With the Bark On

Popular Humor
of the Old South

Compiled and Edited with
Introduction and Notes by
John Q. Anderson

Drawings by Mary Alice Bahler

With

the Bark On

Vanderbilt University Press 1967

Copyright © 1967 by
Vanderbilt University Press
Composed by Western Typesetting Company
Kansas City, Missouri
Printed by Halliday Lithograph Corporation
West Hanover, Massachusetts
Bound by Kingsport Press, Inc.
Kingsport, Tennessee

Library of Congress Catalogue Card Number
67-13998

Printed in the United States of America

The backwoodsman is gone, but behind
him he has left a colorful folk history.
He would swell with pride if he could
only get a glimpse of the shelves of rare
books which have been written about him,
and it would indeed inflate his ego if
he could see the anthologies of his
stories, and the dictionaries and magazines
which contain his colorful words
and phrases. —THOMAS D. CLARK

Foreword

 THE material in this collection appeared in newspapers and magazines between 1835 and 1860; very little of it has been reprinted. Selections were taken from microfilm copies of the New York *Spirit of the Times,* the New Orleans *Picayune,* and the *Richmond Compiler,* Richmond, Louisiana. William T. Porter, editor of the *Spirit,* reprinted many humorous sketches from regional newspapers. Almost half of the sketches included here originally appeared in such papers. Those newspapers and magazines to which Porter gave credit include the *Picayune, Delta, Tropic,* and *Crescent,* all of New Orleans; the St. Louis *Reveille;* the Louisville *Daily Courier;* the *Nonpareil* and *Mercury* of Cincinnati; the *Times* of New Madrid, Missouri; the *Tribune* of Chambers, Alabama; the *Concordia Intelligencer,* Concordia, Louisiana; the *Louisiana Chronicle;* the *Forest Garland;* the *Southern Watch-Tower;* and the *Civil, Military and Naval Gazette.*

Many of the sketches appeared as letters to the editor. Salutations, asides to the editor, and complimentary closings have been omitted. Changes in titles, omissions, and available biographical material about the writers are indicated in the notes. Punctuation has been altered to conform more nearly to current practices, although dashes, exclamation points, and italics have been retained as characteristic of contemporary style.

To my wife, Loraine Epps Anderson, I am indebted for checking microfilm and for editorial suggestions.

JOHN Q. ANDERSON

University of Houston
Houston, Texas
August 1966

Contents

Foreword   vii

Introduction   1

The River   13

   My Grandmother's Trick: Reminiscences of
     Natchez-under-the-Hill by "Yazoo"   21
   A Nightwatch on a Flatboat by "Falconbridge"   25
   The Crack Captain on the Mississippi by "S."   29
   Breaking a Bank by Sol Smith   32
   The Wrong Berth by "Crawfish"   37
   "It's All Right, Captain" by Anon.   40
   The Tallest Snake Story by Anon.   42

The Backcountry   45

   A New Town in Arkansas by "Concordia"   49
   One Man and Two Beds by Anon.   60
   The Yazoo Bottoms Revisited by "Col. J. J. Jenks"   62
   My First and Last Courtship in the Pine
     Barrens by "Neosho"   65
   Poetry and Liquor in East Tennessee by "Roderick"   70
   Selling Chickens to the Legislature by "Phil"   73

Varmints and Hunters   77

   Old Long John and the Bear by "Sulphur Fork"   85
   Bar and Deer Hunting in Mississippi by
     "The Turkey Runner"   88
   Another Bear Fight by "Ruff Sam"   95
   Louisiana "Boys" and Bear Hunting by Anon.   98
   Joe Harris and the Panther by "John of Oxford"   100
   Chunkey's Fight with the Panthers by "The Turkey Runner"   104
   An Alligator for a Present by "Pardon Jones"   113
   Dog Days in Mississippi by "Chips"   117
   A Wildcat Story by Anon.   120
   "Blowed Up" on a Possum Hunt by "Pardon Jones"   122

Fun and Frolic   127

   A Surprise Wedding in Georgia by "Uncle Solon"   133
   A Wedding in Mississippi by "The Turkey Runner"   140

A Wedding Frolic in Arkansas by "Skyscraper"   145
Commemoration Ball in Bates, Missouri by J. N. M. Harding   147
Pretty Gals and Snuff by "Joel Darlin"   150
Ducks in Summer by "Stahl"   154
Fire in the Rear by "Megatherium"   157
The Singing Teacher of Snake Hollow by "Rial Owen"   160

The Professions   165

Primitive Courts in the Southwest by "Amite"   171
Storming an Arkansas Courthouse by "Falconbridge"   176
A Good Witness by Maj. Kelly   181
Mosquito Bait by "Concordia"   183
The Louisiana Law of Cockfighting by Thomas Bangs Thorpe   188
Dental Surgery by "Amite"   191
Uncle Johnny's Tooth Pulling Story by "Obe Oilstone"   194
Irregular Practice of a Regular Practitioner by Anon.   198
The Harp of a Thousand Strings by William Penn Brannon   202
Daddy Donk and the Spirits by "Number Eight"   206
Farewell, Brother Crafford! by William Penn Brannon   209
Shifting the Responsibility by Anon.   212
How to Draw Sinners by "Subscriber"   214
The Good Shepherd by Anon.   215

Jokes and Jokers   219

Fortunes in Prospect by "Jersey"   223
A Snake Story by "Ruff Sam"   227
Catching a Weasel Asleep by Anon.   230
The Beautiful Widow of Shirttail Bend by "Falconbridge"   234
An Arkansas "Sell" by "Plenoir"   238
Why Phil Weston Didn't Rise in the Profession by "The Little 'Un"   241
Getting a Railroad Subscription by Anon.   244

Masculine Amusements   247

A Quarter Race in Kentucky by Anon.   255
Josh Silsbee at the Races by "Thomas the Rhymer"   265
That Big Dog Fight at Myers's by "Obe Oilstone"   269
Up Fool River by "Obe Oilstone"   273
Liquoring on the Mississippi by Anon.   276

Soldiering in Mexico by "Pardon Jones" 279
Seeing the Elephant at the Battle of Buena Vista by "Ruff Sam" 282
The Barrel Movement by "Solitaire" 284
A Breach of Promise Case by "Azul" 287

Politicians, Actors, Yokels in the City   289

Seeing the Elephant by Anon. 298
Electioneering by "Pardon Jones" 301
Fun at the Capitol of Mississippi by "D. V. M." 305
A Texian Hero by Anon. 309
An Intimate Friend by Sol Smith 312
Uncle Billy Brown—"Glorious!" by "Rambler" 317
A "Crack" Hotel by H. P. Leland 322
That Big Fiddle by Anon. 326
A Returned Californian in New Orleans by "Lambda" 328

Index   331

Introduction

Between 1830 and 1860 a great body of humorous writing came out of the area of the United States known as the Southwest, which embraced the present states of Missouri, Arkansas, Tennessee, Mississippi, Alabama, Georgia, and Louisiana, a region now commonly called the Old Southwest.[1] This popular humor was published largely in newspapers and inexpensive books and is variously referred to as Southwestern humor and sometimes more generally frontier or backwoods humor.[2] Much of this writing concerns the American backwoodsman as he developed in the Old Southwest, an extension of popular interest in the rustic who had been portrayed earlier on the stage and in newspapers in the east.[3]

The Southwestern frontiersman emerged in popular humor in the 1830s when A. B. Longstreet started publishing newspaper sketches about country life in Georgia; he collected and published these pieces as *Georgia Scenes* in 1835. The book was widely read and imitated in the following twenty-five years.[4] Also influential in publicizing backwoods humor was William T. Porter's *Spirit of the Times*, a New York weekly newspaper started in 1831 as an imitation of the English sporting magazine, *Bell's Life in London*.[5]

1. Though Texas is not usually included in the Old Southwest, the southern and eastern areas of the state shared the same culture and tradition in the ante bellum period. I have not included Texas, however, because I have treated its ante bellum humor in *Tales of Frontier Texas* (Dallas: Southern Methodist University Press, 1966).

2. Franklin J. Meine, ed., *Tall Tales of the Southwest: An Anthology of Southern and Southwestern Humor, 1830–1860* (New York: Alfred A. Knopf, 1930), and Walter Blair, *Native American Humor* (New York: American Book Co., 1937), were first to indicate the geographical area.

3. The backwoodsman on the American stage is discussed by Jennette Tandy, *Crackerbox Philosophers in American Humor and Satire* (New York: Kennikat Press, 1925), pp. 1-20; Constance Rourke, *American Humor: A Study of the National Character* (New York: Harcourt, Brace & Co., 1931), pp. 15-36; and Richard M. Dorson, "The Yankee on the Stage—A Folk Hero in American Drama," *New England Quarterly*, XIII (1940), 467–493.

4. A lengthy discussion of the origin and publication of the book and its subsequent popularity is contained in John Donald Wade, *Augustus Baldwin Longstreet* (New York: Macmillan, 1924). Poe reviewed *Georgia Scenes* favorably in the *Southern Literary Messenger*, in March 1836.

5. In his book, *William T. Porter and the Spirit of the Times: A Study of the Big Bear School of Humor* (Baton Rouge: Louisiana State University Press, 1957), Norris Yates has made by far the most complete study of this important paper and its editor. I am greatly indebted to that work.

Since horse fanciers and followers of racing were more numerous in the South and Southwest, the *Spirit* was widely read in those areas, and Porter gradually built up a group of unpaid correspondents who sent in reports of races and other sports. At first these sporting epistles contained brief descriptions of local people, particularly backwoodsmen. Recognizing the appeal of local-color material, Porter encouraged his correspondents to include anecdotes, tales, and accounts of backwoodsmen. Within a few years Porter developed a group of regular contributors who became quite skillful in presenting backwoods characters through dialect and description. As a result, the *Spirit of the Times* became the chief outlet for sketches that treated the backwoodsman as a comic character. Along with original contributions, Porter reprinted backwoods sketches from other newspapers, particularly those in the Southwest, such as the New Orleans *Picayune* and *Delta* and the St. Louis *Reveille* and *Journal*. These papers and numerous other weeklies in turn reprinted sketches from the *Spirit*. In 1845 Porter selected a number of the best sketches from his paper and issued them as an anthology which was successful enough to cause him to issue another the next year.[6] At the same time he encouraged his publishers, Carey and Hart of Philadelphia, to print collections by individual writers, notably Thomas Bangs Thorpe and Johnson J. Hooper.

In the last two decades before the Civil War, the *Spirit of the Times* printed hundreds of humorous sketches emanating from the Old Southwest. Most of this material was written by amateurs—lawyers, doctors, engineers, politicians, and planters who enjoyed a good hunting story, a practical joke, or an eccentric character and learned to capture them in print. Some of the writers were indeed journalists, but most of them sought no recognition as authors and hence remained anonymous, using devices to obscure their identity:

6. *The Big Bear of Arkansas, and Other Sketches, Illustrative of Character and Incident in the South and South-West* (Philadelphia, 1845). The collection included twenty-one sketches with illustrations by F. O. C. Darley, one of the most widely known illustrators of the time. Porter published the introduction to the book in the *Spirit*, XV, No. 4 (March 22, 1845), 33. Similar in material is *A Quarter Race in Kentucky and Other Sketches Illustrative of Scenes, Characters, and Incidents Throughout "The Universal Yankee Nation"* (Philadelphia, 1846).

fanciful pseudonyms ("Turkey Runner," "Green 'Un," "Azul") or pen names ("Pardon Jones," "Ruff Sam"). For every writer who was known by name, such as Thorpe and Hooper, many were known only to a few friends and editors, and it is now impossible to identify them from the anecdotes, tales, and sketches that lie buried in old newspapers.

Through newspapers and a few books, the humor of the Old Southwest was widely known for about twenty years, but dependent as it was on contemporary materials, it could not survive the social upheaval of the Civil War. Fashions in popular humor changed immediately thereafter, so that Southwestern humor was largely forgotten[7] until the first decades of the twentieth century when interest in the American frontier, resulting from the theories of historian Frederick Jackson Turner, led scholars to assess the influence of the frontier on American literature. Since the 1920s a number of scholars have studied American humor in this context, and a major share of this effort has been devoted to the humor of the Old Southwest, especially as it influenced Mark Twain.[8] Gen-

7. An exception is Henry Watterson's *Oddities in Southern Life and Character* (Boston: Houghton Mifflin, 1883), an anthology which includes several selections of ante bellum Southern humor. In his introduction Watterson looked back from the 1880s and was nostalgic, apologetic, and mildly bitter. He speaks of that humor as having to do with "a race and a day" that were gone—"the good old time of muster days and quarter racing," he said, "before the camp-meeting and the barbecue had lost their power and their charm; when men led simple, homely lives, doing their love-making and their law-making as they did their fighting and their plowing, in a straight furrow...." He repeats Longstreet's phraseology of fifty years before that the humor of the Old Southwest turned "upon character and incident" peculiar to its place and time. Watterson, more aware of polite literature than the humorists themselves, apologized for the literary value of the selections he anthologized; "it is not my purpose," he says, "to make much boast of its quality" (pp. v–vii, viii).

8. In addition to the studies mentioned above by Meine, Blair, Tandy, Rourke, and Yates, the following works are important: Bernard De Voto, *Mark Twain's America* (Boston: Little, Brown, 1932); Arthur Palmer Hudson, *Humor of the Old Deep South* (New York: Macmillan, 1936); Walter Blair, *Horsesense in American Humor* (New York: Russell & Russell, 1942); W. Stanley Hoole, *Alias Simon Suggs: The Life and Times of Johnson James Hooper* (University, Ala.: University of Alabama Press, 1952); Brom Weber, ed., *Sut Lovingood* (New York: Grove Press, 1954); Kenneth Lynn, *Mark Twain and Southwestern Humor* (Boston: Little, Brown, 1959); Arlin Turner, *Southern Stories* (New York: Holt, Rinehart, & Winston, 1960); Pascal Covici, *Mark Twain's Humor:*

erally, these studies show that American humor in the nineteenth century centered around the country man as a comic figure, first on the stage, then in politics, and finally, as a frontiersman along the westering boundaries of the nation. Types of the rustic emerged in the Down East Yankee (later the "'cute Yankee"), the Kaintuck or riverman of the western rivers, the backwoods boaster (the "Salt River Roarer"), and the Southwestern backwoodsman (variously as hunter, squatter, farmer).

Twentieth-century scholarship has also shown that writers of popular humor, though mostly amateurs, developed skillful techniques for presenting their materials; for example, the framework narrative allows the writer in the first person to set the scene and introduce characters who tell their own stories in dialect, then return at the end to the writer's own commentary.[9] Furthermore, these humorists, particularly those in the Southwest, enhanced their material by use of comic realism, a manner that contrasted sharply to the sentimentality of polite literature of the period. Southwestern humor also developed a body of traditional subject matter. After the pattern set by Longstreet's *Georgia Scenes*, these topics were common: comic fights, gambling, country dances and frolics, horse racing, the militia, fads and fashions, eccentric local characters, and, to some extent, politics and religion. Stylistically, later writers gradually moved away from Longstreet's involved prose toward a more flexible colloquial style and greater use of dialect.

---

the *Image of a World* (Dallas: Southern Methodist University Press, 1962); Milton Rickels, *Thomas Bangs Thorpe: Humorist of the Old Southwest* (Baton Rouge: Louisiana State University Press, 1962); John Q. Anderson, *Louisiana Swamp Doctor: The Life and Writings of Henry Clay Lewis* (Baton Rouge: Louisiana State University Press, 1962); and Hennig Cohen and William B. Dillingham, *Humor of the Old Southwest* (Boston: Houghton, Mifflin, 1964).

A summary and evaluation of these and other studies is presented in my "Scholarship in Southwestern Humor—Past and Present," the principal address at the ninth annual meeting of the American Studies Association of the Lower Mississippi, University of Southwestern Louisiana, Lafayette, Louisiana, October 11–12, 1963. The paper, along with three others presented at that meeting, appeared in a special issue of the *Mississippi Quarterly*, XVII (Spring 1964), 67–86.

9. This technique is fully described by Walter Blair in *Native American Humor*, pp. 90–92.

Porter's selection of the best sketches from the *Spirit* for republication and his praise of successful writers of such pieces encouraged brevity and tightness of construction in order to "make a point," that is, to bring a narrative to a dramatic climax. Porter also encouraged his contributors to vie in topping a story. Cycles of tales thus developed which deal with similar situations.[10] He also encouraged the camaraderie that developed naturally among contributors, especially journalists, many of whom were known to each other, though not always to their readers.

Within the body of Southwest humor, the greatest number of contributors to regional newspapers and to Porter's *Spirit* lived in Louisiana and Mississippi. Several of these writers were New Orleans journalists or other newspapermen who visited the city and wrote about their experiences there. Also, steamboat trips on the great highway of the region, the Mississippi River, were an ideal environment for story telling; they brought together a wide variety of types and classes of people, a mixture that spurred the imagination of many amateur story tellers. Further, social and ethnic contrasts, especially in the Gulf Coast areas of the two states, produced ready-made material for humorous treatment.

Almost all of the major humorists of the Old Southwest—Thorpe, Hooper, Harris, and Lewis—have been studied and reprinted recently. The increasing importance of Southwestern humor as a special development of American humor, as a significant part of American civilization, and as a strong influence on the development of realism in American literature—all these indicate that the minor writers need attention. That is the purpose of the present collection.

The seventy sketches included in this volume were selected from several hundred pieces that appeared in newspapers over a period of about twenty years. Selection was made on the basis of skill in presenting subject matter and of representative qualities. Like the major humorists, the minor writers were not professional authors.

10. Unusual fights, such as Phillip B. January's "That Big Dog Fight at Myers's" in which a man fights a dog, led to imitations; several tales deal with the embarrassment of a traveler who spends the night in the one-room cabin of a frontier family and finds himself having to undress and go to bed before women.

Some of them apparently wrote only one sketch; others, at the most, appear to have written only three or four. Even so, they are in the tradition of the major writers. They used the same techniques and subject matter that distinguish the major humorists. Most of them wrote about specific locales. For example, "Ruff Sam" is concerned with life in the backwoods of Mississippi and views the world from that vantagepoint, even when he is a soldier in Mexico. Alexander McNutt, as "The Turkey Runner," sketches life and manners in northern Mississippi; C. M. Haile as "Pardon Jones," despite his Down East background, looks at character and incidents in the bayou country of south Louisiana; "Rial Owen," also a Yankee, takes backwoods life in Arkansas as his topic; "Yazoo" takes his name and subject matter from the Yazoo bottoms; "Concordia" is at his best writing about the "swampers" of northeast Louisiana; Phillip B. January as "Obe Oilstone" has his Uncle Johnny laugh at and with the fun-loving men of Jefferson County, Mississippi, Vicksburg, and the adjoining parishes in Louisiana west of the river. Even in their single sketches, "Chips" of the River country, "Megatherium" of Louisiana, and "Phil" of Missouri show the same knack for making specific areas memorable.

Others of the minor humorists are more broadly regional. For instance, "Viator," "Azul," and "Amite" seem equally at home in Louisiana and Mississippi, and their sketches concentrate on character and incident of the region rather than those of specific villages. Another group, probably newspapermen, centers in New Orleans: "John Smith," "Lambda," and the anonymous writers for the *Picayune* and *Delta*, doubtless including George W. Kendall and Francis Lumsden.

Though these minor writers were more limited in production and scope than the major humorists, they are usually as skillful in characterization and narration. For instance, Phillip B. January's Uncle Johnny, one of the most delightful topers in Southwestern humor, tantalizes the reader with tales he starts but which his creator does not let him finish. This device creates the impression of an old man who, with his inevitable drink in his hand, relives his adventures with younger drinking and carousing cronies. The realistic portrayal of Uncle Johnny suggests that January patterned him on a man or perhaps a composite of men he knew in Fayette or Greenville, Mississippi, creating character in the way Hooper shaped Bird into Simon Suggs and Lewis based Mik Hooter on Michael Hooter. Porter and his contributors recognized January's talent as is shown in the sustained popularity of "That Big Dog Fight at Myers's," which in turn inspired similar accounts.

Alexander McNutt's account of the activities of fiercely individualistic Chunkey and Jim is sustained throughout six sketches with even more skill. McNutt's manner of presentation of these backwoodsmen and their shadowy mentor, the Governor, departs from the framework tale. The typical "Turkey Runner" sketch, for instance, opens with dialogue instead of the conventional paragraph setting the scene; the effect is that of the opening act of a play. The reader has to listen to Chunkey and Jim for a while before he is drawn into the situation. Furthermore, McNutt's practice of changing point of view—from Chunkey to Jim and back—at first seems confusing, but the reader who has already met them and knows how they think is not disturbed; rather, he is led on to discover how they are going to react in a new situation. If Chunkey is in the right stage of inebriation, he is going to keep on whistling no matter what Jim or the Governor threatens, for they both know that Chunkey always whistles for three days straight after he has been on a spree. Jim, on the other hand, is not going to let Chunkey, the Governor, or anyone else beat him out of his share of the liquor; and though he may be slow in limbering up in the morning after a drinking bout with Chunkey and the Governor, he will soon show his unerring skill in the hunt or his shrewdness in a card game. McNutt presents these characters with such naturalness that the reader feels that they must be based on real people, though they may be simply what fully realized characters in fiction are—more memorable than actual.

C. M. Haile's "Pardon Jones" is a skillful transplanting of the Yankee countryman to south Louisiana. He is, consequently, a blend of the dry humor of the traditional Yankee of the period and of volubility of the country sportsman-politician of the bayou country.

His naivete in politics is disarming, and his Yankee materialism in soliciting a Christmas present from William T. Porter is amusing. With perfect lack of understanding of the irony of the situation, he sends Porter an alligator for a gift with specific instructions on how to use the reptile for a barometer or watchdog, assuming that Porter will be as much at home with alligators as Jones himself had become in his adopted land. Moreover, Haile adroitly transfers "Pardon Jones" from the quiet upcountry atmosphere of south Louisiana to the war in Mexico and makes him a patriotic American soldier. Jones's military experiences, such as the formation of a military band so popular with other outfits, are described in Jones's characteristic country style. Though Jones is by type the comic countryman throughout, he is a memorable addition to comic characters in Southwestern humor.

"Ruff Sam," also the comic countryman, is more primitive than "Pardon Jones," less irascible than Chunkey and Jim, and more the country yokel. Blunt in his manners, crude in his expression, unsophisticated in the ways of the world outside of the Mississippi backwoods, Sam is, as Davy Crockett might have put it, a man with the bark on. Despite his limited understanding of national and military affairs, Sam is one of the backwoodmen whose skill with a rifle won the Battle of New Orleans for Old Hickory and campaigns for Colonel Jefferson Davis in Mexico. Sam's ardent patriotism and his unashamed devotion to his leaders may seem naïve to twentieth-century readers, but American wars have always been won by these simple men who had to do the bloody work with rifles and bayonets. Whoever the creator of "Ruff Sam" was, he knew people well enough to capture them with skill and verisimilitude in print, though the picture he left in only three sketches is a very limited one.

Robert Patterson, editor of the *Concordia Intelligencer* (both before and after Thorpe's stint on that important newspaper) wrote but few sketches that have been identified. If the "Stoke Stout" letters are his, he vividly captured the northeast Louisiana "swamper" with the fidelity shown in Lewis's characters of the same vicinity. As "Concordia"—if indeed those sketches so signed are his— Patterson was the typical newspaperman observing with a clear eye and writing with merciless satire of the fraudulent real estate promotions of the day and picturing graphically the illiterate, impoverished, gullible backwoodsmen who were the victims. In the sketch "Mosquito Bait" (if it is his), he praises in the long introduction the quality of American character that he found on the western fringes of the nation; Patterson belongs with Thorpe (who may have influenced him) as a Southwestern humorist who not only did not scorn the backwoodsman but saw in him an Americanism he did not find elsewhere.

These and the other nameless writers whose sketches follow wrote to amuse newspaper readers of their own day, but in so doing they left a brilliant panorama of life in the Old Southwest. They could hardly have imagined that readers more than a century later would be able to share their gusto and lust for life and to see through their eyes the mighty Mississippi sometimes made sordid by men; the vitality and sometimes earthiness of backwoods weddings and frolics; hunters around campfires telling tales of animals and men; lawyers entertaining men with lusty stories in bars and on the long rides on the circuit; doctors and preachers in their more amusing moments with men's bodies and souls; men and boys of all levels of society pulling jokes, mild and brutal, on each other; men drinking great quantities of whiskey, betting on horses, gambling at cards; men fighting each other, fighting wars, persuading their fellow citizens to elect them to offices; men living vicariously in the characters created by players and entertainers; city men enjoying the antics of yokels in New Orleans, the metropolis of the Old Southwest.

The minor humorists made an important contribution to the humor of the Old Southwest, which, in turn, contributed to the rise of realism in American literature. Aside from the glimpses of American culture of the nineteenth century these writers provide, they are today, as they were in their time, to be enjoyed.

The River

Rivers dominated the geography of the Old Southwest, and the Mississippi dominated the rivers. Almost all roads and streams led to that great highway whose meanderings determined the pattern of settlement. Before the beginning of the nineteenth century, rough and rowdy keelers who called themselves "half-horse, half-alligator" guided their loaded keelboats down the Mississippi, reloaded them, and poled them up again. They patronized the dance halls and gambling dens of the river towns, such as "Yazoo" describes in his reminiscences of Natchez-under-the-Hill in 1824. Tales of their fighting, drinking, and "Salt River roaring," especially of their heroes such as Mike Fink and Little Billy, became part of the lore of the river.[1]

Next came the western frontiersmen who built flatboats and rafts, loaded them with liquor and produce, and guided these clumsy craft down the tributaries of the Mississippi and thence to New Orleans, where they sold their products, broke up their crude boats and sold them for lumber.[2] Because so many of these men came from Kentucky, all of them were called "Kaintucks." To the Latin peoples of New Orleans, the Kaintucks, like the keelers, were inordinately fond of fighting with fists and hunting knives and drinking until they became insensible. After their celebrations in the "good-time town," these frontiersmen walked back home over the Natchez Trace. In the popular imagination, Kaintuck was synonymous with the lank, belligerent, ignorant but shrewd backwoodsman. Though the Kaintuck is usually shown in his antics in New Orleans,

1. See Walter Blair and Franklin J. Meine, *Half Horse Half Alligator: The Growth of the Mike Fink Legends* (Chicago: University of Chicago Press, 1956); and *Mike Fink; King of the Mississippi Keelboatmen* (New York: Henry Holt, 1933).
2. See Leland D. Baldwin, *The Keelboat Age on Western Waters* (Pittsburgh: University of Pittsburgh Press, 1941).

"Falconbridge" describes the toil and danger
of flat-boating in 1838 when as a young
man he went down the river.

The "heroic age," as Blair and Meine call it,
of the keelers and Kaintucks was largely over
by the 1820s when the Mississippi was conquered
by steamboats. The mechanical marvel of its
age, the steamboat soon dominated the river
and its tributaries.[3] The steamers brought people
to new lives in the new land, supplied them
after they settled, hauled away the cotton and
produce, and took them downriver to New
Orleans for business and pleasure. Thus the
arrival of a steamboat—whether a crack boat at
Vicksburg or Louisville or a creaking packet
at the head of navigation on the smallest
tributary—was an event; one never knew what
strange cargo—human, animal, or vegetable—
it would bring. The whistle for departure was
also exciting, especially of the downriver
steamer, for at the end of the journey was the
Crescent City, "a city of beguiling sin, a
strangely foreign playground for the Americans
of the upriver plantations, a racing mecca of
the nation."[4] The steamboat was a world all its
own as it glided through space and time and
touched the real world of work, fever, and
worry only when it stopped "to wood up."
Competition for passengers brought increase in
size, luxury, and speed; as "Viator" wrote in
1849, "All that we have come to care about
in these United States is to get on. . . .
We are all passengers."[5]

Through the eyes of passengers the river and
steamboats are seen in the popular humor of
the period. Since the captain was a glamorous

3. For discussions of steamboats,
see Louis C. Hunter, *Steamboats
on Western Rivers* (Cambridge:
Harvard University Press, 1949);
Herbert and Edward Quick,
Mississippi Steamboatin' (New
York: Henry Holt, 1926); and
Charles H. Ambler, *A History of
Transportation in the Ohio
Valley* (Glendale, Calif.: The
Arthur H. Clark Co., 1932).
4. Hodding Carter, *Lower
Mississippi* (New York: Farrar &
Rinehart, 1942), Rivers of
America Series, p. 253.
5. *Spirit*, XIX, No. 34 (Oct. 13,
1849), 397. "Viator" contributed
sketches from various places
in the South.

figure to passengers, he is the subject of many sketches. The captain was usually a businessman who operated his boat as a business enterprise and was sensitive, therefore, to public opinion. Several types of steamboat captains appear in humorous sketches: the captain who was always willing to race a rival boat (sometimes endangering the lives of passengers by over-taxing engines); the captain who stopped at isolated landings on the lower river and took orders from people for goods in New Orleans; the captain who went to extremes to please all customers (and sometimes displeased all); the captain who was down on his luck and had to run a broken-down boat on a small tributary; the captain who, failing to get a full load of passengers in New Orleans, went about the streets crying up an epidemic of yellow fever and soon had his boat loaded.

Even more intriguing to contemporary commentators were fellow passengers. Any steamboat on any western river in the 1840s carried an assortment of travelers more varied than Chaucer's Canterbury pilgrims: businessmen, journalists, students, preachers, doctors, lawyers, gamblers, adventurers, bear hunters (such as Jim Doggett of "The Big Bear of Arkansas"), adolescent runaways (such as Henry Clay Lewis, the "Louisiana Swamp Doctor"), families moving west, planters' wives and daughters. In addition to this cross-section of Americans, such a steamer might also carry traveling English writers, Frenchmen, Germans, and a host of Irish emigrants stowed away on the lower deck amid baggage and produce.

A steamboat trip from New Orleans to

Louisville or Cincinnati, even in the later days
of speedy boats, was long; passengers had to be
entertained. Ladies generally kept to the ladies'
salon where they talked or read the latest
French or English novel from the boat's library;
gentlemen resorted to the social room where
they drank and talked at the bar or gambled
at poker, euchre, whist, loo, or faro. Perhaps the
most common type of amusement was simply
sitting on the deck watching the scenery and
telling stories. It was an age of storytelling,
and the leisure of a steamboat journey was the
very climate in which oral lore lived and
breathed. A typical yarning session might range
over many subjects: steamboat captains and
boats, hunting and hunters, horse racing and
gambling, actors and entertainers, backwoodsmen
and city dwellers. Each storyteller, freed from
time and space and from those who might
question his facts, gave rein to his imagination
and shaped his tale to his audience—
introduction, action, conflict, climax, and quick
denouement. By the time his audience was
through laughing or expressing amazement
at his tale, another storyteller was ready with
his own tale. And as the hours passed, tales
grew taller and taller, episodes more carefully
sharpened, and audience reaction more
stimulating. In the mouths of experienced
raconteurs human experiences were distilled into
drama, and in the memory of some the best tales
were stored until the amateur writer could get to
pen and paper to set them down and mail them
to Editor Porter of the *Spirit*. Such is the
background of some of the best stories set on
steamboats, such as Thorpe's "The Big Bear of

Arkansas" and Lewis's "Rattlesnake on a
Steamboat."[6] Tales were told over and over
again—as shown in "The Tallest Snake Story"
which follows—passing back and forth between
the oral and written tradition, for as J. Frank
Dobie says, "A story belongs to the man
who can tell it."

The humor of the Old Southwest naturally
concentrates on the amusing side of steamboat
travel, and though characters and events are
realistic enough to convince the twentieth-century
reader that he is actually looking at life as it was
on a Mississippi steamer, he should realize
that tragedy sometimes rudely interrupted
pleasure trips. Snags and sawyers lurked in the
muddy waters, waiting to rip open the bottom of
a boat; fires broke out in the cargo; boilers
exploded; collisions were common in the fogs
of the lower Mississippi; disease, especially the
dreaded cholera, spread up the river with the
flood of emigrants and reached epidemic
proportions in several different years after 1832.
Steamboat accidents were the most common of
dangers by far. By 1840 more than two hundred
accidents had occurred on the western rivers,
and nearly two thousand lives had been lost.[7]
By its very nature, popular humor ignored these
grim facts. Yet the very newspaper that printed
a humorous sketch of experiences on a steamboat
would carry a detailed account of a steamboat
explosion, such as that written by H. A. Kidd,
editor of the New Orleans *Crescent*, who was
blown up in 1851 on the *Anglo-Norman*
and lived to tell the story.[8]

Not only did the "western waters," as the
Mississippi and its tributaries were called,

6. Thomas Bangs Thorpe, "The
Big Bear of Arkansas," in
William T. Porter, ed., *The Big
Bear of Arkansas, and Other
Sketches* (Philadelphia, 1845);
*Odd Leaves from the Life of a
Louisiana Swamp Doctor* by
Madison Tensas, M. D., [Henry
Clay Lewis], (Philadelphia, 1850).
7. Hunter, *Steamboats on the
Western Rivers*, pp. 277-278.
8. "Experience of a Blown-Up
Man," *Spirit*, XX, No. 48 (Jan.
18, 1851), 567-568. The writer,
seated on the deck immediately
above the boiler when it
exploded, was blown clear of
the boat but managed to stay
afloat until he was picked up by
another steamer.

dominate the lives and imaginations of people in the Old Southwest, but easterners went in great numbers to see the paintings of the Mississippi done by artists on huge continuous canvases.[9] As a result, the steamboat contributed more metaphors to the language than did any other form of public transportation, as Mody C. Boatright has pointed out.[10] Among these words and phrases are "to bust a biler" (to be angry), "to get steam up" (to talk volubly), "to wood up" (to drink), " to get up a head of steam" (to begin something vigorously), "to hit a snag," "to miss the boat," "to blow off steam," and "to blow for a landing."

On the waters of the rivers that swept down the Great Valley of the Mississippi, whether in the flood of spring or the placid flow of winter, moved myriads of people in the first half of the nineteenth century, and with them went comedy and tragedy. In the sketches that follow, comedy has the forefront of the stage; so rarely does tragedy appear that it is easy to forget that it was sometimes there.

9. *Description of Banvard's Panorama of the Mississippi River, Painted on Three Miles of Canvas, Exhibiting a View of Country* 1200 *Miles in Length, Extending from the Mouth of the Missouri River to the City of New Orleans, Being by Far the Largest Picture Ever Executed by Man* (Boston, 1847).
10. "Frontier Humor: Despairing or Bouyant?" *Southwest Review,* XXVII (Spring 1942), 334.

My Grandmother's Trick:
Reminiscences of Natchez-under-the-Hill

by "Yazoo" of Mississippi

§ "Yazoo" may have been a printer on the *Whig*, Yazoo City, Mississippi, or connected with some other paper in Yazoo County. In 1841 he wrote letters back to the *Whig* from Pass Christian, Mississippi, a popular watering place. In December 1843, he published two other sketches in the *Spirit* — "Trout Fishing in Mississippi," XIII (December 24, 1843), 43, and "A Dinner in the Yazoo Swamp," XIII (December 30, 1843), 44. He knew "Concordia" of the *Concordia Intelligencer*, Vidalia, Louisiana, who speaks of him in "A New Town in Arkansas," *Spirit*, XIV (March 9, 1844), 2. In a letter dated July 23, 1845, from Yazoo City, "Yazoo" introduced "Cupping on the Sternum," the first sketch that Henry Clay Lewis, then a resident of Yazoo City, printed in the *Spirit* (Anderson, *Louisiana Swamp Doctor*, p. 33). The following story was printed in the *Spirit*, XIII, No. 44 (December 30, 1843), 523.

LANDING at Natchez in the winter of 1824–5 about ten o'clock in the evening, I thought I would stop for a few minutes Under-the-Hill with the view of ascertaining, if possible, what peculiarity it was that had made *"Natchez under-the-Hill"* so celebrated throughout the Union. I walked up the street and entered the first door I saw open. The room into which I entered was a brilliantly lighted saloon, around which two gaily dressed, sylph-like forms were whirling in the waltz. A few spectators had, at this early hour, collected to witness the extraordinary scenes that were nightly enacted at these places. They appeared to be principally Kentucky boatmen and were wedged in the corners or stuck around the room flat against the wall, affording as large a space in the center as possible for the dancers. On an elevated platform, serving as an orchestra, sat some four or five musicians; two violins, a clarinet, and bass drum, I noticed particularly; and in front of them as a kind of figure head, stood a black boy of some twelve or thirteen years of age, dressed *a la Turk*, who flourished and beat a tamboureen in the most fantastic manner — producing sounds that would in all probability have slept until the Day of Judgment but for the skill and *genius* of this performer. On my entrance the waltz was stopped and an exciting reel struck up by the band, while the imp of the tamboureen redoubled his exertions, grinning and chaunting in melodious cadence some stanzas of which I caught but the concluding line of each verse:

The old woman she_____ _____in the haymow.

One of the beautiful creatures I have mentioned came up to me and desired me to dance with her, while others equally beautiful and as gaudily dressed came flocking in with a like request to those standing about the room. The invitation to dance I declined. "Then d--n you, treat me," said she, which I instantly did and *retreated* into an adjoining room, the door of which stood invitingly open. Here a scene presented itself which made a lasting impression upon me. Immediately in front, as I entered, stood a roulette table, revolving like the flood wheel of a tubmill, from which I ever and anon heard the ominous exclamation of "Double O black!" On the right, around a table, sat some half dozen or more persons betting at faro. Some bet with silver coin, some with bank notes, and a few who seemed to be the largest bettors with "checks" or counters.

"Split again, by ---!" said one, as the dealer cried "Jacks a pair," who took one-half the stakes upon the Jack, and continued, "Ace, Tray—Ten, Four."

"D--n that catharpen; it has twice split me wide open," said another of the bettors; a third cursed the Queen as a faithless ---, whilst a fourth lost in sullen silence. I observed, however, one who was betting with counters to win several large bets in succession without lifting his money from the table. The checks, which were circular pieces of bone or ivory, were paid him and piled up, one above another, to a great height. The large amount now pending induced the barker to ask the bettor whether he "went" the whole amount. "Yes, by ---, I'll pile my paralee to the ceiling," replied the desperate gamester.

Just at this moment my attention was attracted to a different part of the room where the proprietor appeared to be endeavoring to eject some person from the house who was greatly intoxicated. "I won't go," said the drunken man, "until I have won five hundred dollars or lost my pile." "You're a fool," said the landlord; "put your money up and go home." "If I'm a fool my money ain't," replied he, and he offered to bet any amount on anything. In one hand he held five $100 bank notes and in the other a deck of cards. The money he scattered about the room seemingly regardless of its value—falling himself against the counter and sometimes upon the floor. His money was picked up and handed to him by the considerate land-lord, who urged him by every argument in his power to put up his money and go home; this he declined doing, and as a dernier resort, the landlord proposed to me, who was looking on with some interest at the strange scene, to win his money and return it to him, when sober.

"If you don't," said he, "some gambler will and keep it."

This seemed reasonable and looked kind in the landlord, and I felt half disposed to put the scheme in execution. The drunken man had laid out three cards and placed $500 as a stake upon the counter, which he offered to bet that he *could name and turn any of the three cards,* or he would bet the same amount that no one else could do so. The cards he had previously shown were the Jack of Clubs, the Tray of Spades, and the Nine of Diamonds. He was now about to add to his beastly intoxication by taking another drink and in doing so had partially turned his back upon the cards he had laid out. At this stage of the game, a plainly dressed man, whom I took to be a farmer from the neighborhood, stepped up to me and said he would join me in carrying out the suggestion of the landlord—that it was a charitable act and one that we ought not to hesitate to perform for our fellowman. The gentleman put his hand into his pocket for the money to stake, but immediately recollected that he had left his pocketbook at the hotel where he stopped to avoid the risk of having his pocket picked while Under-the-Hill. He then appealed to me to furnish the money for so praiseworthy an object, alleging that he would not have me do so if the game was not a certain one; and to make assurances doubly sure, he lifted one of the cards, while the man's back was turned towards us, and turned up one of the corners, showing me that it was the Nine of Diamonds, which, said he, "You can name and turn for the bet—the bent corner will not be observed and you can win the money without risk."

I had taken out my pocketbook, not for the purpose of staking the money, but merely to see if my money was safe, and as I ran over the notes, my companion and friend, as he seemed to be, half soliciting and half forcing, took from my hand five notes of $100 each and placed them with the $500 already on the counter, observing with a wink that he would hold the stakes. He now desired me to name and turn a card for the money; this I was about to do when the drunken man asked the privilege of shuffling the three cards, which was of course granted, and with the dexterity of Signor Blitz, or the "wonder working Adrian," he smoothed down the corner which had been turned up and turned up the corner of one of the black cards, in precisely the same manner. This, of course, I did not observe. "Now," said he, "name and turn a card for the money staked." I examined the backs and turned the card with the corner bent; it proved to be the *Jack of Clubs!* I cast my eyes towards the holder of the stakes—he was in the act of handing them over to the winner, who had suddenly become quite sober, and who, as he pocketed the money, cooly informed me that it was *"all fair"* and that I had lost my money upon *"My Grandmother's Trick."*

I turned to leave this den. The roulette was still whirling its endless round, the small ivory ball vainly endeavoring to enter the *compressed compartments upon which the bettors had staked;* faro was catching in hockley and "splitting open" more victims, and as I passed through the ballroom the little nigger was still thumping the tamboureen and singing:

The old woman she_____ _____ _____in the haymow.

A Nightwatch on a Flatboat

by "Falconbridge"

§ Under the pseudonym "Falconbridge," Johnathan Falconbridge Kelley
wrote numerous sketches for the *Spirit*. A journalist, he started a
newspaper in Pittsburgh and later worked on papers in Ohio, where
he died in 1854. In an obituary in the *Spirit*, XXIV, No. 25 (August 5,
1854), 295, "Arcola" said he was "a writer of no ordinary calibre."
Some of his sketches were collected and published as *The Humors of
Falconbridge* (Philadelphia, 1856). Kelley was also the author of *Dan
Marble: A Biographical Sketch of That Famous and Diverting Humorist,
with Reminiscences, Comicalities, Anecdotes, Etc., Etc.,* (New York,
1851). The following story was printed as "A Fearful Tale of the
Mississippi," *Spirit*, XVIII, No. 2 (March 6, 1847), 13.

IN looking at Banvord's great panorama of "the Father of
Waters"—the running, roaring, majestic Mississippi[11]—a few evenings since, I was reminded of a fearful scene I once encountered
upon that notable stream. In the year 1838, I went down to New
Orleans as second mate and assistant cook on a flatboat from Zanes-
ville, Ohio. I need not detail the preliminary circumstances of getting
under way or heaving to day after day and night after night—the
desperate leaps I made in jumping ashore with the rope—the tumbles
I made in the mud—and the duckings I got in the water, which was
just then (March) considerably colder than that used in "hot punches,"
generally speaking.

It was a rough drizzly night, and the double-dyed hues of the
"silent watches" hung around "our devoted barque" which, in
consequence of the Stygian darkness and inclemency of the night,
we had tied up to the right hand bank of the Mississippi about ten
miles below "Lost Prairie."

If my memory serves me correctly, it was *thar* and about the hour
of two a.m. I was called from my *stateroom* (two old quilts upon
some barrels of flour—part of our freight) to go on deck and stand

11. See note 9.

my watch until day broke. A watch, of course, is very essential and is strictly kept on boats tying up along the plantations as the colored population along the banks have a great penchant for robbing and plundering flatboats whenever a favorable opportunity offers. Nor are the niggers the only professors of the business for cutthroats and highwaymen of lighter complexion than charcoal have frequently made descents upon flatboats, taken the freight, and in hundreds of cases murdered the unguarded crew.

We had tied up in a very suspicious place, close in under some tall cottonwoods, and my shipmate that had been on watch remarked to me that he believed "some d-- cuss was prowling around the cottonwoods, waiting a favorable chance to crawl aboard in the bow and levy on a barrel of flour or a few hams." The bow of a flatboat is generally open; the roof—excuse me—the *deck* projects over the open space in the bow, thus sheltering what may stand or be placed beneath; under this deck, seated on a barrel, I took my watch with a small pistol in my trowsers' pocket and a pretty smart chance of a stick at my fingers' ends.

Having whistled and hummed most of the popular airs of the day to keep myself awake, I began to feel very drowsy. All of a sudden I caught a glimpse of something moving about and dodging around the cottonwoods. Presently I espied another. I kept my eyes sharp about me while a tingling cold feeling began to seize upon me, and I had a strong inclination to sing out "Help!" "Fire and blue blazes!" But, thinks I, I'll hold on a spell and see if they make any attempt to come aboard, and if they do I'll pull the trigger of my pistol and shoot one of them and that will arouse my fellow seamen in the cabin. Again I saw them: one came down very close to the boat which lay rather too far from the bank to be slipped on board of, but to my surprise one of the invaders approached with something in his hands that looked like a rail or board, which was evidently intended to assist in getting into the bow of the boat or knock out my brains with if I stirred! I felt transfixed to the barrelhead, and my fist froze fast to my trowsers pocket upon my brass barrelled pistol. Had the power to do so remained in my limbs, I should unquestionably have scrambled on deck and broke for the cabin.

I could just make out the dusky figure with the rail standing close to the boat, but it was evidently impossible for him to see me in the double darkness of my situation. "Hallo! de bote?" said the fellow in a quite low call, and by his accent I of course discovered he was a Negro. "Hallo! de bote?" he again called in a low hoarse whisper.

The Negroes are in the habit of thus calling out, and if they are answered by anybody, they make some inquiries about the price of bacon or whiskey and finally sneak off; but if no one answers, they naturally conclude all hands are asleep, and there is an opening for plunder.

He then disappeared and in an instant returned with two others. The plank or rail was carefully laid on to the bow, and to my horror one of the villains began to come aboard! I was speechless and glued fast to the barrelhead with fear, but what was my utter horror and consternation to see right before me the hand of a white man, armed with a heavy horse pistol! It was evident now that robbery and *murder* were about to take place! Now or never was the time for me to make a desperate movement. It was plain I should be discovered if I kept still—should have my throat cut and be quietly thrown into the swift, deep stream. My mind was made up in a moment, and my self-possession returned as suddenly. Slowly drawing my pistol, just as the fellow put his head fairly under the deck and within two feet of my own, I pulled the trigger.

A heavy fall of a man's body upon the bottom of the boat and a terrific yell of anguish or horror that roused the crew who came running forward in confusion and fright announced the dreadful fact that I had fallen from the barrel in my sleep, firing off my pistol by the concussion in my pocket, setting my trowsers on fire, and raising a lump on my forehead against the bottom of the boat about the size of a goose egg! In fact, I was just about *killed dead* for a few minutes, and it required considerable vinegar and whiskey to resuscitate me. The Lord only knows where the *ball* in the pistol went to, but with the exception of tearing the leg out of my old trowsers and setting them on fire, I felt no serious effects from the malicious little projectile. I swore, of course, that I had been assailed— shot and knocked down by a score of ruffians and cutthroats, and from the appearance of matters the supposition was feasible enough.

Daylight appeared; we cut loose and left the scene of my fearful adventure.

The Crack Captain on the Mississippi
by "S."

§ This story appeared in the *Spirit*, XVII, No. 11 (May 8, 1847), 122. The author is unidentified.

SOME men rise to distinctions, as you know, in one line of life, others in a different one, according to the bent of their genius; for, as Long Tom said, "You can't make a soldier of a cock, or a sailor of a goose." As Napoleon in war and Newton and La Place in philosophy rose like top-sawyers over all mankind, so doth Capt. Stecke stand out in popularity along the "coast"[12] above all others for iron memory and his accommodating disposition, especially where the softer sex is concerned....

His "hard sense," you must know, has never been impaired by the vulgar art of reading, all dependence on writing has been carefully excluded from his system of mnemonics, and as for cyphering he carries all that "in his head." Charged on his trips going and returning with all sorts of commissions by all sorts of people, he was never known to forget one iota from a sugarboiler down to a sugarbowl.

In fact, the perennial fountain of his overflowing popularity is in his readiness to attend to the *smallest matters*. In that respect he may be compared to the great Elephant Nero that with his great flexible trunk he could lift up with equal grace a horse or a hobnail. So Capt. Stecke is equally to be trusted to sell a bale of cotton or to buy a cambric needle. He was commissioned on one trip by the women along the coast to bring back from New Orleans one hundred and

---

12. In "Pummelings by the Way," "Attackapas," *Spirit*, XVII, No. 44 Dec. 25, 1847), 13, says: "The captains on the Mississippi are proverbial for their disposition to oblige, between Baton Rouge and New Orleans. The packets will always stop for a ball of twine or a letter, and yet the people on the 'coast' are always complaining. It was only a few weeks since that an old lady refused to ship any more on the *Magnol* because Thomasson refused to stop until she could complete her dozen of eggs; she had eleven and the hen had gone to lay, and yet the Captain would not wait just five minutes to oblige a lady."

twenty-three different articles, none of which cost more than a picayune![13]

Among a thousand instances of his placable temper, let me relate one that can be vouched for. You may commend it to our racing boats on the Hudson, but I doubt that they will imitate his example.

Early one morning, somewhat sooner than usual, the Captain was seen coming down under high pressure at twelve knots an hour, loaded down to the water's edge. He came to Donaldsonville on the starboard side of the river to take off some lady passengers—for the ladies, you must know, will any time wait two days to go with Capt. Stecke. Having "all aboard," he was laying on his steam to be off again when down ran an old Creole woman crying, "Ah! *Capitaine* Stecke, *mon ami,* you please wait one leetle moment. You see, I av leven eggs, *mais* I want to send one *dozaine;* I no spec you so soon, *pardonnez mois.* My 'en gone to lay one more egg. Ah! *mon chere Capitaine,* you please wait one leetle moment. I want you buy me one pape de pins, one ankerchief, red and yellow shek ankerchief, and one poun wat you call de *mackibaw.*"

"Certainly, Madam," was the prompt and hearty response of the Captain, "anything to accommodate a lady."

As might be expected, the passengers fretted, and fumed, and protested, but it was "no go" with the Captain, whose motto is

> *When a lady's in the case*
> *All other things give place.*

Fortunately, it was but a brief trial of their patience, for in a very few moments out flew the old lady's hen from her nest—*cackle! cackle! cackle!*—in higher glee at the great feat she had performed than old Rough and Ready after one of his hard-fought battles. "*Ecoutez! Ecoutez!*" cried the old lady as the familiar sound caught her impatient ear, and away she ran, coming back in the twinkling of an eye with a round dozen of fresh eggs in the same little old basket that for years had been the familiar acquaintance of Captain Stecke on his way to New Orleans.

13. A Spanish-American coin worth one-sixteenth of a dollar in circulation in New Orleans until 1857 when Congress repealed the law of 1793 which permitted circulation of foreign money; Fayette Copeland, *Kendall of the Picayune* (Norman: University of Oklahoma Press, 1943), p. 23.

Thus steams his boat up and down, filled with odds and ends, and if the prayers of the ladies can avail, so will he continue as long as the great Father of Rivers shall pour its turbid waters into the bosom of the dark blue sea.

Breaking a Bank

By Sol Smith

§ Sol Smith (1801-1869) was an actor and theatrical manager. Aspects of his career in New Orleans are discussed in John S. Kendall's *The Golden Age of New Orleans Theater* (Baton Rouge: Louisiana State University Press, 1952), 186-209 and *passim*. In addition to many sketches in the *Spirit*, Smith published three books, *Theatrical Apprenticeship* (1845), *Theatrical Journey Work* (1845), and *Theatrical Management in the West and South* (1868). The following story appeared in *A Quarter Race in Kentucky and Other Sketches*.

CAPTAIN Summons is a very clever fellow, and the *Dr. Franklin was* a very superb boat, albeit inclined to rock about a good deal and nearly turn over on her side when visited by a breath of air in the least resembling a gale. Captain Summons is a very clever fellow. All steamboat captains are clever fellows—or *nearly* all. But what I mean to say is Captain Summons is a *particularly* clever fellow!—a clever fellow in the widest sense of the term, a fellow that is clever in every way, anxious that his passengers shall be comfortably bestowed, well fed and attended to, and *determined* that they shall amuse themselves "just as they d––n please," as the saying is. If he happens to have preachers on board, he puts on a serious countenance of a Sunday morning, consents that there shall be preaching, orders the chairs to be set out, provides Bibles and hymn books for the occasion, and himself and his officers, whose watch is below, taking front seats and listening attentively to the discourse. Likely as not, at the close of the service he will ask the reverend gentleman who has been officiating with his back in close proximity to a hot fire in a Franklin furnace to accompany him to the bar and join him in some refreshments! If there are passengers on board who prefer to pass the time away in playing poker, euchre, brag, or whist, tables and chairs are ready for *them*, too—poker, brag, euchre, and whist be it! All sorts of passengers are accommodated on the *Dr. Franklin;* the rights of none are suffered to be infringed; all are free to follow such employments as shall please themselves. A *dance* in the evening is a very common occurence on this boat, and when cotillions are on the *carpet* the captain is sure to be *thar*.

It sometimes happens that at the commencement of a voyage, it is found somewhat difficult to reconcile *all* the passengers to the system of Captain Summons, which is founded on the broad principle of equal rights to all. On the occasion of my voyage in the *Doctor* in December, 1844, I found myself surrounded by a crowd of passengers who were *entire strangers* to me, a very rare occurrence to one who travels so often on the western rivers as I do. I wished my absence from New Orleans to be as brief as possible, and the *Doctor* was the fastest boat in port at the time of my leaving the Crescent City. I resolved to secure a berth in her and trust in luck to find a St. Louis boat at the Mouth.[14]

I don't know how it is or *why* it is but by strangers I am almost always taken for a preacher. It was so on this voyage. There were three Methodist *circuit* riders on board, and it happened that we got acquainted and were a good deal together. From this circumstance I was supposed to be *one of them*, which supposition was the means of bringing me into an acquaintance with the lady passengers who, for the most part, were very pious, religiously inclined souls. We had preaching every day and sometimes at night, and I must say in justice to Brothers Twitchel and Switchell that their sermons were highly edifying and instructive.

In the meantime a portion of the passengers "at the other end of the hall" continued to play sundry games with cards, notwithstanding the remonstrances of the worthy followers of Wesley who frequently requested the Captain to interfere and break up such unholy doings. The Captain had but one answer. It was something like this: "Gentlemen, amuse yourselves as you like; preach and pray to your hearts' content—none shall interfere with your pious purposes; some like that sort of thing—I have no objection to it. These men prefer to amuse themselves with cards; let them—they pay their passage as well as you, gentlemen, and have as much right to *their*

14. That is, Cairo, Ill., transfer point at the junction of the Ohio and Mississippi Rivers.

amuse*ments* as you have to *yours,* and they shall not be disturbed. Preach, play cards, dance cotillions—do what you like, *I* am agreeable. Only understand that *all games* (preaching among the rest) *must cease at ten o'clock."* So *we* preachers got very little comfort from Captain Summons.

Up—up, up—up we went. Christmas day arrived. All the *other* preachers had holden forth on divers occasions, and it being ascertained that it was my intention to leave the boat on her arrival at Cairo, a formal request was preferred that *I should preach the Christmas sermon!* The ladies (God bless them all!) were *very* urgent in their applications to me. "Oh, *do,* Brother Smith! we *want* to hear *you* preach! All the others have contributed their share to our spiritual comfort—you *must* oblige us—indeed you must!" I endeavored to excuse myself the best way I could—alleging the necessity of my leaving the boat in less than a hour—my baggage was not ready—I had a terrible cold. Many other good and substantial reasons were given, but all in vain—preach I must. "Well," thinks I, "if I must, I must."

At this crisis, casting my eyes down towards the social hall and seeing an unusual crowd assembled around a table, I asked one of the brethren what might be going on down there. The fattest of the preaching gentlemen replied, "The poor miserable sinners have filled the measure of their iniquity by opening a *faro bank!"* "Horrible!" exclaimed I, holding up my hands and "Horrible!" echoed the ladies and missionaries in full chorus. "Cannot such doings be put a stop to?" asked an elderly lady, addressing the pious travellers. "I fear not," groaned my Methodist contemporary (the fat one). "We have been trying to convince the Captain that some dreadful accident will inevitably befall the boat if such proceedings are permitted, and what do you think he answered?" "What?" we all asked, of course. "Why, he just said that, inasmuch as he permitted *us* to preach and pray, he should let other passengers dance and play, if they chose to do so and that if I didn't like the 'proceedings' I complained of *I might leave the boat!* Yes—he did, and, moreover, he mentioned that it was eleven o'clock and asked me if I wouldn't 'liquor'!" This announcement of the Captain's stubborness and impiety was met with a general groan of pity and sorrow, and we resumed the conversation respecting the unhallowed faro bank. "It is much to be regretted," remarked the elderly lady who had spoken before, "that *something* can't be done." She continued appealing directly to me and laying her forefinger impressively upon my arm, "Brother Smith, cannot *you* break up that bank?" "Dear Madam," I answered, "you know not the difficulty of the task you impose upon me—*Faro banks are not so easily broken up* as you may imagine; however, as you all appear so anxious about it, if you'll excuse me from the sermon, I'll see what can be done." "Ah! that's a dear soul!"—"I knew he would try"—"He'll be sure to succeed!"—"Our prayers shall not be wanting!" Such were the exclamations that greeted me as I moved off towards the faro bank. Elbowing my way into the crowd, I got near the table in front of the dealer and was for a time completely concealed from the view of my pious friends near the door of the ladies' cabin. I found the bank was a small affair. The bettors were risking trifling sums ranging from six to twenty-five cents.

"Mr. Dealer," I remarked, "I have come to break up this bank." "The deuce you have!" replied the banker; "let's see you do it." "What amount have you in the bank?" I inquired. "Eleven dollars," was his answer. "What is your limit?" asked I. "A dollar," he replied. "Very well," said I, placing a ragged Indiana dollar behind the queen. "Turn on." He turned and the king won for me. I took the two dollars up and let him make another turn; I replaced the bet and queen came up in my favor. I had now four dollars which I placed in the square, taking in the five, six, seven, and eight—and it won again! Here were seven dollars of the banker's money. I pocketed three of them and bet four dollars behind the queen again; the jack won and the *bank was broken!* The crowd dispersed in all directions, laughing at the breaking up of the petty bank, and I made my way towards the ladies' cabin where my new friends were anxiously awaiting the result of my bold attempt. "Well, well, well," they all exclaimed. "What success? Have you done it? Do let us hear all about it!" I wiped the perspiration from my brow, and putting on a very serious face I said solemnly, "I *have broken that bank!*" "You have?" they all exclaimed. "Yes, I'll be d---d if he hasn't!" muttered the disappointed gamester, the keeper of the late bank who was just going into his stateroom. In the midst of the congratulations which were showered upon me, I received a *summons* from the Captain to come forward with my baggage — we were at Cairo.

The Wrong Berth

by "Crawfish" of New Orleans

§ Several sketches concerning going to bed in an embarrassing circumstance were printed in the *Spirit*, the most widely known, "Going to
Bed Before a Young Lady," being credited to Judge Douglas of Illinois.
This story appeared in the *Spirit*, XX, No. 36 (October 26, 1850), 522,
reprinted from *Civil, Military and Naval Gazette*.

A VERY amusing thing occurred on an excursion on board
the steamer_____from this city to the watering places, via the
Mississippi.

About sunset on the evening of Saturday, June, 1850, the fine
steamer_____left her moorings and gently made her way down to
the "Father of Water." Wishing to take a farewell look at the City of
Juleps, I went up on the hurricane roof[15] and there beheld a scene
beyond description; as far as the eye could reach the upper part of
the city it beheld a forest of masts, and then, as it descended, came
the steamboats from all parts of the valley of the Mississippi, then
comes what is termed the Picayune Tier, then again another forest
of masts, and last, though not least, the Government wharf and its
vessels, and so on, until the last glimpse of the city and environs
vanishes from the eye, the beautiful plantations, which are unequalled
by any in the world, on the coast now meet the view.

There were some fifty passengers aboard, among whom were
French, Spanish, Irish, Dutch, and, in fact, a sprinkling of all nations.
While gazing at the above-mentioned spectacle, I noticed a fat, short,
pursy, round, pumpkin-faced Frenchman; the hair on his head had
emigrated to his upper lip, which made quite an extensive moustache, say about five inches in length; his coat was one of the striped
kind and looked as if some mischievous cur had stolen the tail of it;
and to sum up the whole, he was the queerest piece of unfinished

15. Most steamboats had three decks—main, boiler, and hurricane; after Texas was
admitted to the union, a fourth deck called the "Texas" was added; Quick, *Mississippi
Steamboatin'*, pp. 95-96.

humanity I ever beheld. He was jabbering French constantly, but there was more to be understood from gestures than from what he was trying to get through with in English.

Having quite forgotten the little Frenchman, I was sitting soliloquizing upon the excursion and the scene around when I was accosted by Monsieur Paroe (the French gentleman's name). "How de do. Sair, vaire fine boat, he fly—no, not fly—he, he, bump trou de wata plenty times in one minute." I made no reply to his observation, but catching a chance to call his attention to something on shore, I slid down stairs with a rush.

When the boat was fairly under way some distance down the river and everything snugly arranged, our attention was called to the bell—the bell of the boat, the supper bell, the bell of all belles—whose sound makes all, great and small, "stoop to conquer" their appetites. While enjoying a fine and delicious supper (which the South ern boats, and especially those of the Mississippi, are famed for), I again noticed Monsieur Paroe and the manner in which he *got through* at his supper. He would raise up his moustache with his left hand and with his right deposit whatever it might be in his *breadbasket*. I think they set three tables, and I noticed Mons. Paroe at the third table, not quite *through*.

Supper over, I again retired to the hurricane roof where I seated myself in a large comfortable armchair and while enjoying a delicious Havana drove all thoughts of the past from my memory; all around was dark and gloomy with nothing to disturb the deathlike stillness save the hoarse voice of the 'scape-pipe and the splashing of the wheels in the water as the steamer ploughed her way down the mighty Mississippi. Probably I would have remained in this pleasant mood until midnight had not a mosquito very politely reminded me where I should be; so rising up with two or three yawns, I descended to the cabin. Everybody had retired but myself, and as I am seldom behind in the fashion I went to my berth and had pulled off *my everything* and was about retiring to bed when I was aroused by a terrible scream, apparently from some lady, followed by an exclamation of "Got tam!" I was dressed and on my way to the scene of trouble in less than two minutes. The cabin presented a different aspect from what it had ten minutes previous; passengers, stewards, cook, chambermaids, and others were making their way to the ladies' cabin, all with anxiety depicted on their countenances.

I arrived just in time to see Monsieur Paroe hauled out of one of the ladies' staterooms by a gentleman, the husband of the lady in whose room poor Frenchy had been found. Paroe was the picture of despair; in his hasty exit from the room he made out to grab from the berth a sheet in which he was wrapt up to the eyes. The poor fellow was so frightened that what hair he had (in the place where the wool ought to grow) actually *riz right up* and pitched the handerchief off that he had tied around his head. His moustache stuck out like two frying pan handles; you might have hung a fifty-six on them. It appears that he got a ticket from the clerk with No. 3 on it, and not being acquainted the usages of the boat he by mistake got into the ladies' cabin. When he felt like going to roost, as they say out West, he bolted into No. 3 where there was quite a pretty lady wrapt in the arms of Morpheus. Monsieur Paroe entered, shut and bolted the door, and quietly began to undress himself with his back to the berth; he never thought for a minute of looking into the berth, being positive that he was right; he had No. 3 on his ticket and was in stateroom No. 3. He had finally got off all his clothes with the exception of his shirt; he drew from his coat pocket a fancy colored handkerchief and tied it around his head; and being very sleepy he gave one yawn, raised the mosquito bar, and jumped into bed. Oh ye Gods and little fishes! the scream that saluted his ears! He was lost for a moment to all sense of feeling. "Got tam!" were the only words he used to express his astonishment. At that moment the husband who had just come into the cabin rushed to his wife's room. Finding the door bolted, he seized a heavy armchair and with one blow drove it in with a terrible crash. Lo! he beheld the poor Frenchman sitting on the side of the berth with his legs dangling and petrified with astonishment. Fortunately for him, the Captain arrived just in time to save him from the enraged husband. One of the passengers who spoke French was called upon as interpreter, and the dispute was settled to the satisfaction of all parties.

"It's All Right, Captain"

by Anonymous

§ The following story appeared in the *Spirit*, XXIII, No. 21 (July 9, 1853), 249.

As the fleet steamer R_____ was coming up the Mississippi not long since, several way passengers came on board at Vicksburg, and among others a giant looking middle-aged Kentuckian, who very soon became the subject of curiosity, wonder, and general remark. After travelling a short distance, the party, except "our hero," made their way to the Captain's office and paid their fare to the place of destination. The next day, the clerk made bold to call on the delinquent passenger who had taken no berth but had passed the greater part of his time in sleeping in his chair, and with his usual urbanity of manner asked the Kentuckian to give him his place of destination as it would help him in making up his book, intending his question also as a gentle hint for him to pay his fare.

The giant rose from his lethargy and replied, "I'm going up the river a-piece—It's all right, Mr. Clerk."

The clerk, not being much the wiser from this answer, again politely asked, "At what point do you intend to land, sir?"

"Don't land at *no point*, Mr. Clerk. It's all *right* though."

Here the clerk left our old hero and went to consult the Captain, who at once lost his wonted good humor as the clerk related the result of his interview with the delinquent customer. The Captain proceeded forthwith to bring the matter to a focus and accosted the Kentuckian, saying, "How far are you going to bear us company up the river, Uncle?"

"Oh! I'm going a-piece up with ye—but it's all *right*, Captain!"

"But sir," said the Captain, "you have neither paid your fare nor given the clerk your place of destination, and you are old enough to know the custom of steamboat men that when a man refuses to pay his fare or to give a good reason for not paying we put him ashore immediately."

"W-e-l-l, Captain, 'spose 'tis your custom, but it's all *right!*"

Here the Captain lost his patience and resolved to put him ashore forthwith. The Captain accordingly ordered the pilot to land and told the Kentuckian to make ready to go ashore, to which he very graciously replied, "It's all right, Captain."

The boat landed; the plank was put out, and the giant was told to walk, to which he readily assented, saying, "It's all right."

After the Kentuckian was on terra firma, the Captain gave him a short blessing for giving him the trouble to land and threatened him a top dressing if he ever saw him again, etc. The old man responded again with an air of triumph, pointing to a fine looking cottage just above him on the bank, "It's *all* right, Captain, that's my home. It's *all right.*"

The Tallest Snake Story

by Anonymous of Louisiana

§ The following story was printed in the *Richmond Compiler*, I, No. 34 (February 22, 1842), 2. The *Compiler* was founded in 1841 in Richmond, Louisiana. The only known file of the paper ends July 22, 1844; this bound volume is owned by Mrs. S. B. Bettis of Tallulah, Louisiana, and has been copied on microfilm and deposited in the University of North Carolina library. See John Q. Anderson, "The *Richmond Compiler*, 1841-1844," *Louisiana Historical Quarterly*, XXXIX (October 1956), 419-441.

JUDGE "Blowhard" is the appropriate appelation under which a very distinguished member of the Mississippi legislature has revelled for many years past. The Judge's heart is the home of every feeling and sentiment that can adorn or lend a beauty to the nature of man; his brain is the seat of lofty thought and of warm, devoted, patriotic sentiments. However, as his name intimates, the Judge occasionally indulges in extending to a winding ligament the product of the sheep's back, or as we render it in our vernacular "spinning a yarn."

Not many months since, the Judge was seated in the deepest reverie in the social hall of one of those majestic steamers which float upon the waters of our noble Mississippi River. Supper was over, and the passengers gradually dropped one by one at the side of the Judge and before he was well aware of the fact he was surrounded by a host of the jolliest fellows that ever "run a saw," stole an apple, or ate an oyster. The passage had been a long one and as usual exceedingly monotonous. The passengers resorted to light and mirth inspiring anecdotes in order to drive the lazy hours along, and, as we will soon see, some of them drew heavy drafts upon their imagination. Hunting stories which are old as the hills and familiar as household words were rehearsed and palmed off as original. The "deep" was called upon to furnish its volume of interesting incidents and produced many a startling tale of horror and of hair-breadth escape; the devotees of Old Isaac, sir-named Walton, gave their portion when the conversation turned upon the keenness of some of the faculties of the brain.

One man boasted of having seen a fly at a hundred yards; another that he had *heard it step*. This was a fit time for the Judge to run his "saw"; he remarked, "Gentlemen, I was one day standing on a high bluff on the Ohio and had a clear view of that noble stream for twenty-five miles; I cast my eye down at the fartherest point from me and discovered a turkey gobbler sitting upon a limb of a very fine tree." One little blinkey-eyed, snub-nosed, carrotty-haired, stuttering Yankee here poked in his jaw and asked the Judge, "How do yeow know it was a g-g-gobbler?" "How did I know!" said the Judge, as he cast a look of withering contempt upon his interrogator. "How did I *know* it was a gobbler? Why I *seen his beard!*"

The conversation dropped here for a moment. It was taken up again in a few minutes, however, by a Hoosieroon who boasted of the size of his trees and the luxuriance of his land. This started the Judge again, and he remarked, "Gentlemen, I had a tree on my plantation which was so large that it furnished lumber enough for a two-story frame house, built all my stables, Negro quarters, and made rails enough to fence in all my plantation." The snub-nosed Yankee popped his jaw in again and remarked that *his* "Uncle Ben had a tree so large that the boys used to climb upon it to shoot squirrels, and they frequently went out so far upon the limb that they *couldn't hear one another's guns when they fired!*" The Judge appeared to be stumped; once more did he dart a look of supreme and ineffable contempt upon the last speaker and remarked between his teeth that "the last story was a *lie.*"

Snake stories next came up. Wonderful snake stories were told by many persons. Here the Judge thought he was at home. No one *could* beat him in *that* line he was sure. His eyes were seen to glisten with his anticipated success, and he drew himself up with the most exquisite pomposity and remarked, "My place grows the largest serpents in all creation. I was out 'a-snaking' one day and killed a rattlesnake that was *forty-nine* feet long and had *thirty-eight* rattles!" After this "highly concentrated mental accouchement," the Judge threw himself back in the chair, stuck out his legs, looked at the

Yankee, and seemed to say, "Beat *that* if you *can*, d--n you." The Yankee was not to be stumped; he slipped in his gab again and said, "I w–was r–riding l–long through the W–Wisconsin Territory; I saw something m–m–moving cross the road and w–waited about half an hour for it to go by, but it d–didn't do it; I t–t–turned my horse down the thing and had to ride a mile and a half before I could get to a place *small enough for my horse to jump over!* And g–g–gentlemen, I never *did* find out *how big that snake was!*"

The Judge was "busted," "swunk up," and had to give in. He retired to bed immediately and has never been known to tell a story since that time.

The Backcountry

The Rivers which were the great highways of the Old Southwest were about the only highways. As soon as the traveler got off the steamboat at a landing, he found himself in the mud. And the farther he went from the river, the dimmer the road became until it eventually turned into a trail or vanished altogether. Excepting the Natchez Trace and a few military roads, not a trail existed over thousands of acres of the country. No wonder that the traveler through the backcountry frequently got lost and desperately sought for a place to spend the night. When he found a lonely cabin or a tavern at a stream crossing, he was hardly in any mood for the coarse food and poor accommodations he found. But as Thomas D. Clark has pointed out:

The spirit of the frontier on the whole was one of rough good-natured cordiality and hospitality. A backwoodsman meant what he said when he greeted new arrivals with 'Light stranger! light and hang your horse to a tree—walk in—we'll spare you some liquor, and gin you something to gnaw on.'[1]

Of course, many travelers, especially foreign ones, did not understand that frontiersmen were on the move, that they cared more for the future than the past, and that they had little regard for social amenities. Clark continues:

It never occurred to the average frontiersman that his personal habits, table manners, mode of speaking or general appearance was anything to excite a stranger. Where the French and English peasants were tractable, governable, and meticulous, the American was careless about his dress, his homestead, and his manners. As one of his most sympathetic historians has said, he was 'blunt, straightforward, and independent in his discourse.' He was 'intractable, beyond control.'[2]

1. "The American Backwoodsman in Popular Portraiture," *Indiana Magazine of History*, XLII (March 1946), 2.
2. *Ibid.*, p. 7.

Popular humor, of course, capitalized on this independent spirit and the eccentricities of the backwoodsman. In its concentration on unusual characters and incidents, the humor of the Old Southwest presents an exaggerated picture of the backwoodsman. Against this caricature may be posed the flattering picture created by one of the frontier humorists:

> ...the ruder but not less noble specimens of human kind that are dwellers of the Western tier of the States...are of taut strung nerve, and as the flash of the simeter [sic] when drawn for furious fight, found not the less true than the hard steel....those noble specimens of nature's man that form the bare-breasted wall of our vast frontier—the bold Backwoodsmen of the South and West—and sculptured art is shamed by these noble patterns of her proudest efforts....good citizens, and pure patriots they are, performing all duties devolving upon them, and though sometimes judging harshly of the law, yet ever ready for the right and ready for its defence by argument or arms, to stand by a friend or nobly extend forgiveness to a fallen foe and lending to him a helping hand when conquered. Such, such are the men we tell of, and would have them known and esteemed.[3]

Despite his noble-savage theme and his florid prose, this writer, living as he did on the last frontier in Louisiana, had adequate opportunity to observe backwoodsmen and evidently did not dislike what he saw.

But it is not the picture presented by the defender of the countryman or by the serious historian that has survived in the popular mind; it is, rather, the denizens of Dogpatch, the mountaineers of cartoons, and the hillbilly of movies and television. The humor of the Old Southwest to some extent contributed to this

3. *Spirit*, XIV, No. 24 (Aug. 10, 1844), 279. From the introduction to "Mosquito Bait" (printed in the section entitled "The Professions"); "Concordia," the author, was probably Robert Patterson, editor of the *Concordia Intelligencer*, Vidalia, La.

cherished American myth by creating backwoods types and preserving them in print. In view of the humorists' concentration on character and incident, the presentation of the backwoodsman is not as vicious in its class distinction as some twentieth-century critics claim. Were that so, then it is difficult to account for their implicit—and sometimes stated—admiration of the plucky spirit of the man of the backwoods, especially of his skill in repartee and his refusal to be worsted by the man of the town.

A New Town in Arkansas

by "Concordia" of Louisiana

§ "Concordia" was probably also the author of the "Stoke Stout" letters published in the *Concordia Intelligencer* and reprinted in the *Spirit of the Times.* The "Yazoo" in this sketch is the writer of that name referred to in the preceding section. This story appeared in the *Spirit,* XIV, No. 2 (March 9, 1844), 13-14.

SOME years ago during the rage for speculation,[4] it was no unusual thing for the pencil in sketching the topography of any new town to make all crooked places straight and rough places smooth and plain; all was made beautiful to the eye and every sense of taste was gratified as the delighted beholder with intent gaze stood fixed before the promised seats of future greatness, which with glowing language were described as surpassing beyond all dreams of comparison all existing cities, towns, or villages. It was our lot when the fever raged fiercest to realize the full truthfulness of those brilliant picturings of fancy, to dream of the reality, and to gaze upon its rude and unformed inception; for it was but the semblance of a thought we looked on when we beheld the new, delightful, and eligible town of Belleair, situated upon the Arkansas River, about so many "miles from the mouth and contiguous to the most fertile region of the State and the healthiest part of the Union; situated high and commanding where the cool breeze constantly fanned the fevered brow and the sunshine, ever beaming clear, glows from the heart." Thus in glowing words and flowery language ran the advertisement which told of other divine and sundry felicities too numerous to mention.

We had driven fast and far; there were four of us penned up in a

4. In the early 1830s an era of deceptive prosperity was stimulated by public land sales in the West, and as a result a huge surplus was created in the national treasury. The famous "Specie Circular" of July 1, 1836, required land agents to accept only specie for public lands rather than notes on local banks; land sales declined, eastern financiers called in loans, Western banks went broke, and a severe depression followed and lasted several years.

small stagecoach, cramped and confined, in a space smaller than nature fitted us to occupy; a morning's ride—hot, dusty, and most disagreeable—was followed by a severe thunder gust and drenching shower in which we reached the ferry that was to convey us to the promised land, the town of Belleair, far famed and most widely known and spoken of through the region. "Won't we go it in the way of a big rest!" said a big Kentuckian. "I'll *julepize* with a vengeance," said one of the Orleans gentry. "I'll make the whiskey *slide!*" said Yazoo, an interesting individual not unknown to fame and claiming a "clearing" in the then new purchase of Mississippi. We listened to their bright dreams of bliss as we stole a sly glance towards the opposite shore, and we smiled quietly as the ferryman upon being asked where the town was replied, *"Close by, stranger; don't fret. I reckon I'll show you just sich another town as ain't to be seen every day."*

There was something sarcastic, a dash of *insinuated sourness* about the fellow's speech that lent us new light, and again we smiled.

The river was crossed, and our stage *bogged* in most gallant style.

"Come," said one of the company, "let's walk to the town and send hands down to extricate the stage and horses."

"Aye! aye! do as you choose, gents," said our sour Charon, as his tongue protruded out of his dexter cheek some inch or so while his left thumb rested on his nose and the other digits of his hand performed various fife-playing movements most indicative of a non-comatibus return for the promised start after hands.

We *took* in an instant and took occasion to ingratiate ourselves into the good graces of this uncouth specimen of the backwoods waterman. While our companions trudged manfully through mud knee-deep for a mile to attain a point three hundred yards distant, we most philosophically seated ourself upon a stump and unfolded the ferryman. Said he, *"Stranger, it's all humbug! This country is all humbug! Belleair is all humbug! Everything about here ain't like nothing no where else, and so it's all humbug. There ain't no town here*—nothin but a log cabin that Dick Swike built cause the folks what own the new town give him a lot to start the town! Dick, poor fellow, is got a wife and three children and he couldn't live no where else, and so he thought he might's well stand a chance of dying off here in this sickly hole; *and maybe, stranger, if it ain't the sickliest place this side of t'other, I don't know where the next is. Tha' is all sick now!"*

This was cold comfort for us, for we had fasted and with the *fast* had travelled far and felt as if a feast would best suit our feelings. We strolled leisurely toward the town where we found stakes marking tier on tier of streets, and on an old gum stump some ten feet high was stuck a whitewashed board on which was scrawled with charcoal "Broadway." It was unnecessary for us to look for the "Park"— it was around and about us. We entered the solitary cabin of the city which should in some future day rival the oft-told glories of Old Troy and make Venice pale and startle with wonder and surprise the pigmy ports of modern times. We *entered* and beheld on an upturned washtub our *Orleannois* with arms folded and doleful gaze fixed upon the puncheon floor. *Old Kentuck* was fuming and cursing most violently the outrageous imposters who had attempted to pass this *place* off as anything of a *place. Yazoo* commenced cavorting about the way they did things "in the Purchase" and wound up by saying that he would be "half slung" if the proprietors of Belleair should not be lynched for thus "taking in" us four interesting strangers. "Why," said he, "I've walked all about the house, and they hain't got even a speck of bran, and the cow has run off, and a weasel killed the last chicken last night, and the whiskey barrel is empty, and the only thing I have seed is about a half a barrel of soap-grease! What do you think of that boys! *Soap-grease,* I say, soap-grease! Will you have it fried, biled, briled, roasted, or stewed, or will you take it fricasseed with a few corncobs? It is the *only* chance, and we'll have to stand it, boys. As for me, I'll take mine raw, and—pitch it out of the window!" and away went the barrel of soap-grease as Dick entered his castle.

He opened his budget of complaint and misfortune with the comfortable assurance that our stage could not be extricated before the following morning and then unfolded his own miseries. He told us "whar he was from, what brought him thar, why he staid, why he couldn't get away, his prospects, the sickness of his family, the death of his chickens, the loss of his cow, the support of himself, wife, and four children, during periods of scarcity" and talked about the "ager and fever."

'Twas a budget of blues poor Dick heaped upon us, and he, poor fellow, from the speechless astonishment with which we listened to the tale thought we feasted on it; on and on he went, misfortune on misfortune piled he upon us, until finally Kentuck broke the charm by asking, *"Why don't you lie down and die, old fellow?"*

Good nature and true earnestness seemed breathing in the question, while Kentuck's eye glistened and his features glowed with that benignant brilliancy which tells that the heart within feels conscious of the commission of an act of good. So supremely ridiculous was the scene, so *malapropos* the implied advice that the balance of our crowd yelled a loud laugh, Yazoo leading the cry. Dick retired to superintend the grassing of our two horses, and shortly afterwards his wife entered bearing under each arm a yellow-haired urchin while the balance of the interesting family hung to her dress, screaming, squalling, and kicking most noisily, un-angelic music, awful to the ear and stunning to every sense and feeling.

"Well!" exclaimed this specimen of_____the unadulterated slattern, *"I 'spose, men, as how you want some supper?"*

"Yes," we replied most voraciously and veraciously, for it was as Yazoo said a "nateral truth that we were as hungry as a pack of Indian dogs," and they, reader, are fed, feasted, and fattened upon hunger and 'tis said sometimes grow sleek with gaunt famine—i.e., they die from sheer want and swell when dead.

"Well, 'spose we ain't got nothing?"

"O!" replied we with a bland conciliatory smile—one of our winning electioneering smiles—"we can do tolerably well upon anything rather than nothing."

"Stra–a–nger, you've travelled 'fore today—you are up to we poor folks' ways—you've bin in the Injun country and know a thing or two."

Her sallow complexion assumed for an instant a long forgotten hue, her lips parted, she smiled and her eyes glistened with pleasure, as we replied by thanking her for the compliment and directed her thoughts to the future glories of Belleair. *It was her hobby,* and upon this *streak* as they say in Ohio, she was a perfect monomaniac. She talked, fumed, raved, screeched, and became a demon, not of destruction, but of enterprise and improvement—took us from our seat on a three-legged settle and made us travel through mud and water almost knee-deep that we might be made acquainted with the splendid site of Belleair. Streets, alleys, lanes, and squares were pointed out; names from every city and all lands were scattered round this skeleton village thick as the liquid mud which floated, streaked, or stood in pools on every hand. We returned to the house and the dame said in uncouth phrase, *"Men, I'll feed you.* Sit down—be at home—make yourselves comfortable."

Picture to yourself, reader, a twelve-foot unbarked log cabin, built of the greenest sort of pecan—two beds occupying one-half the room—an uncouth bureau, the remnant of some forgotten time of prosperity, half the drawers without handles and the rude veneering in patches peeled from its face—a triangular piece of what was once a shaving glass occupying its top together with sundry and divers other "small doings," tawdry as the most perverted taste could pine for. One third of the opposite side of this Tremont, Astor, Barnum's, Galt, or St. Charles[5] of Belleair was taken up by an extensively laid-out but unfinished fireplace whose upper story admitted rain by the bucketsfull and gusts furious as the highly-concentrated northwest could send. Over the usual place occupied by the mantelpiece hung a roughly stocked rifle upon a couple of pegs protruding from the wall; washtubs in all imaginable positions; pots, kettles, stew pans, firedogs, piggins, and bowls were scattered most picturesquely about various portions of the room; at intervals above the medley of misery and discomfort peered severally the heads of Kentuck, Yazoo, and Orleans (or as he was familiarly called by Kentuck, "Polly Bouze"), and our humble self, plain Bob. In the rude, familiar, and expressive parlance of the region, "the dame hustled about most awfully" from the corner drawing a few glazed half-gallon bowls, the requisite

5. Famous hotels of the time in Boston, New York, Baltimore, Louisville, and New Orleans.

number of plates, a couple of knives, and two single-pronged forks. Long and patiently watched we her busy bustling efforts to show off her small stock of industry for she seemed to act upon the belief that the bigger the show the better the meal. Coffee was eventually made just outside the door and a huge cornpone baked with tolerable judgment, save that it was rather "soft" when done. On the table and in its center, the very spot for display, stood a broken tumbler filled with a black liquid substance resembling the soap-grease so ruthlessly destroyed by Yazoo. He looked upon it with stolen glances while the busy notes and movements of preparation of the dame were in progress, and with that remarkable idiosyncracy which some-times troubles the mind his whole attention became riveted on the darkly filled tumbler; he was fascinated, and it was to him as the serpent eye to the charmed bird. It was a specter endowed with talismanic powers—'twas the ghost of the soap-grease! and bitterly did Yazoo rue the hour when fortune tempted him to destroy the tub.

"Men, come to supper" was the uncourtly phrase which bade us to the feast, and we were soon seated on tubs, settles, and blocks around the board. The dame poured full to the brim the half-gallon bowl with brown liquor which filled the coffee pot; in color, body, and taste it resembled, as we found by future trial, the unsweetened washing of half-grown Irish potatoes. We turned and with our most gentle tone requested her to give us but the quantity necessary to fill a common sized cup. "For," said we, "unless under extraordinary circumstances, we never drink more than that quantity of strong coffee." She replied to our remark by a smile compounded of pity and contempt and filled to the brim the bowl, observing, "Stranger, you don't know what coffee is." And with truth we confessed our ignorance of the particular variety before us. It was a strange com-pound of bitterness—washy, and most unpalatable; and to cap the climax, to fill to the highest top sparkle the half gallon of disgust before us, the Ganymede of Belleair observed, "We ain't got no sweetnin, men, 'less you sweeten your coffee with that wild honey in the tumbler." Yazoo breathed free at this announcement and was "himself again"; Richard-like he prepared for the furious fray, dived into the cornpone, and quaffed with Leviathan capacity from the bowl of bitterness. The dose was too much for us. We went through the form of eating as a matter of necessity, stayed old nature with a few crumbs of pone, raised with studied care the coffee bowl, and sipped but sufficient to moisten our tongue. Supper was finished and we rested on the spectral feast. Yazoo, with rude wit, spoke of the delicate flavor of that salmon; Kentuck replied with some witty remark as to the peculiarity of the ham — its utter absence! Orleans, moody, discontented, and "very much disgust," as a French friend of ours says when subjected to anything disagreeable, sat as we have seen an owl of forlorn and antiquated appearance perched in the gloomiest recess of the gloomiest glen.

A change came over the spirit of the scene. Dick, our worthy landlord entered and threw upon the hearth a "lighted light'ood," or pineknot, as the chandelier of Belleair's St. Charles.[6] He looked around moodily upon our crowd and with wandering gaze scanned the festal board until his eyes rested upon our unfortunate bowl. "Who," asked he with vengeful tone and flashing eyes, quivering limb, and lip compressed, "Who didn't drink that coffee?" Lifting his slouched hat from his head and dashing it like a glove of a mailed knight in old chivalric times upon the floor, he demanded "Who *didn't drink that coffee?* Tell me, wife," in a Forest-like whisper —"tell me who!"

"One of them men," replied she in that tone of suppressed discontent we have sometimes but seldom heard uttered by woman's angered tongue, without, however, identifying the individual.

With extraordinary presence of mind, we asked him the price of a lot such as No. 2 upon the splendid plat lying on the bed and which to while away the time we had been examing. The current of thought was changed, calm as the sea in summer's calmest hour; he seized the bait, and we rested from the fear of furious frays. He looked over

6. An allusion to the famous chandelier in the St. Charles Theater, New Orleans, built in 1835 and the fourth largest theater in the world at the time. The widely publicized chandelier weighed two tons, had 23,000 pieces of cut glass, lighted by 176 gas burners; it was decorated with twenty-six eagles and stars surmounted by a gilded cornice of fleurs-de-lis. The theater burned in 1842; Copeland, *Kendall of the Picayune,* p. 18.

the map; glowing satisfaction lighted his countenance, humanizing the fierce expression which an instant previous made his face a demon's. He pointed out the peculiar advantages of that lot, its nearness to the landing and vicinity to the public square, the gardens, park, and halls of justice. "It is," said he, "the choice lot of the town, and it's the one I wanted to buy myself." On and on, like an untamed steed for the first time chased, he wandered with the glowing thought within him burning and for an hour told the future glories of Belleair. Another hour passed and still the tale in wonder grew. Glory lit all the future time of this inceptive city, and for an instant we dreamed that a flashing of gas lights illuminated the streets, which beneath the lightning's lurid glare seemed to assume form and fashion—and the treetops and darkened shades of the dense forest took shape of castle, citadel, and long lines of buildings in ordered rows arranged themselves all city-like. In an instant the dream was past, and stern reality stared at us with skeleton feature as Kentuck observed to the infernal city builder, "Stranger, will you show me my room?" "You can lay your pre-emption[7] just wherever you like, stranger. Here's two beds—me and my family calkatlate on occupying one, two of you the other, and the balance of you can float on the floor." And truly was it a floating affair for the rain continued and increased, and independent of that soothing sound its dripping produced at times upon the worn or wearied we were blessed with its veritable presence, streaming as it did in no gentle flow through various apertures of the roof. It would form pools for an instant and then course in mimic rivers along the puncheons. The "Old Father of Waters," the beautiful Ohio, the muddy Arkansas, the quiet Thames, the dark-rolling Danube, the Ganges, and Afric's headless, mouthless stream, undescribed Niger—all, all were before and around and about us in miniature: cascades leaped, and fountains sprouted, Niagara, Montmorency—the lakes of Old England, and lagoons of Venice, and fiords of Norway in infant revelry played,

---

7. Frontiersmen often settled on public domain in the territories and waited to buy land until the government offered it for sale. The practice was called pre-emption. In 1841 the federal government passed the Pre-Emption Bill entitling squatters then on public domain to buy their land.

sported, or slept beneath our every glance.

Bright reader, think ye, was the prospect for repose? Kentuck and Yazoo "floated" the vacant bed; our business habits had induced us to throw furtive glances of inquiry toward that bed, and we gloried in not being victimized. It is useless to describe its varied population for generation on generation of different sizes, degrees, and races of the vermin family had "squatted" and then built permanent settlements, given birth to families, reared them, and then died, leaving hundreds of hungry, living, crawling, biting representatives for each of the handful which formed the first "settlement"—a myriad horde of pigmy monsters, in their sphere leviathans, of might and power and most prone to phlebotomizing all of human kind who dared invade their "homes and firesides." Orleans and ourself, with an eye to the nature of our floating grant and with matchless skill in the line of un-civil engineering, spread ourselves jointly and collectively upon a bearskin and blanket, located longitudinally with the building in order to shy the big leaks, but to little effect for our first doze was interrupted by a hunch from Orleans, who proposed a remove of our bedding about one foot farther north as a new leak had opened its youthful Niagara upon his feet. We accommodated ourself to his proposal, and lo! we were half drowned from another which had opened with fierce flow directly upon our face. Again we floated with like success, and again, and again; whereupon leaving Orleans to battle with the fluvial element we vacated our pre-emption and roosted on a couple of chairs; this in half an hour proved fatiguing, and we groped back to our watery lair. Again we took the chair and again the floor, thus alternating, taking the discomfort of each position in broken dose like most unpleasant medicine until the grey dawn peeped through the open cabin chinks and the rain rested for a time. We were comfortable for a time, when we were aroused by a shriek from Kentuck and the loud, death-threatening, and thrilling war-whoop of Yazoo, who had been partially educated amongst the Choctaws. Kentuck would in his half-dreamy sleep order a charge while Yazoo, skilled in woodcraft and Indian tactics, directed his imaginary command to take to the trees as the only means of escape or protection from the murderous fire dealt amongst them by the enemy dreamed of as human but felt most tangibly and touchingly amid their slumbers.

'Twas a rich scene, and although weary and somewhat worn we enjoyed·it to the full, quit our blankets and walked the floor, watching the maneuvers of the sufferers until the broad day with its full flashings of light broke their troubled slumbers.

Our own position and that of our companion Orleans upon first awaking was of itself a touch of the supremely ridiculous — for owing to the peculiar topography of the puncheon floor, but a single position could be occupied by either of us — a departure in the slightest degree from this would throw us amongst the young mountains and twixt peaks, or deep valleys which covered the face — not of the country but the floor. As our eye opened a young biped of the Chanticleer family was roosting comfortably upon one of us and on the breast of the other lay a huge specimen of the "Felis Catus," the biggest specimen of the "tom cats" of the region. Our companions here aroused and without waiting an instant for anything more in the eating line, we went to work to extricate our stage, and as if freed·from a miserable nightmare we shook the mud of Belleair from the soles of our feet and departed, most thoroughly determined never again to trust ourselves within the limits of a *new town* and particularly one destined to be *a place*.

Our landlord with the coolest *nonchalance* and an air of conscious pride at having served us well drew upon our pockets most liberally, exacting three times the ordinary charge.

The bubbles of '37 burst and Belleair, the biggest, burst with them — a dilapidated log cabin marks this spot of intended greatness and no human being lives within ten miles of the future Troy. Dick and his interesting family migrated yet farther West, and it's possible we may again in our wild rambles stir them up at some future day.

The lone log cabin of Belleair stands a melancholy memento of departed greatness; for there was greatness in and around the place — greatness of thought in the belief that it should become a place — greatness in the enterprise exhibited by the master minds of the owners and builders up of the incipient metropolis. They had planned causeways of miles through the low swamp surmounting it — impassable sloughs were made most passable on the paper plat — half a dozen railroads in their mad dreaming could center nowhere else — the noble stream upon whose banks it grew up, flourished and faded was made navigable by their strange course of reasoning — the free airs of heaven were here in this wet nurse of disease made by them wondrous free, freer, balmier, and more salubrious. All was fairyland glowing with loveliness and light, and in fine it was boasted of as the very place from whence Adam and Eve were driven for that disobedience whose melancholy results are even in this very effort so strongly exemplified.

The shrill cry of the bittern, the screech of the dark night bird, and hissing of reptiles now fill the charmed air with music most horrible; and when the sunlight rests upon its fens, even then in the broad glare of the bright light, sadness sits supreme around it, while the huge mutterings of the alligator calling to her youngling brood are varied only by the softer cadences of the frog family whose metropolis Belleair has become.

One Man and Two Beds

by "N. of Arkansas"

§ Charles Fenton Mercer Noland, who died in 1858, was a planter and newspaperman of Batesville, Arkansas, who wrote numerous sporting epistles for the *Spirit* signed "N. of Arkansas." He also wrote humorous sketches under the name "Pete Whetstone," a "rough and rude backwoods character" from Devil's Fork of the Little Red River. Born in Virginia, Noland attended West Point briefly, dropped out, and migrated to Arkansas. He served as a lieutenant in a company of mounted rangers in the Black Hawk War and returned to Arkansas about 1835. In addition to running an upland cotton plantation, he edited a Whig newspaper and served in the state legislature. (Yates, *Porter and the Spirit*, p. 63 ff.) The following sketch was printed in the *Spirit*, XXIII, No. 2 (February 26, 1853), 17, reprinted from the *Southern Watch-Tower*.

PETE WHETSTONE of Arkansas was once travelling on horseback through the interior of the state and called one evening to stay all night at a little log house near the road where entertainment and a postoffice were kept. Two other strangers were there, and the mail rider rode up about dark. Supper being over, the mail carrier and the three gentlemen were invited into a small room furnished with a good fire and two beds which were to accommodate the four persons for the night. The mail carrier was a little shabby, dirty, lousy-looking wretch, with whom none of the gentlemen liked the idea of sleeping. Pete Whetstone eyed him closely as he asked:

"Where do you sleep tonight, my lad?"

"I'll thleep with you, I reckon," lisped the youth, "or with one o' them other fellars, I don't care which."

The other gentlemen took the hint and occupied one of the beds together immediately, leaving the other bed and the confab to be enjoyed by Pete and the mail boy together as best they could. Pete and the boy both commenced hauling off their duds, and Pete getting in bed first and wishing to get rid of sleeping with the boy remarked very earnestly, "My friend, I'll tell you beforehand, *I've got the Itch*, and you'd better not get in here with me, for the disease is *catching*."

60

The boy, who was just getting in bed too, drawled out very coolly, "Wal, I reckon that don't make a bit o' difference—I've had it now for nearly these theven years," and into bed he pitched along with Pete, who pitched out in a great hurry as if he had waked up a hornet's nest in the bed. The other two gentlemen roared, and the mail boy, who had got peaceable possession of a bed to himself, drawled out, "Why you must be a thet o' darned fules; Mam and Dad's got the eatch a heap wurth than his, and they thlept in that bed last night when they was here at the quilting."

The other two strangers were now in a worse predicament than Pete had been, and bouncing from their nest like the house had been on fire, stripped, shook their clothes, put them on again, ordered their horses, and though it was nearly ten o'clock they all three left and rode several miles to the next town before they slept, leaving the imperturbable mail carrier to the bliss of scratching and sleeping alone.

The Yazoo Bottoms Revisited

by Col. J. J. Jenks, Yazoo Co., Mississippi

§ This sketch was printed in the *Spirit*, XXI (November 8, 1851), 453, as "Letter from 'Curnill Jinks'" and signed "Jeems Johnsing Jenks, Jr., Curnill of the 43d Regt of Yazoo Rapscallions." This satire of the people of Satartia, Mississippi, may have been written by William C. Hall, a native of Yazoo County. For a time he was a journalist in New Orleans and in 1849 and 1850 published several "Yazoo Sketches" in the *Delta*. These humorous sketches greatly exaggerated the traits of residents of Satartia, particularly Michael Hooter and his family. According to tradition in Yazoo County, Hooter once threatened Hall if he continued the sketches. Hall did not publish any others after April 1850, unless this letter and "Letter from Mike Shouter," *Spirit*, XXVI, No. 47 (January 3, 1857), 556-557, are his. See John Q. Anderson, "Mike Hooter—the Making of a Myth," *Southern Folklore Quarterly*, XIX (June 1955), 90-100.

YAZOO is the home of my four fathers and four mothers. Here it was that I tuk my fust lessons in leapfrog and larnt to wear breeches. Them ole oaks what sighs in the nite wind and howls in the tempest lent me ther shadows in my earliest attempts at backer chawin, an as for cussin, I don't know when I begun. Cum to think, I blieve I must have commenced in the cradle. My early edication was sooperintended by a larned ole hoss named Dorsey,[8] who knowed everything on this habitable yearth, sepen common sense. He couldn't tell the muzzle of a gun from a hole in the ground, and how in the name of sense could you spect him to teach the young how to *shoot*?

If you should ax me whar I've bin and what I've bin doin since the last time I seed you, I would anser in the langwidge of the Arch Inimy: "Gwine to an fro in the yearth en walkin up and down in

---

8. Perhaps Dr. Washington Dorsey (1811–1845), a native of Kentucky and graduate of Transylvania College who practiced medicine in Yazoo City from 1832 until his death. He was the preceptor of Henry Clay Lewis who, as a humorist, was later widely known as "Madison Tensas, M.D." See Anderson, *Louisiana Swamp Doctor*, pp. 18 ff.

it." You know that I'm a grate feller for moseyin about in strange places and that, like Noey's dove, I can't find a spot of dry ground wharon to rest the heel of my boots. But here I am at last on the ole stompin ground, "chawing the cud of sweet an bitter fansys," an facin up agin a quart of the best ole "red eye" you ever stuck a knife into.

You orter seed me the day I arriv, when I fust cum in site. If you'd seed them niggers, the way they did run an holler an shout out and rip and tear, you'd thought that the very hevens and the yearth was cumin together. If I didn't think they was gwine to eat me up, dod wallop me!

Things has changed mightily sinse I left here. To be sure, the hills is thar yet, but the trees don't look so green, the birds don't sing half so merrily, an instead of old, familiar faces, thar ain't nuthin to be seen but unfamiliar graves!

The only part of the country what don't seem to have changed none is that all-fired town what they calls Satartia, an it ain't a bit poorer nor a bit meaner than it was ten years ago. Like the feller what was born with his face turned wrongside-outards, its buty ain't to be spyit. How this town cum to be and who was the people that fust bilt it, history don't give no account of. Its sposed to have been founded by that oncertain individooal that walloped Billy Patterson, in company with the illustrious *hero* and the *shero*, his wife, "what butt the bull off the bridge." I'm mityly puzzled what to compare the place to. Sumetimes I think of the last of pea time, and finally I've settled down on the proposition that its the little eend of meanness, sharpened down to a pint! The people are a curious generation. Ther faces is as yaller as a ripe simmun, supposed to cum from eatin dirt, and ther stomicks is all swelled out like they'd swaller'd pumpkin seed and washed um down with hot water. I seed a gal here tother day, said to be a great buty, whose face was all towseled up with bumps an carbuncles so that her features put in mind of the knots on the bark of a black-jack saplin!—pledge you my word I thought she'd bin struck with lightnin! The principal vegetable production of the country round is composed partly of bars an panters, snakes, skeeters, coons, possums, young babies, jimpson weed, and a slite sprikklin of Injuns an mulattoes. The great peculiarity of the country is that the children is mostly orphans an nobody knows where is ther daddies.

Stopt at the house tother night of an old bar-hunter and was almost chawed up boudaciously with muskeeters, cause the old feller didn't have no [mosquito] bars to keep um out. Shure nuff, cum to talk to the nabors bout why the ole cuss didn't keep muskeeter bars, they sed that he and his wife and children had ther faces so wrinkled up an turned catterwompus like, that the skeeters couldn't lite on um long enuf to bite. I tuk a privit look myself outen one corner of my eye at his daughter Sal, an, pledge you my word, I thought I should er raised up my very bread-basket, I laffed so! Talk about yure "Gorguns, hydras, and Chymera's dyer!" She can beat um all holler; an as for her har, Medusy's sarpent ringlets warn't a patchin to it!

The principal artikles of dyet 'mongst the people here is acorns, blackberries, simmons, whiskey, and terbacker, and I am told that cotton seeds and young gourds for dessert is bein rapidly interduced.

The chills an fevers prevails hear to a grate ekstent an is handed down from father to son to the tenth generashum, as it turns its viktims so yaller in the face that it is amost impossible to tell a white man from a nigger eksept by his manners, an in that case, the nigger very often has the advantage. I've hearn thar is one feller here what has bid defiance to this disease of the shakin ague, for when a fit comes on him, he's so ever lastin lazy he won shake a lick! The nabors here say that that same chap hates to work so bad that he's spent the last ten years of his life trying to invent a chewin machine to save himself the trouble of eatin his vittals. How true this is, can't for certain say.

I'm gwine to leave this evenin for the Ohier river and the Mammuth Kaiv, an evry whar else, an if some of them all-fired stemebotes an ralerodes don't bust ther bylers an blow me into the middle of next week, I'll rite you again.

My First and Last Courtship in the Pine Barrens

by "Neosho" of Mississippi

§ The following story appeared in the *Spirit*, XXIV, No. 13 (May 13, 1854), 152.

THOSE were my halcyon days in the Southwest when I had just concluded my preparatory studies for the bar, and with my license in my pocket had sallied forth on first circuit of fees and fortune. No person who deemed himself entering upon a career of greatness could have had a more "vaulting ambition." Law and love were my topics; every idea concentrated in them. I aimed for success and distinction in both. I had two systems of special pleading, one governed by arbitrary rules, the other by romance — law in the courts and love to the ladies. I balanced Chitty with Byron[9] in my saddlebags, and when not displaying my legal lore to the Judge, I was quoting the poetry of passion to the fair ones. But poetry like "full many a flower is sometimes born to waste its sweetness on the desert air," and the germs of awakening hope and affection are often nipped ere they bloom.

Our circuit extended over a pine barren country larger than Massachusetts. Court and bar rode the circuit on horseback familiarly together, through rain or sunshine, o'er bog or stream. The dwellings were few and far between but we were a social, jolly set, generally carrying our "provender" with us, and he was the cleverest fellow whose "baldface" held out the longest.

It was the fall circuit. A bright October sun was setting over the low pine ridges that bordered the valley of Bogue Chitto, as tired but merry and full of "sperits" we lighted at the door of the "oldest

---

9. Thomas Chitty, English author of legal textbooks; George Gordon, Lord Byron (1788–1824), the English romantic poet beloved of romantic young men who aped the so-called Byronic pose and costume.

inhabitant," a man by the name of Essig, to spend the night. This was a place of great interest to me. It was a spot uppermost in my thoughts. I had dreamed of it nightly since I was informed that Essig was wealthy and had two accomplished daughters. Here, thought I, is the theater of my *love* ambition, the arena for the exercise of my peculiar talents. Push boldly was the resolve, and I determined to fall in love at first sight.

The Judge and members of the bar who were all older than myself and not aroused by the same stimulus soon retired to their rooms, and I had the field open to myself.

I determined to make a conquest. I felt Napoleonic. I resolved to approach with the skill of a general and batter down the outworks first. There were the old gentleman and lady. I not only resolved, I *acted.* What! thousands of broad acres and one hundred and fifty Negroes to be divided between two amiable and accomplished girls! What would a man not do to win the prize? But Essig was a singular man; his family partook his singularities. Like members of Congress, he was fond of using big words, and like them, too, he often misplaced them. He had commenced life with the partner of his bosom and only two hands. He had settled in the wilderness on the banks of a stream that bore a beautiful and sonorous Choctaw name. He had raised cotton. He had grown, prospered, flourished. Every year added to his "cleared" acres, his bales of cotton, and his Negroes until he was now the richest man in his county—a thousand broad acres in the beautiful valley before us with the white opening balls glittering like snow in the fresh moonlight. It indeed woke in me a vision of delightful anticipation. There were no schools, however, in the neighborhood, and the girls were severally sixteen and eighteen before they were sent to boarding school where they remained six months and returned with all the accomplishments which such an education could give. What education they acquired from the "old folks at home" prior to this time the sequel will show.

I had been introduced to them at the tea-table; how my heart fluttered! They were certainly pretty brunettes with rather sleepy eyes; but whenever I gazed at them, Negroes and acres intruded themselves on my thoughts, and I overlooked coarseness of hands and those little asperities which will sometimes exhibit themselves, notwithstanding a few months boarding-school polish. I was not mercenary in my thoughts—far from it—I was merely *ambitious.* I left the table, walked on the porch in the incipient stage of love, and determined to batter down the first outwork—old Essig.

The home—or castle—of Essig was a singular affair; like his fortunes, it had been built piecemeal. You could discover by each pealed pine-log cabin that it had been built year after year in regular progression. The first cabin he built was still standing. As his wants and means increased, he had added building after building until there was a long row of pine-log huts extending a hundred yards with an L, in which was kept the neighborhood postoffice and a grog-shop. Here the neighbors congregated of a Saturday evening, drank "baldface" which they sweetened with brown sugar stirred with their fingers and drank out of big tin cups. As the "fall fights" were about to commence, there was a larger "sprinkling" gathered together on the evening alluded to than usual.

I met Essig on the porch, with his pipe in his mouth, looking grave and dignified while "the glow of humanity beamed from his nose." Now, thought I, is the time for assault.

"You have a beautiful place here—a lovely view, Mr. Essig."

"Yes, sir, magni*fish*unt! magni*fish*unt, sir! Bottoms, sir, rich as grease, sir! bales to the acre—bales, sir, and—sir, the most tall, *gi*-gig-antic pines, for a mile on both sides in circumference, sir!"

This was a heavy broadside, but I stood up under it. The workmen had been busy all day; when we arrived they were hammering away like a boatyard in full blast. They were constructing a porch or two, building some outhouses, and fresh shingling the long row of cabins. I again commenced the assault.

"You seem to be making considerable improvements here, Mr. Essig."

"Yes, sir—*yes!* I intend to make a *portoricoro* in front of my house and a *pizzarazzaro* in the rear, and a *dissevered* department for the disaccommodation of my *majestics,* sir, when I hope I shall be able to *detain* travellers in a more *hostile* manner than usual, sir!"

I finally reeled under the fire, when the *grocery birds* came to my rescue. The first "fall fight" had commenced. There was a general "free fight" and a running fire of "Hurrah, Dick!" "Give it to him, Tom!" "Peg him under the short ribs!" "Grapple him under-holts!" and a thousand such classical phrases in backwoods fisticuffs when old Essig rushed from the porch to the scene of battle near the post-office and grog-shop. With an air of chagrined dignity he roared out, *"Persist!* gentle*men,* I say by G–d, *persist!* or I'll *discomborbirate* the whole d––––d possum-cum-it-at-us of you. I'll let you know, gentle*men,* by G–d, that I permit no *hospitalities* about my house, gentle*men!"*

After this sally I retreated into the stockade to try my luck in an attack upon the old lady. I found her seated in what she called her *parlor* with her blushing daughters. The room had been recently ceiled. Smiling matronly under her spectacles which became admirably her vegetable countenance—for the point of her turn-up nose was trying to look at her carroty hair, now slightly sprinkled with gray—the old lady beckoned me to a seat. I took it, straightened out my light blue unmentionables, smoothed down my buff vest, and imagined that I looked exceedingly interesting. Casting my most bewitching look at the girls, I remarked to the old lady: "You are getting your room finished quite neatly and comfortably. Do you design to have the ceiling papered or painted?"

"Well—*raly,* I don't know. I think I'll have it painted, but for the life of me I can't think what color is *beautif*ullest. What do you think?"

I answered at random, "As for my part, Madam, I would prefer a sky-blue or a pea-green."

"Oh, yes—yes—that suits my taste *zackcisely*—a *skeye*-blue, yes—it looks so much like the *canister* of heaven!" And the old lady adjusted her spectacles piously and benignantly. Here was a thundering cannonade, but I rallied. Seeing a piano on one side of the room, I observed: "I see you have music here, Mrs. Essig. I suppose the young ladies perform."

"Oh, yes. There's my daughter Jane sings like a *martingill,* and Susan plays on the *peranner* admirable."

Here I felt conquered but turned to Miss Susan, who played so "admirable," and solicited a performance, but with *ahems* and coughs and blushes, she declined. "Now do, Susan," said Miss Jane imploringly. "I know you can accommodate the young gentleman — now do play 'Rustic Facility!'" At this new name of "Haste to the Wedding" I beat a retreat to the door. I stood leaning against one side gazing out on the scene contemplating what should be done next when the girl that sang like a "martingill" came and leant against the other.

It was one of those sweet October evenings of the Southwest when the balmy air seems to waft romance on its wings. Love seemed to sigh in every gale, and I was sighing for something to love. The pine woods had taken fire in the ridges beyond the Bogue Chitto. There was a long waving line of light undulating beautifully over the hill. The giant pines stood like mail-clad warriors as the flames flashed and crackled around them. The columns of smoke rose like the smoke of a volcano while the moon glimmered chastely through the near pines, and the stars peeped out of the deep blue sky like angels' eyes. The night wind sighed in music through the pine leaves, bearing with it a delicious aroma, and I again felt the slightest possible sensation of love stealing over my heart, notwithstanding my defeats. I turned towards Miss Jane with romance bounding in every pulse and love beaming in my eyes and observed, "This is a beautiful scene. See the flames how like a serpent they wind over the hills, the inverted cone of smoke, and the moon and the stars which are the poetry of heaven."

"Yes — yes — it's quite roman-*tic* and picture-*sque!* It reminds me of what I read of in a history book where the Emperor Ner-ro set fire to the city of Rum and fiddled by the light."

This shot destroyed all further efforts. I was totally demolished. I did not faint, but I made a presipitate retreat to the grog-shop where with a pint of "baldface" I immediately extinguished every rising sentiment of love and drowned the memory of my disastrous defeat.

I continued my circuit a wiser but less *loving* youth, and I would advise all young barristers never to mix *love* with law nor balance Chitty with Byron.

Poetry and Liquor in East Tennessee
by "Roderick" of Roarer's Vale, Tennessee

§ Yates, *Porter and the Spirit,* pp. 78, 212, says that "Roderick" was one of the pen names used by George Washington Harris, author of sketches in the *Spirit* and later the book *Sut Lovingood* (1867). According to Yates, Harris wrote his first full-length sketch for the *Spirit,* "A Knob Dance—A Tennessee Frolic," in response to comments by the "Man in the Swamp" who questioned Harris's use of dialect. A letter supposedly written by "Roderick" but "possibly written," Yates explains, by the "Man in the Swamp" suggests that "Sugartail" (one of the names used by Harris) and the "Man in the Swamp" were collaborating on a book. "Harris made a trip to New York about this time [1845] and may have discussed this proposed book with Porter," Yates observes, "but the volume seems to have died a-borning." This story was printed in the *Spirit,* XV, No. 38 (November 15, 1845), 446, as "Sayings and Doings in East Tennessee."

WELL, hurrah for Buncombe[10]—they had a schoolmaster there once. He was some in a *"bar fight,"* sure. He knew less, could whip harder, and drink more on ordinary occasions than any other schoolmaster betwixt _____ and Capt. Shines' stillhouse. But when Christmas come—Oh, Lordy! but didn't he set the liquor deep 'till after that time the Buncombe boys converted and made him both temperate and religious? That's what I am trying to get at, to tell you how it was done—and it's *truth,* too—"you'd better believe it."

Not many years since, this teacher of Dilworth and Knight of the Hickory took one rare and unparalleled Christmas frolic in the usual quiet town of A————. His scholars had barred him out in the morning,[11] at which he was well pleased no doubt for after a little negotia-

---

10. A frequent reference in popular humor, Buncombe refers to the county of that name in North Carolina and is synonymous with "bunkum" or "bunk," that is, claptrap. Supposedly a representative made a flowery and irrelevant speech in Washington and when asked about it said, "I was not speaking to the House, but to Buncombe."

11. The custom of students' "barring out the schoolmaster" on one day in the spring to get a holiday is the subject of one of the sketches in Longstreet's *Georgia Scenes.*

tion he gave them a week's vacation as is the custom in Buncombe. He had been drinking and *cavorting* mightily the whole day; so when night came on he was pretty much "how came you so?" He did manage, however, to wend his way, though a serpentine one, to Mr. S————'s tavern, where many of the "young bloods" were gathered, cracking jokes, relating hairbreadth 'scapes, and drinking occasionally, many of them just because it was Christmas night and they had nothing else to do—and whenever they drank, likewise did the pedagogue—"Uncle Simeon" is the cognomen he was best known by. They had taken but few rounds when it was quite evident he had worshipped with too fervent a devotion at the shrine of Bacchus, and before the barroom clock struck nine "King Alcohol" had him down. By ten he was fast locked in the embraces of Morpheus. At half-past ten the stage left for the East—over the *roughest, rockiest* road—oh, hush! I've travelled it, and if you would call a road rough that took three passengers with a light coach, four good horses, and two bottles of old cogniac twelve hours to go twenty-four miles and upset only three times, then it was *rough* some! But that was when roads were bad all through the "Old North State." Well, when the mail-coach left that night, it carried only one passenger and that one where they usually carry trunks. It was "nobody else" but the schoolmaster. The coach had been rolling along about three hours, and nothing had been heard from the baggage. The driver had become a little anxious about the fate of "Uncle Simeon" and determined to get down and examine when he reached the top of the ridge he was ascending. Just as he had come to that determination, he heard a groan and soon after another; by this time he was at the top and the road was slightly descending and rocky before him; behind the coach he knew nobody was dead. He cracked his whip, and Uncle Sim thought the d———l had him *certain*. Such "weeping, wailing, and gnashing of teeth" as there was behind that coach, never did they "hear tell of" in Buncombe. The driver could occasionally hear—"Have mercy on me," "O, Mr. D———l! where am I?" "O, Lordy! Lordy!! They *told* me whiskey would kill me and the D———l would get me; and now he has done and got me sure enough. What are you doing with me, Mr. D———l?

Oh, where am I? Am I dead and in ————, or where am I?"

Just then the driver spoke in a most unearthly voice, "Uncle Sim, I've been expecting you down here some time. Bill Yaney, that you whipped to death, is waiting to pour blazing brimstone down you!"

Uncle Sim: O, don't, please, don't let him do that, Mr. Satan. I can almost feel it burning in me now. Let me go back, please do, I'm suffering, *dreadful*.

Driver: If I'll let you go back will you quit drinking, get religion and join the church?

Uncle Sim: *Yes, Sir-ee,* and *thank* you into the bargain.

The driver thinking the poor fellow had suffered enough, halted, unbuckled the straps, drew him forth, headed him towards A—————, and told him to keep the big road and he would get back to the settlement again. As the driver bade him "good night," and was mounting his box, "Why," said he, "you talk mightily like Jim Stokes, the stage driver, Mr. D———l."

Late the following day he passed through A————— without calling as usual at Jo Gray's grocery. The story got wind how Uncle Sim had been to "Kingdom Come," driven by the D———l, and Buncombe was too small to hold him. He closed his school and left that "fair countrie" for the Far West. Report says, however, that he has kept his promise to the D———l who drove him that night and is a sober man and good citizen where he resides.

Selling Chickens to the Legislature

by "Phil," Jefferson City, Missouri

§ This tale appeared in the *Spirit,* XXII, No. 21 (July 10, 1852), 252.

WHILE the Legislature of Missouri was in session a few years ago, a green fellow from the country came to Jefferson to sell some chickens. He had about two dozen, all of which he had tied by the legs to a string, and this, being divided equally and thrown across his horse or his shoulder, formed his mode of conveyance, leaving the fowls with their heads hanging down with little else of them visible except their naked legs and a promiscuous pile of outstretched wings and ruffled feathers. After several ineffectual efforts to dispose of his load, a wag, to whom he made an offer of sale, told him that he did not want chickens himself, but that perhaps he could sell them at that large stone house over there (the Capitol), that there was a man over there buying on speculation for the St. Louis market, and no doubt he could find a ready sale.

The delighted countryman started, when his informer stopped him.

"Look here," says he, "when you get over there, go upstairs, and then turn to the left. The man stops in that large room. You will find him sitting up at the other end of the room, and he is now engaged with a number of fellows buying chickens. If a man at the door should stop you, don't mind him. He has got chickens himself for sale and tries to prevent other people from selling theirs. Don't mind him, but go right ahead."

Following the directions, our friend soon found himself at the door of the Hall of Representatives. To open it and enter was the work of a moment. Taking from his shoulder the string of chickens and giving them a shake to freshen them, he commenced his journey towards the Speaker's chair, the fowls in the meantime loudly expressing from the half-formed *crow* to the harsh *quaark* their bodily presence and their sense of bodily pain.

"I say, sir,"—Here he had advanced about half down the aisle, when he was seized by Major Jackson, the doorkeeper, who happened to be returning from the Clerk's desk.

"What the devil are you doing here with these chickens; get out, sir, get out," whispered the doorkeeper.

"No you don't, though, you can't come that game over me. You've got chickens yourself for sale, get out yourself, and let me sell mine. I say sir, (in a louder tone to the Speaker) are you buying chickens here today? I've got some prime ones here."

And he held up his string and shook his fowls until their music made the walls echo.

"Let me go, sir (to the doorkeeper), let me go, I say. Fine large chickens (to the Speaker), only six bits a dozen."

"Where's the Sergeant-at-Arms," roared the Speaker — "take that man out."

"Now don't, will you, I ain't hard to trade with. You let me go (to the doorkeeper); you've sold your chickens, now let me have a chance. I say, sir, (to the Speaker in a louder tone) are you buying chickens to----"

"Go ahead," "At him again," "That's right," whispered some of the opposition members, who could command gravity enough to speak — "At him again." "He'll buy them." "He only wants you to take less — at him again."

"I say, sir, (in a louder tone to the Speaker) — cuss your pictures let me go — fair play — two to one ain't fair (to the Speaker and Sergeant-at-Arms), let me go; I say, sir, you up there (to the Speaker), you can have em for six bits! won't take a cent less. Take em home and eat em myself before I'll take---- Drat your hides, don't shove so hard, will you! you'll hurt the chickens, and they have had a travel of it today, anyhow. I say, you sir, up there----"

Here the voice was lost by the closing of the door. An adjournment was moved and carried and the members almost frantic with mirth rushed out to find our friend in high altercation with the doorkeeper about the meanness of selling his own chickens and letting nobody else sell theirs, adding that if he could just see that man up there by himself he'd be bound they could make a trade, and that no man could afford to raise chickens for less than six bits.

The members bought his fowls by a pony purse,[12] and our friend left the Capitol, saying, as he went down the stairs, "Well, this is the darndest roughest place for selling chickens that ever I come across, sure."

12. "Pony purse"—money taken up in a collection.

Varmints and Hunters

Bear, deer, panther, wildcat, turkey, and waterfowls made the forests, canebrakes, lakes, and streams of the Old Southwest a hunter's paradise. In some areas, it was said that the animals would not flee from man because they had never been hunted. Even after much of the land had been settled and county-seat towns dotted the area, game remained so plentiful that wild meat was a staple food. No man had to go far to hunt, and almost all men hunted.

Wild animals were, in fact, so much a part of the frontiersman's everyday life that it is no wonder that he used them, as did his primitive ancestors, to express his concepts of strength, agility, cunning, and endurance. Thus his language abounded in animal metaphors.

In the Old Southwest there were essentially two types of hunters, the professional and the competent amateur or, more generally, the countryman and the townsman. The professional hunter, always on the fringes of the frontier as it moved westward, is remembered in Cooper's Hawkeye, in Daniel Boone, and to some extent in Davy Crockett. The hunter found his escape from civilization by retreating into the canebrakes and other submarginal land too difficult for the farmers to clear; there he lived on a limited scale the semiprimitive life that his freer predecessors had. He was of great use to the amateur hunter who employed him as a guide, learned skills from him, and sometimes became friends with him. The Jim Doggetts, Mike Hooters, Jims and Chunkeys of the popular humor are but lightly fictionized accounts of many hunters of their kind.

The other type of hunter, the amateur, was a

townsman who did not make his living off the
land but who frequently responded to the
age-old impulse to become man the hunter.
Whether a doctor, lawyer, or merchant, he may
have been reared in the country and hunted as a
boy; consequently, on every possible occasion
he got together with his friends and went
hunting or fishing. Numerous hunting epistles
in the *Spirit* indicate that parties of townsmen
went by boat or horseback to remote areas,
employed a guide or professional hunter, and
camped out for several days. They took along an
adequate supply of food and liquor, since
eating and drinking were an important part
of the expedition. After the day's hunt, they
gathered around the campfire, and some of the
best sketches in the *Spirit* came out of such
settings, "Campfire talk in print,"
Blair calls them.[1]

Many of these hunting sketches describe the
initiation of the greenhorn into the ritual of
the hunt, of camp life, and of animal lore.
Standing behind this masculine custom is the
primitive conflict between the will of man
and the strength and cunning of animals.
Primitive man drew pictures of the animals he
was about to hunt and attempted to control
them by sympathetic magic; he passed his
discoveries on by word of mouth. For him,
hunting was an utterly serious matter. Echoes
of hunting rites, artistically treated, may be
seen in Faulkner's "The Bear" in which Sam
Fathers lets the boy see the majestic buck,
symbol of the hunted, and then smears the
boy's face with the blood of the first deer he
kills. Civilized men unconsciously reflect

1. Blair, *Native American
Humor*, p. 80.

the ancient superstitions concerning death and violence in the hunt; they, too, must learn the ritual of the hunt, the skills of the chase, and the lore of animals, usually from the professional hunter or the experienced huntsman. The beginners may develop "buck fever" ("buck ager," frontiersmen called it) at the crucial moment and panic, run, or perhaps shoot the wrong animal, and so they become the butt of jokes in camp. Another form of hazing was exaggeration of the ferocity of certain animals or giving the neophyte false information.

In the Old Southwest, bears made the most lasting impression on hunters, if popular humor is an indication. The bear was ferocious and difficult to hunt, but bears furnished meat, fat, and clothing to sustain people in the first stages of settlement. Davy Crockett said that he killed forty-seven bears in a month and one hundred and five in a season to obtain meat and cooking fat.[2] Jim, according to his creator "The Turkey Runner," killed sixty bears in a season, some of them weighing 700 pounds. Jim explains why bears are difficult to hunt:

> ... they come to water at a certain place and jist as regular as a parson to his eatin; every bar has his waterin place, and he comes and goes in the same path and in the same foot tracks, always until he moves his settlement; and jist you break a cane, or limb, or move a chunk or stick near his trail and see how quick he'll move his cabin! Oh yes, a bar is mighty particular about sich things — that's his *sens* — that's his trap to find out if you are in his settlement.

Bear hunters spoke familiarly and meaningfully of "he-bars" and "she-bars," and sometimes when carried away in reciting hunting stories

2. *Life of Col. David Crockett Written by Himself* (Philadelphia, 1860), p. 157.

completely personified them. A good example of this tendency is Mike Hooter of Yazoo County, Mississippi, the main character in a cycle of tales by William Hall and Henry Clay Lewis. Among the five sketches which Hall published in the New Orleans *Delta* is one in which Mike describes a Yazoo bear that caught a hunter off guard, slipped the powder out of his gun, and then thumbed his nose at the man while he snapped the gun. The same Hooter in Lewis's "The Indefatigable Bear Hunter" gets into a fight with a bear and has his leg so mangled that the Swamp Doctor has to amputate it. While he is recuperating, Mik (so Lewis spelled the name to avoid the wrath of Hooter, who lived just across the Mississippi from where Lewis wrote in Louisiana) claimed that the bears and panthers came up in the clearing outside his cabin and taunted him because he could no longer harm them.[3] In addition to this personification of animals, an even more primitive form of animism is seen in the hunters' custom of giving names to their favorite rifles— Crockett's "Betsy," Hooter's "Bar Death," and Long John's "Death in the Path"—and sometimes even to hunting knives. Certainly, hunting dogs were often characters in their own right—Trail, Lead, Loud, Holdfast, Singer, Boss, Juno, Brutus, Caesar, Pete—and even Polk and Constitutional.

Next to the bear, the panther figured largest in the experiences of people of the Old Southwest. Feared because of its methods of attack, fighting ability, and unearthly scream, the panther occupied a special place in the lore of the frontier; though twentieth century scientists

3. [William C. Hall], "Mike Hooter's Bar Story. A Yazoo Sketch," *Spirit*, XIX, No. 49 (January 6, 1850); reprinted from the New Orleans *Delta*. "The Indefatigable Bear Hunter," *Odd Leaves from the Life of a Louisiana Swamp Doctor*, reprinted in Anderson, *Louisiana Swamp Doctor*, pp. 233-244. For a discussion of the Hooter cycle of tales, see John Q. Anderson, "Mike Hooter—The Making of a Myth," *Southern Folklore Quarterly*, XIX (June 1955), 90-100.

maintain that the panther does not scream like a woman in pain,[4] in folk belief it did. Hunters respected the panther because it was dangerous, not because it was useful as the bear was.

Game animals were so much a part of the life of the Old Southwest that experiences with them were sometimes so bizarre that the truth seemed incredible to outsiders. Every community had its wise old bear, panther, or fox — even alligators — that continued to outwit even the most skillful hunters. Jim Doggett's bear in "The Big Bear of Arkansas" permitted the hunter to kill it simply because its time had come. The drama of the hunting tale often carried the storyteller into fantasy. As Derek Colville has said, "Often the distinction between real life and the tall tale is so blurred as to be scarcely perceived."[5] And as Mody Boatright concludes after analyzing the tall tale, it cannot be faked. He cites J. Frank Dobie as saying that the authentic "liar" must know "what he is lying about"; that is, he must know his subject so well that he knows where to take liberties.[6]

The hunting story always seems to move toward myth: pitting man against a worthy foe in nature and allowing him to triumph in spite of difficulties; the animal becomes symbolic of the forces of nature and of the uncertainties of life against which man must do battle and win — at least in his myths.

Man the hunter, whether professional or amateur, is treated humorously for the most part in the newspaper sketches of the Old Southwest — hunting and roistering with male companions of his own kind, venting on

4. "Many folk tales repeat the savagery of cougars, their numerous attacks on man, and their bloodcurdling screams, but authentic unprovoked attacks on man are far less numerous than those of the domesticated bull." William B. Davis, *The Mammals of Texas* (Austin 1960), Bulletin No. 27, Texas Game and Fish Commission, p. 111.

5. "History and Humor: The Tall Tale in New Orleans," *Louisiana Historical Quarterly,* XXXIX (April 1956), 161.

6. Mody C. Boatright, "The Art of Tall Lying," *Southwest Review,* XXXIV, No. 4 (Autumn 1949), 360.

animals the violence and brutality that seem part
of his nature — in that pristine period before
the frontier closed so that he could no longer
so freely express his impulses as man the hunter.

Old Long John and the Bear

by "Sulphur Fork," Bayou Chicot, Louisiana

§ This story appeared in the *Spirit*, XIX, No. 48 (January 19, 1850), 566; reprinted from the New Orleans *Delta*.

OLD Long John, the Bear Hunter (as he always called himself), almost everyone west of the Mississippi is familiar with the name, has almost as wide fame as the name of Daniel Boone. So long as the creeks and rivers continue to run through his old hunting grounds—Boggy Gutt, Beaver Creek, Turkey, Darbone, Calcasieu, and their tributaries—so long will his fame last. On the first named is where he first settled after he came to this country in the year 1810. Being a great place for game at the time, it was the only inducement for his settling there, except that he also had a fine range for cattle and hogs. I have often heard him say that he never would have left old Carolina but for the want of a range for stock and the scarcity of game. He was a man six feet four inches in height, weighed one hundred and eighty-five pounds, and was as erect as an Indian. His eye was more like an eagle's than any man's I ever saw. He died in his eighty-fifth year, about fifteen years ago. One month before his death he could stand on a level plane and jump thirty feet in three jumps. This will give some faint idea of what kind of specimen he was of the human species. In fact, I think he was the finest looking man I ever saw of his age. I have often sat up with him in his pine log cabin of long winter nights by a cheerful pine-knot fire and heard him relate some of the most thrilling accounts of himself, and others too, in the old Revolutionary War; and about hunting wild hogs, and bear and panther fights—some of which I know I never can forget and one of which I will relate as he told it to me, word for word as near as I can remember.

Old Long John, the Bear Hunter, said: One mornin in May in the year 1810—least ways it was blackberry time—I took Old Death in the Path (the name of his rifle) on my shoulder and belted Old Butcher around my waist, and off I started to look for a deer up

Boggy Gutt. After I walked two or three miles and seein no deer, I begin to look for sign of other varmints. Now mind you—be G—— sirs, this is the truth I am tellin, and I want you all to listin. I know (said he) that it is a matter of long ago given up that all old hunters will lie, and I must acknowledge that I will lie a little, too, if you corner me too close about a bar fight—that is, if I have to shoot more than one time at it. It always discomboborates me to fight a bar in a canebrake with an empty gun, onless my dogs is mighty good— then I don't kere a fig; I jist walk right into em with Old Butcher (his knife). But if the dogs ain't true I always git mad, and then I am jist as apt to go right off from it as any other way. And, as I was sayin, I was lookin for sign, and sure enough, be G—— sirs, I soon found plenty, right fresh and soft bar sign. I followed it up twill it come to a big bottle-ended holler stump of a tree that had been broke off about fifteen foot above the ground. I examined it well; I saw scratches and nail marks plenty on the stump; so I lent Old Death agin the tree and laid Old Butcher down by her. I thot I hearn something nestling inside the stump; so I tuck off my shoes and up it I went. When I come to the top, I looked in, I did, and what do you think I seed? Why two cub bar, be G—— sirs, rolling and playing down thar jist like two little niggers. Well, says I, you're jist the critters I have been wanting for a long time for pets for the children. So I jist lumbered right down among them, I did. Then if you could a bin thar to a hearn the fuss they kept up—sich hollerin and screaming! Oh! it beat any baby crying I ever hear, all holler. I got mad at last and begin to slap first one then tother to try to make um hush, but instead of that it made um ten times wors. I luckily kept my belt on; I let it out a few holes bigger and slipped one under it on each side, I did.

Then, for the first time, I seed my sitivation. Now the holler of the stump was heep bigger at the bottom nor it was at the top, and I could get no foothold to climb out by. Man! I tell you, I was getin to feel mad then!—and them critters keeping sich a fuss, I could hear nothing else while they kept squalling. I jist sot down, I did, and studied, and studied, and studied what on yearth I should do to get outen this holler stump. Why you might jist as well try to climb out of a forty foot well that warn't curbed. I begin to think maybe the Old She might come along arter a while to suckel her young. Then I thought to myself, says I, I am in a nice fix here, a mile from home, in a holler tree, and no gun nor knife, and every prospect of a fight with an Old She, be G–– sirs! Man! I tell you, I was mad then! All at once while I was a-studyin about it, I heard the allfiredist rippet outside you ever heard; the Old She had come sure enough. Oh! I was mad then, I was. All at once a thought struck me. I knowed that an Old She or a bar of any kind, indeed, could not bear to be fingered behind much, so I intended to act accordin. When she entered the top of the stump, she made all look dark below, I tell you, she did! I got on my feet and waited twell I could jist cleverly reach her, I did—you know they always come down tail foremost. As soon as I could reach her, I grabbed her behind with both hands, and I give her the whoop, I did. If ever you saw a skeered bar—and I was mad, be G––, sirs—she took me faster than any railroad car twell she landed me about ten foot from the root of the stump, flat on my belly, she did. Oh man! I was mad! but sort a stuntified like by the fall. Before I could get Old Death, she was clean outen sight, and a-running.

Bar and Deer Hunting in Mississippi

by "The Turkey Runner," Vicksburg, Mississippi

§ Under the pseudonym "The Turkey Runner," Alexander Gallatin McNutt wrote six sketches for the *Spirit*, a series in which Chunkey and Jim are the main characters. Yates, *Porter and the Spirit of the Times*, p. 82, says "the characters of the two hard-drinking, hard-fighting, fun-loving, sharp-dealing backwoodsmen . . . are sustained to a degree matched among Porter's contributors only by Hooper and his Simon Suggs yarns."

McNutt, self-made lawyer and planter, was governor of Mississippi from 1838 to 1842. He was widely known as a story-teller. Frank E. Everett, Jr., in "Vicksburg Was Center for Famous Lawyers" (Anniversary Edition of the *Vicksburg Evening Post*, July 1, 1963, p. 6 of the section "A City is Born"), says of him: "No more colorful or controversial personality ever lived in Mississippi . . . educated in his home state, Virginia, young Alex settled in Vicksburg about 1820 and may have been the first lawyer in Vicksburg. After a slow start he acquired a considerable estate by 1835. Entering politics, where his talents lay, the tall, large McNutt became an adroit stump speaker and popular leader. Elected Governor, he inducted [induced?] the state to repudiate the Union and Planters Bank bonds causing a national scandal and outcry. Many contradictory appraisals of McNutt exist to this day."

The following tale was printed in the *Spirit*, XIV, No. 8 (April 20, 1844), 91.

"YES, Capting, they war *lower*, I tell you—why, God bless your soul, honey, they war not only powerful thick, but some on em war as big as common sized horses, I *do* reckon; cause why, nobody ever had hunted em, you see. In the winter time the overflow, and in the summer time the lakes and snakes, bayous and alligators, musketoes and gallinippers, buffaloe gnats and sand flies, with a small sprinkle of agur and a *perfect cord* of congestive, prevented the Ingins from gwine through the country! Oh, no, the redskins would rather hunt fat turkey and deer in the Azoo [Yazoo][7]

7. A local pronunciation in which the stress apparently was on the first syllable, A'-zoo, the *a* having the sound of the *a* in *ale*. The word *Yazoo* now is generally pronounced Yaz'-oo, the *a* having the sound of the vowel in *mat*.

Hills and pine lands t'other side of Pearl River to killin fat bar on the Creek or Sunflower."

"Well, Jim, I think they were right; you must have been among the first hunters in the country."

"Yes I *do* reckon when I first went into that country, from the Azoo Hills to the Mississippi, there never had been but *mighty* few hunters. Why thar ar places thar now whar the deer ar tame as sheep and whar the bar don't care a dam *for nobody!* Fact! ask Chunkey."

"That is very remarkable; what is the cause?"

"Cause they've never been hunted; no, sir, never hearin the crack of a rifle nor the yelp of a dog; why thar ar more nor a hundred lakes and brakes in them diggins that hain't never been pressed by no mortal 'ceptin varmints. You know more nor half the country is overflowed in the winter, and t'other half, which is a damned sight the biggest, is covered with cane, palmetto, and other fixings; why it stands to reason, and in course no man ever *had* hunted em. Why, sir, when I first went to the Creek————"

"Let the Creek run, Jim; tell us about the bear!"

"Well, sir, the bar war very promiscuous indeed, and some ov the old hees war mighty mellifluous, I tell you. I had no sens about bar *then*, but thar warn't no cabin or camp in the whole settlement, and in course I soon larnt ther natur by livin 'mongst em. A bar, Capting, an old *he* bar, ain't no candidate or other good natured greenhorn to stand gougin and treatin. Oh no, he ain't, but he's as ramatugenous an animal as a log cabin loafer in the dog days, jist about, and if a stranger fools with him he'll get sarved like that white gal what come into my settlement."

"How as that, Jim!"

"Why *perfectly* ruinated, as Buck Brien says."

"You don't mean to say, Jim, that you—"

"Yes, dam'd if I diddent. Ask Chunkey, or—"

"Oh I am satisfied with the girl. Go on with the bear."

"Well, let's licker—(after drinking)—a bar is a *consaity* animal, but as far as his sens do go he's about as smart as any other animal; arter that, the balance is clear fat and fool. I have lived 'mongst em and know ther natur. I have killed as many as seven in a day and *smartly* to the rise of sixty in a season. Arter I'd been on the Creek about two months, up comes the Governor and Chunkey; the Governor 'tended like he wanted to see how I come on with the clearin; but, sir, he were arter a spree, and I know'd it, or why did he bring Chunkey? Everything looked mighty well; the negers looked fat and slick as old Belcher's [in] catfish season. I'd done cut more nor two hundred acres of cain and had the rails on the ground. I'd done—"

"Come, Jim, keep the track!"

"Well, Capting, they war mighty savagerous arter likker; they'd been fightin the stranger mightly, comin up and war perfectly wolfish arter some har of the dog, and dam'd the drop did I have, so I started two negers with mules and jugs to the pint (Princeton, Washington Co.) and the ox team arter a barrel. Well, sir, the day arter the jugs come, and we *darted* on em, (giving a sigh) but Lord, what war two jugs in *sich* a crowd? They jist kept Chunkey from dyin as he was so dry he had the rattles; next day the barrel come and then we *krack*-ovienned[8] up to it in airnest. *You* know what kind of man Chunkey is when he gits started—if he commences talkin, singin, or whistlin, no matter which, you'd jist as well try and stop the Mississippi as him. Why I have knowd him to whistle three days and three nights in a stretch—the Governor couldent eat nor drink for Chunkey's whistlin, and at last he gits mad and that's the last thing he does with anybody what *he* likes, and, says he to Chunkey—

'Chunkey, you have kept me awake two nights a-whistlin, and you must stop it tonight, or you or me must quit the plantation.'

Chunkey said, 'Governor, I don't want to put you to no trouble, but I can't stop in the middle of a chune, and as you have known

8. "La Cracovienne" was a lively character dance which the Viennese ballerina Fanny Elssler (1810-1884) performed in her sensational tour of the United States in 1840. Her characterizations of the fiery Hungarian, Pole, Russian, and the like were new to ballet; her lively movements and short costumes aroused a great deal of comment in the public press. Her second tour included New Orleans and Havana; she returned to Europe in 1842, having made almost a million dollars in the United States; *The Dance Encyclopedia*, comp. and ed. Anatole Chujoy (New York: A. S. Barnes, 1949), pp. 166-173.

the plantation longer than me, I expect you can leave it with less trouble.'

The Governor jist roar'd, and gin Chunkey a new gun and—"

"Stop, Jim, you have forgot the bear."

"Well, whar was I, Capting—oh, I remember, now! Well, when the barrel come we *did* lumber; Chunkey he soon commenced singin and I to thinkin about that white gal. We went on that way nigh a week and then cooled off. One morning I and Chunkey had gone down to the Creek to git a bait of water, and I knowd the bar would be thar as it war waterin time with them."

"Why, Jim, have they a particular time to water?"

"In course they has; they come to water at a certain place and jist as regular as a parson to his eatin; every bar has his waterin place, and he comes and goes in the same path and in the same foot tracks, always, until he moves his settlement; and jist you break a cane, or limb, or move a chunk or stick near his trail and see how quick he'll move his cabin! Oh yes, a bar is mighty particular about sich things—that's his *sens*—that's his trap to find out if you are in his settlement. Why, Capting, I have watched him—"

"Jim, you have left yourself and Chunkey on the bank of the Creek, a-waterin! Are you going to stay there?"

"Well, we set down on the bank and took our stand opposite the *biggest kind* of sign, and sure enough presently *down* he come; a bar don't lap water like a dog; no, they sucks it like a hog. You jist ought to see him rais his nose and smell the wind. Well, he seed us and with that he *ris!* He war a whopper, I *tell you!* He looked like a big barn, and he throwed them arms about awful, honey. It war about 120 yards to him, but I knowd he were my meat without an accident, so I let drive, and he took the Creek; then out he went and scampered up the bank *mighty quick,* and then sich a ratlin among cane, sich a growlin and snortin, sich a breakin of saplins and vines, I reckon you never *did* hear! I knowd, in course, I had him. I throwed a log in and paddled across—found his trail and lots of har and fat, but no blood!"

"That was very strange, Jim; how did you account for that?"

"Why he were too fat to bleed! Oh, you think I am foolin you, but you ask Chunkey. It is freekquently the case. I follered his trail about a quarter and a half a quarter, and *thar* he lay; so I jist hollered to Chunkey to git two negers and a yoke of stears to take him to the house. How much do you reckon he weighed?"

"I have no idea, Jim."

"Now, sir, he weighed, without head, skin, or entrails, 493 pounds, and his head sixty pounds! You don't believe me! Well, jist ask Chunkey if I hain't killed em smartly over 700 pounds! Killin him sorter got my blood up, and I determined to have another. Chunkey had been jerkin it to the licker gourd mighty smart and was jest right. 'Chunkey,' says I, 'let's gin it to another!' 'Good as —,' says Chunkey. 'Who care for expenses? a hundred dollar bill ain't no more in my pocket nor a cord of wood!' With that we started down to the Bend; we haddent been thar long when in comes an old buck; he was a smasher, and one horn were broke off. I telled Chunkey now's his time as I scorned to toch him arter killin a bar. Chunkey lathers away, and *ca chunk!* he went into the creek; he then gin him a turn with t'other barrel; the buck wabbled about a time or two and sunk, jist at the head of the little raft at the lower end of the clearin. I knowd he'd lodged agin the drift, and determined to have him, and if you'll believe me, I'd been workin at the gourd since I'd killed the bar. I pulled off my coat and jest throwed myself in; I swim out to the place and *div*—you know the current are mighty rapid thar. Well, I found him, yes—if I diddent. But, Moses! warn't I in a tight place *that* time? Well, I reckon I were. I'd been willin to fight the biggest *he* on the creek and gin him the first bite to have been out!"

"Why, Jim, what was the matter?"

"Arter I'd got in I couldent get out—*that* was the matter! You see the drift were a homogification of old cypress logs, vines, and drift-wood of every description for nigh three hundred yards long, and the creek runs under thar like it was arter somebody; the trees and vines and prognostics of all sorts ar sorter nit together like a rock, and you couldent begin to git through em. Well, Capting, I thought my time had come, and I knowed it war for killin that cub what I telled you about. And, sir, it would have come if it haddent been for the sorritude I felt afterwards. You see the young cub was standin in the corner of the fence eatin roastin ears, and I was goin to the—"

"But, Jim, you have told that once, and I don't want to hear it again."

"Well, I tried to rise, but I'd as well tried to rise down'ard. I then tried to swim up 'bove the raft, but I found from the way the logs and vines were tearin the extras off me that I were goin further under, and I was gettin out of wind very fast. I knowd thar was but one chance, and that was *to go clean through!* So I busted loose and set my paddles to goin mightily; presently my head bumped agin the drift! I div again and kept my paddles a-lumberin! Chunk! my head went agin a log, and then I knowd the thing were *irrefrangably out,* but I div agin, still workin on my oars smartly until I hung agin! 'Good bye, Chunkey!—farewell, Governor,' says I. But, Capting, I were all the time tryin to do *something.* Things had begun to look speckled, green, and then *omniferous,* but findin I were not gone yet by the way I were kickin and pawin and knowin I were goin *somewhere* and expectin to the devil, there ain't no tellin how long or powerful I *did* work! The first thing I recollect after that was gittin a mouth full of wind! *Fact!* I'd done gone clean through and were hangin on to a tree below the raft! But, sir, I were *mighty* weak and couldent tell a stump from an old he, and 'spected smartly for some time that I were in the yother world, and commenced an excuse for comin so onexpectedly! However, presently, I got sorter right, and when I found I were safe I reckon you never did see a man feel so *unanimous* in your life, and I made the water fly for joy."

"Well, Jim, what had become of Chunkey? He did not leave you?"

"Yes, if he diddent! He'd commenced gettin dry afore he shot the deer, and when Chunkey wants a drink, if his daddy was droundin, Chunkey would go to the licker gourd afore he'd go to his daddy. I went to the house, and thar he was settin at the table, jist a-rattlin his teeth agin the bar's ribs; the grease war running off his chin; he held a tin cup in one hand 'bout half full of licker; his head were sorter throwed back; he were breathin sorter hard, his eye set on the Governor, humpin himself on politics. 'Dam the specie currency,' says Chunkey, 'it ain't no account, and I'm agin it. When we had good times I drank five-dollar-a-gallon brandy and had pockets full of money.' 'But,' says the Governor, 'you bought that brandy on credit and never paid for it!'[9] 'What's the difference?' asks Chunkey! 'Them what I bought it from never paid for it! They bought it on credit from them foreigners and never paid for it, and them foreigners, you say, are a pack of scoundrels, and I go in for ruinin em, so far as good licker is concerned.' 'You are drunk,' says the Governor, and then—but Capting you look sleepy! let's licker and go to bed."

"No, I am not sleepy, Jim."

"Well, then, I'll tell you how I sarved Chunkey for leavin me under the raft. Moses diddent I pay him back? Did I ever tell you about takin Chunkey out on Sky Lake, makin him drunk, takin his gun and knife away from him, and a puttin him to sleep in panter's nest?"

"No, you never did; but was you not apprehensive they would kill him?"

"Apple—hell! no! If they'd commenced bitin Chunkey they'd have been looed, as that's a game Chunkey *invented!* But here he comes, and if you mention it before him it puts the devil in him. Let's licker!"

9. Reference to the argument over "hard" and paper currency.

Another Bear Fight

by "Ruff Sam" of Mississippi

§ "Another down-at-heel and disreputable letter-writer," says Yates (*Porter and the Spirit*, p. 99), "is 'Ruff Sam,' purportedly a Mississippi backwoodsman who served for awhile as a volunteer in the Mexican War. After his return, dialect letters based in part on his supposed war experiences appeared in New Orleans newspapers and subsequently in the *Spirit of the Times*."

The following letter, reprinted from the *Picayune*, appeared in the *Spirit*, XVIII, No. 2 (March 4, 1848), 14. The other two letters are reprinted elsewhere in this volume.

I'M rite from the backwoods of Mississippi, and as I told you onct 'bout my fite a Bony Vista,[10] the folks have been pesterin me to death to tell em sumthin of the bar an panther hunts I've had, how many I kilt and wether I was kilt or no, 'twill I've gis' determined to tell em of a rale swingin hunt I had last October.

You see, I left these parts in Ceptember and went strate hum. I arriv thar, and arter shakin hans with all the wimin folkes and kissin all the galls, the boys raised a bar hunt, and nuthin would do but I must go 'long. Thar was Bill Beenyard and Long Jim—but thar is no use in givin names for you doesn't know em—depend on it, thar was a parcel on em. We all got reddy at Squire Startises at the forks of the road, kalkulatin we'd start out next mornin by crack of day. Sure nuff next morning kum—I shuck myself an got out in the yard, kummenced blowin for the dogs. The other boys hain't much usen to huntin, so they was snorin 'bout that time. I blowed agin and here kum the dogs a-howlin and wagin thar tales, an a-lookin so eager—but I hadn't orter sed that Boss was a-wagin his tale cause he got it bit off onct by a darned old she tiger cat, an tain't never growed out yit. The boys kum a-stretchin themselves and axed me what all fired thunder that was. You see they hearn my horn and took it for thunder—I'm prodeegeous on a wind insterment an I

10. "'Seeing the Elephant' at the Battle of Beuna Vista" by "Ruff Sam" appears in the section "Masculine Amusements" following in this volume.

sorter skeered em—but I insured em it wouldn't rain nor nuthin, an everything bein fixed off we put. They wanted me to go long with the krowd, but I wasn't goin to do nuthin of the kind, so I tole em they'd fine me at the big bend in the kreek and then struck for the kanebrake.

Thar hain't never been a place yit whar Ruff Sam couldn't git throo. I whistled for Boss and gin him a few injunkshuns, such as "Look him up, sir-r-r!" "Mind what you 'bout, you bob-taled raskel!" —sorter urgin of him on—didn't mean to hurt his feelins, and he noed it. You ort to ha' seen him—Lord, how he riggled himself— a-camellin on the groun'—a-kockin his ears, a-histenin his tale, and a-whinin an cuttin setch numbersome kapers that you'd ha' thot he had tread in a wass ness. He seed I wasn't arter no turkeys nor deer for he never let on he noticed em.

We had pushed throo 'bout a mile of kane break when I began to *feel* a varmint of sum sort nigh me, and Boss felt him too. 'Twas powerful dark—the sun wasn't more an up, an it didn't stan' no chance for the kane, 'twas so 'mazin thick. "What is ail you, you skoundrel?" sez I, a-turnin roun to Boss. Thar he stood, his legs spraddled out and his grizzly sides a-swellin in an out like a pair of bellewes. "What on the airth is the matter?" sez I, a-gittin mad—I patted him on the back an a-coaxed him; 'twant no use—he wouldn't budge. That made me rale feerce and rip, rip, diff! I gin it to him in the ribs with my fist shet up. "Now, what ails you?" sez I. Boss looked at me an said, jest as plane as a dog kin say, he was skeered. I know'd sumthin most orful was kummin, or Boss would never ha' been skeered. I stopped and considered, an I mout ha' taken a little sumthin what I have 'long in a goard, but I won't say I did. I studdied on an speclated, and I mout ha' taken a nuther drop or so, but I won't swar to it. I looks at Boss, and sez I, "Boss, is you goin to foller me, or is you not?" He wanted to sodger out of the skrage, an I seed it in him; his har was stanin strate out all over him. Sez I, "If it's a whale you shall fite him, you kowardly Mexikin raskil!" You must ha' knowed I was savage, or I never would a-called my dog a Mexikin! Suddenly I hearn sumthin, and turnin I seed one of the most stonishin big she bars that ever wored fur standin afore me, within ten foot. When she seed me a–lookin at her she grunted, as much as to say, "Who's afeered!" Sez I, "Say your prayers quick; I wants your hide!" and lets drive with my rifle. Jest as I fired she throed her head round, an it took her in the shoulder. That riled her tremendious, and she kum at me afore I kould say who's who. I looked round and seed Boss a–watchin on close by, jest as the kritter closed in with me. "Charge her in the rair!" I shouted out to Boss. Zip! I kum down with the butt eend of my rifle, smashin it to pieces. She shuck her head an grabbed for me; but feelin the enimy a–worryin her in the rair, she wheeled. That gin me time to git out my old bowie knife, and I flanked her with it rale quick. She manoovered an kum to the charge agin in a bilin swet, bitin an showin fite in dead airnest. I was a–fallin back for a new position as my foot slipped, an kefetchup! I kum on my back! I thot the thing was out then an kommenced thinkin 'bout kingdom kum. She got me in her arms rale sure nuff, an if you say she didn't squeeze me, you doesn't know nuthin tall 'bout it. I tried to breathe, but the wind in me was so skase I kouldn't. She hugged me so tite that my fingers got as strate as stix; my head begin to swell 'bout the size of a whisky barl, an I sorter thot I mite bust or brake or sumthin if she presd me much harder. Presently I hearn her a–tremblin, and then she loosend her holt an rolled over on her side. I laid still 'twill I got to my usual size and then riz up to look for Boss. I was willin to quit. Thar was Boss, one of the bisiest dogs you ever seed, a–findin what she was made outen — he naterally had his head clane in the hole I had made in her with old bowie. The bar was dead, an me an Boss had licked her!

I was a–skinnin of her when the boys kum up, an sech a nuther spree we had arter we got to the Squire's I never spects to have agin.

Louisiana "Boys" and Bear Hunting

by Anonymous of Louisiana

§ This anecdote first appeared in the *Concordia Intelligencer*, Vidalia, Louisiana, during the time when both Thomas Bangs Thorpe and Robert Patterson were editors. Rickels *(Thorpe,* p. 74) lists it as Thorpe's. It was reprinted in the *Spirit*, XII, No. 26 (August 19, 1843), 291, from which the following version was taken.

AN old gentleman of some ninety winters had resided in an adjacent parish for the last forty years. A short time previous to his death which occurred about three weeks since, he was engaged with a couple of his sons in an exciting bear hunt. Bruin had been for some days committing various depredations in the vicinity and at length trespassed upon the old gentleman's premises, thereby arousing his ire. He called upon his two sons to aid him in the chase. The hunt continued from early dawn even when his sons or, as the old veteran called them, his *boys*, retired from the field and left him alone to achieve the glory of the day.

Fast, far, and furious fled bruin, but the old man's perserverance waxed not faint; like the well-trained hound, he followed fresh upon the trail and at length had the good fortune to get a sight of the bear some fifty yards distant upon the banks of a small slough where he had stopped to quench his thirst. The old man raised his faithful gun (an old favorite of thirty years standing and as true as tried steel when aimed by his unerring hand), the shrill, sharp crack broke upon the ear, and bruin fell. He was immediately butchered in the most approved style, his skin rolled up, containing a portion of "the fleece," the choice morsel of the hunter.[11] The old man, unchafed by long travel, took up his homeward way.

Upon reaching his cabin home, he found his sons resting from the

11. Webster's unabridged dictionary lists as one of the meanings for "fleece," "The meat taken from either side of the hump of the buffalo" *Local, U.S.* Cf. *depouiller* (n.) French colloquial word for "Fleece" and *depouille* (n.), "skin" or "hide" of an animal, the word buffalo hunters are said to have applied to the layer of fat under the skin.

toils of the day. Seating himself, he told them the incidents of the chase and exhibited the huge skin. While discussing "the fleece" which the good wife had cooked to a nicety, he lectured his boys upon the degeneracy of the youth of these latter days. He wound up his exhortation by observing: "Who'd a–thought it! Who'd believe that my boys could be beat bear hunting by their old father! Oh, how times have altered since I was young; the boys of my early days thought nothing of a week's chase—this is a fact, boys—you ought to be ashamed of yourselves!" The *elder boy* thus censured by the ninety-year-old veteran was only *sixty-five* and the younger but *sixty* years of age.

Joe Harris and the Panther

by "John of Oxford," Nubbin Ridge, Mississippi

§ Subtitled "A Reminiscence of Wolf River," this story was printed in the *Spirit*, XIX, No. 31 (September 22, 1849), 366.

IN the spring of 1832, at which time the Cholera Asiatique first made its appearance in this country, I took a trip to the Western District of Tennessee (then a great point of attraction for persons from this quarter of the world and from some portions of Virginia), where I spent some three or four months in and about the little town of La Grange and in scampering over the flower-enamelled prairies and park-like woodlands of the then almost wilderness country of Northern Mississippi. It was like a new existence to me! Young and enthusiastic, I would not have exchanged my horse and gun for the proudest position among the highest places of fashionable life, the echo of my own ringing shout for their sweetest music, and my mid-day snack of plain bread and meat taken by the side of some bubbling wildwood spring or sparkling streamlet whose flowing chrystal served to temper the draught of old Monongahela[12] which rounded off the repast—these I would not have exchanged for the daintiest array of chicken fixins that ever tempted and tickled the palate of an epicure.

In rambling about in this way I fell in with a good many strange characters as may be supposed, and among them all no one for the time more attracted my attention than the hero of the little adventure I am about to narrate.

I first saw him in the streets of La Grange on some public occasion and was immediately struck with his light but round, compact, and

12. Often "Monongaheely" in colloquial language; a name for whiskey, much of which was made on the Monongahela River in West Virginia and Pennsylvania and shipped west. Other names for liquor in this sketch are "baldface" and "the corn." For still other names, see the section "Masculine Amusements" following in this volume.

sinewy figure, the admirable carriage of his head, and the quiet, composed self-possession of his manner.

Although clad in the simple garb of a plain countryman, he would have been singled out in a crowd anywhere by a close observer. I drew the attention of Gray, an Indian trader, to him and asked whom he was. He immediately informed me and then proceeded to give me the following account of him. He was the youngest of three brothers, the eldest, Bill and Sam, being tall, rawboned, fair-haired, fair-complexioned men, noisy, insolent, and quick to quarrel, and constantly engaged in fights, in which, by the way, from their great pensonal strength and activity, they generally proved victorious.

Joe, on the other hand, was about the middle size with dark skin and eyes and his bullet head covered with short crisp curls of the jettiest black. Quiet and cool in his general demeanor, he seldom ever got into a difficulty, but when he chanced to be drawn into one gave ample proof that he was by no means behind any of his family in fistic prowess and accomplishments. It happened on one occasion at a quarter race (at a little place familiarly known in those days as Pin Hook[13] but set down, I believe, on the map of the state as Van Buren) that Joe got mixed up in a fight with one of the bullies of the neighborhood and was knocking the conceit out of him "hand over fist" when Bill, the eldest brother, who was standing by and hadn't had a fight for more'n a week, took the fight off Joe's hands and demolished the fellow in the twinkling of a bed post.

After the affair was over and before they had time to liquor on it, Joe took Bill one side out of earshot and very deliberately remarked to him, "Look here, Bill, I'll tell you what it is; I've no objection in the world if you see that a feller's a–gittin the better of me that you should cut in and get us apart, but I've no notion when I've got a feller as good as whipped that you should run in and take all the credit of the fight! Tain't the first time you've done it; and if you ever do it again, I give you fair warnin, I'll turn right round an lick you like h–––! Now mind if I don't!"

13. Pin Hook as a name of scorn was also given to villages in Texas and Louisiana; John Q. Anderson, "Some Mythical Places in Louisiana," *Louisiana Folklore Miscellany*, Louisiana Folklore Society Publication No. 3 (May 1958), 1-10.

"Very well," says Bill, who was well aware that Joe would be apt to be as good as his word, "I'll try and remember!"

They then walked back to the crowd and clinched the understanding with a smile of "baldface"!

A few weeks after the conversation and fight aforesaid, Bill and Joe walked down into the river bottom, either to hunt up some cattle or hogs or to look for timber stock. Bill had his rifle but Joe was unarmed. After forcing their way some half a mile or such matter through the thick underbrush, composed in part of the red buckeye with its brilliant blossoms, they were suddenly startled by a low savage growl which sounded uncomfortably near, and ere they could look about them or make any preparation, a large female panther sprang with a wild shriek of exulting rage from a limb overhead full upon the shoulder of Joe and attempted to fasten her teeth in his neck.

To twist himself around and seize the animal by the throat was to the intrepid borderer but the work of an instant, and then commenced the struggle for life and death, fist and foot against teeth and claws. Of little service, however, were the monster's teeth for such was the vice-like tenacity of the backwoodsman's grasp and the wiry tension of his sinewy arm that the animal never once got her head near enough to his person to seize him, but the claws did tearing service. In a few minutes, poor Joe was as naked in front as he was when he came into the world and as crimson red from top to toe as ere a buckeye blossom that bloomed around him. Meanwhile, with untiring vigor and energy he had poured an incessant storm of blows from his iron fist into the ribs and chest of his savage antagonist, which began after a while to writhe evidently under the punishment and finally confined its efforts to struggles to get away. But that was no go! There was no such thing mentioned in the bill of the play! At length perfectly exhausted with his exertions and loss of blood, the gallant Joe staggered to a seat, the body of the panther now perfectly dead slipping from his nerveless grasp with its ribs and brisket beaten to a perfect jelly. After recovering his breath somewhat and while with Bill's assistance endeavoring to staunch the blood which still flowed pretty freely, he noticed the rifle lying down by Bill's side and called out, "Why, Bill! why the h–ll didn't you shoot the infernal cretur when you seed it doin me so?"

"Hum!" says Bill. "Very good reason why! Didn't you tell me t'other day, if I ever mixed in a fight of yourn agin when you was getting the best of it that you'd lick me? say? If I'd a–seed the panther have you down and puttin it into you, I'd a–shot him; but long as I seed you was gettin the best of it, I wouldn't a–toch it for half of Fayette County, d--n if I would!"

Feeling very much interested in the hero of such an adventure, I soon after sought an introduction to Joe and in the course of conversation referred to the affair. He acknowledged the corn and to gratify my curiosity rolled up his sleeves and opened his bosom to show me the remembrances left by the panther. Besides several deep marks on his face, his arms and chest were perfectly seamed, as also he informed me were his lower limbs. If his stripes had only been colored, he could have beaten a zebra and given him two in the game. I have not deemed it necessary to be particular as to the correctness of the names, but the truth of the incident itself was vouched for by many respectable persons besides the hero (who seemed to be notoriously known on account of that very circumstance) and his scar-covered body which told a tale of itself.

Chunkey's Fight with the Panthers

by "The Turkey Runner," Warren Co., Mississippi

§ Another in McNutt's series of sketches about Chunkey and Jim, this story appeared in the *Spirit*, XIV, No. 12 (May 18, 1844), 139. Porter included it in his first anthology of backwoods sketches, *The Big Bear of Arkansas and Other Sketches* (1845), where he introduced it as follows: "In the 'Spirit of the Times' of the 20th April, we published the first of a series of original hunting stories, written expressly for this paper by a most acceptable correspondent who promises to rival in fame the author of *'Tom Owen the Bee Hunter'* who made his debut as a contributor to the sporting literature of the day in these columns, as also *'N. of Arkansas,' 'The Shingle Splitter,'* and others, whose articles are now read and admired throughout the world."

*C*OCHUNK! went Jim into the middle of the floor, jest at the crack of day—(Jim is a labor-savin man and don't pull off his socks or breeches when he goes to bed). He commenced chunkin the fire, and then "Ah!" says he, feelin for the tin cup—"*Gluck, gluck, gluck*" went the licker—then "Ah!" agin. Presently he went to the door and shouted to the foreman, "Sound that horn, Hembry; tell the niggers in the kitchen to holler to the niggers in the quarter and the niggers in the quarter to lumber the holler back agin to the kitchen, for hell has *surely* broke loose!" Then "Ah!" says he agin and in he comes.

"Chunkey!" says he.

"What's bursted, Jim?"

"Hell *has* bursted and no mistake! the ground is kivered with snow!"

I sprung and sure enough *thar* was the snow, the first that ever fell in the Creek, jest follerin civilization. I *knowed* thar'd be howlin, smashin of teeth, burnin of brimstone, and a-worryin of the "stranger" on the Creek today, and so I reckon did the dogs cause when Hembry blowed the horn they come a-shoutin like so many devils. Jest imagin, Captin, thirty full-grown dogs, a cross of the blood on the old Virginna fox hound, keen as a bowyer [bowie knife], and a 'zactly of Jim's opinion that hell *had* bursted and signifyin as plain as they could if huntin's goin on *they'd* take a chance.

Well, we splurged about till breakfast time gettin up and cleanin guns, countin balls and dividin powder. "Bring out them bar sassage and deer melts; I'll take a little jaw-exercise," says Jim, "and then, Chunkey, we'll locomotion," his eye all the time lookin like a live coal of fire and every muscle jumpin for joy. "Look out, bar!" says he.

"Lay low and keep dark, painter," says I.

"Deer, don't you come nigh me," says Jim, and then commenced singin

> *Oh, rain, come wet me, sun come dry me,*
> *Take care, white man, don't come nigh me!*

and strikin a few licks of the goin-and-comin double shuffle.

"Hurrah for Sky Lake," says I.

"Hurrah for the Forkin Cypress drive," says Jim, takin a drink and cuttin a few pigeon wings with his left leg. "Them's the licks, Chunkey, what makes a gal say 'yes.' Now, mind, Chunkey, no deer or wild turkey, no wild hogs or cub, nothin but bar or painter!" "Agreed," says I, and then we bulged. Captin, you've hearn Jim say he's hard of hearin? Well, he is, sometimes, specially when he don't want to hear; but *that* mornin he was wide awake all over and could have hearn an old he grunt in a thunder storm! "I'll carry the horn, Chunkey; if you blow I can't hear you, and when I want you I'll blow, and you can."

I diddent 'spect anything then, but you'll see.

Well, we had our big guns, them the Governor gin us; they throw twelve to the pound and war made by that man what lives in Louisville—what's his name? He promised to send me a deer gun gratis for two young painters, but he ain't done it. Jim's gun were in bar order that mornin, and if you'd jest say varmint above your breath, *click* it would go cockin itself. We haddent crossed the creek two hundreds yards afore yelp, yelp went old Rambler. "Cuss them dogs!" says Jim, "that's a deer!" Big Solomon went to examine the sign. "No it ain't, Massa Jim—it's a painter *sure!*—look at her long foot and sharp nail, and see hear whar he's been ridin pigs! Cuss his saitful countenance!" "It's a wolf," says Jim, "or a dog! Run down to the rossin-gum tree, Chunkey, and I'll go to the Cypress crossin log; he's bound to go one way or the yother to git out."

Well, I husseled off to the rossin-gum and Jim to the foot log, and afore we got to our stands the dogs had him gwine like a streak; away he went down to the Pint, and I knowed that's no place for him, and presently I heard em comin back — nearer and nearer — here they is! — don't they make the snow fly, and jest look at him! Look at them yaller eyes! — them ears laid back and them meat hooks a-shinin! Ain't he stretchin himself! Ain't them dogs talkin to him with "tears in their eyes!" Yes, they is, boss, and now I'll git him! *Bang!* Oh, dam you! you've got it! I know you is! you ain't shakin that tail for nothin! Yes, thar's blood on the snow! But ain't he "gittin out de way?" Never mind; them dogs will shuck him afore he's much older, and if they don't Jim's yager will. *Bang* went Jim's gun and then all were still. "Howdy, wolf! how do you rise?" says I, and started. When I got up Jim were shakin him. He were a smasher but too full to run.

Another lickerin and cussin a spell, we took a "bee line" for Sky Lake. Goin along we lickered freely, and arter a while Jim said, "Chunkey, I can slash you, shootin at that knot!" "Well, I reckon you can, Jim," says I, but you know he couldent, Captin, I wouldent shoot cause we hadent any ammunition to spare. "Keep them dogs in and break for the Forkin Cypress, Sol," says I, "and make a cane camp, and Sol, do you hear, jest let them dogs loose, and I'll swaller you, wrong and foremost!" "Massa Chunkey is risin," said Sol, and then he busted.

Lots of deer war 'tinually passin; some on em stood feedin jist as careless as a loafer with a full belly — they know'd they was safe. The day was mighty clear and yaller; it warn't very cold, but still the snow diddent melt but floated round sorter like turkey feathers in the wind, and in the tall cane it fell round us like a fog. When we got to the Forkin Cypress, Sol soon had a camp done, and I and Jim started to look for sign.

We haddent been gone long when I hearn Jim's horn and made to him; thar war sign at the foot of a tree, and *thar* was his track in the snow. "Shall we nail him, Chunkey?" "*In course,*" says I. Well, he hollered to Sol to turn the dogs loose and *hear* they come; they jest fell onto the trail like a starved dog on a bloody bone. They circled about among the switch-cane and priscimmon bushes a long time afore they could make it out. Presently I hearn em give some short licks, and I knowed he war up. "Thar's a cry for you!" Away they go, further and further, presently you can jest hear em, and then they are clean gone. I hearn Jim shoutin awhile, and then his mouth is lost. I started on spectin to meet em comin back, and in about an hour I hearn Jim's voice—*who-whoop.* "Ah, *bar,*" says I. "Whar's your friends?" I soon hearn Jim agin, and presently I hearn the dogs, like the ringing of a cowbell, a long way off. They come up the ridge, and then bore off to the thick cane on my right; then they hushed awhile, and I know'd they's a-fightin. Look out dogs!— *thar,* they are gwine agin; no, hear they comes! Lay low and keep dark! I put down another ball and stood for him. I heared the cane crackin and cocked my gun! Here he comes—here he is! I hearn him snortin; wake snakes! *Ain't that lumberin?* Thar, they've got him agin, and now the fur flies. I crawled through the cane tryin to git a shot afore the dogs seen me. *Thar they is,* but which is *he?* Dam that dog's head! *Bang!* Whiff, whiff, said the bar, and with that every dog jumped him. The cane's a-crackin and the dogs a-hollerin. I jerked my bowyer [bowie] and plunged in, and thar they war hung together like a swarm of bees! Thar lay Singer on the ground, limber as a rag, and the bar had Constitutional down. I felt the har risin on my head and the blood ticklin the end of my fingers. I crept up behind him and *zip, zip, zip* I took him jest behind the shoulder-blade, and *he war done fightin.* He sot down and sorter rolled his head from side to side, the blood runnin off his tongue and his eyes full of dirt. He haddent got a hundred yards from the place whar I'd shot him. It war a death shot and blinded him, and thar side of him lay Singer and Constitutional, two of the best dogs in Jim's pack.

H--l! I gin a shout and Jim answered. Presently, I seen him cummin, *blowin* like a steamboat and mad as hell; he always gits mad when he's tired, and when he seen them dogs he commenced breathin mighty hard and the blood filled the veins in his neck as big as your fingers. Presently he commenced cussin, and then he sorter got easy. After a while he turned in and cleaned him; we warn't more than a quarter and a half from the camp whar we soon got, both mighty hungry and tired. Sol cooked the liver jest to the right pint, and we giv it Jessy. We spent the balance of the evenin in drinkin, braggin, and eatin spar ribs roasted brown. Jim made Sol sing

> *Oh, she waked me in the mornin, and it's broad day.*
> *I looked for my canu [canoe], and it's done gone away.*

till we went to sleep.

Next morning when we waked it war sorter cloudy and warm, and I and Jim were cloudy and warm, too. The wind war howling mightly.

"Now, Chunkey, let's have a painter today, *or nothin.*"

"*All sot,*" says I.

Well, arter breakfast Jim says, "Chunkey, you must take the right side of the Lake, and I'll take the yother till we meet—and, Chunkey, you must *rush;* it ain't more nor eight miles round, but your side *may* seem long as you ain't been to the ground. Let's licker out of *my* gourd, you ain't got more nor you'll want. Keep your eye skinned for sign and listen for my horn."

"Hump yourself," says I, and we both started. Well, I worked my passage through cane, palmettoe, and vines until I were tired. I haddent hearn Jim's horn and pushed on the harder to meet him; every once and a while I'd think *hears the turn of the Lake,* but when I'd git to the place *thar it was* stretchin out big as ever. Once I thought I hearn Jim's horn but couldn't quite make it out. I kept movin; hours passed and no Jim or end of the Lake; I'd seen lots of bar and painter sign, lots of deer, and more swan, wild goose, and duck than you ever will see, but I paid no attention to em and spected I'd taken some wrong arm of the Lake and were lost. It were gettin towards night, and I spected I'd have to sleep by myself, but you know I dident mind that as I war used to it. But it war the first time in my life that I'd ben lost and that *did* pester me mightly. Well, sir, arter studyin awhile, I thought I'd better put back towards the camp, mighty tired and discouraged. I then throw'd my gourd round to take a drink of licker, and it were *filled with water!* fact!—thinks I, Chunkey, you must have been *mighty* drunk last night—that made me sorter low spirited like a 'oman, and my heart were weak as water. It had commenced gittin sorter dark, the wind were blowin and groanin through the trees and rivers, and the black clouds were flyin, and I war going along sorter oneasy and cussin when *a painter yelled out, close to me!* I turned with my gun cocked but couldent see it; presently I hearn it agin, and out it come and then another! "Here's hell!" said I, taken a crack and missin to a certainty and away they darted through the cane. I drap'd my gun to load, and, by the great Jackson, there warn't a full load of powder in my gourd! I loaded *mighty* carefully and started on to pick out some holler tree to sleep in. Every once and awhile I'd git a glimpse of the painters on my trail. "Painters," says I, "I'll make a child's bargain with you; if you will let *me* alone, *you* may *go long;* and if you don't here's a ball into the head of one of ye'er, and this knife!—*hush*, if my knife warn't gone I wish I may never taste bar's meat! I raised my arm trimblin like a leaf, and says I, "Jim! *I'll have your melt!*" Well, I *war* in trouble sure! I thought I war on the *Tchule a Leta Lake* and *witched!*

Well, I did! Oh, you may larf, but gist imagine *yourself* lost in the cane on Sky Lake (the cane on Sky Lake is *some*—thirty miles long, from one to three miles wide, thick as the hair on a dog's back, and about thirty feet high) out of licker, out of powder, your knife gone, the ground kivered with snow, you very hungry and tired, *and two painters follerin your trail,* and you'd think you was bewitched too!

Well, here they come, never lettin on, but makin arrangements to have my skalp that night—I never lettin on but determin'd they shouldent. The har had been standin on my head for more nor an hour, and the sweat were gist *rollin* off me and that satisfied me a fight war brewin atween me and the painters! I stopped two or three times thinkin they's gone, but presently hear they'd come creepin along through the cane, and soon as they'd see me they'd stop, lay down, roll over, and twirl their tails about like kittens playin; I'd then shout and shake the cane and away they'd go. Oh, they thought they had me! *In course they did,* and I determined with

myself if they *did let me go*, if they diddent attack an onarmed man
—alone and lost, without licker, dogs, powder, or knife—that the
very first time I got a painter up a tree with my whole pack at the
root, my licker gourd full, and I half full, my twelve-to-the-pound-
yager loaded, and my knife in shavin order, I'd let *him go!* Yes,
dam'd if I diddent!

But what did *they* care? They'd no more feelin than the devil! I
know'd it wouldent do to risk a fight in the cane and pushed on to
find an open place whar I could make sure of my one load and rely
on my gun barrel arter. I soon found a place whar the cane drifted,
and *thar* I determined to stand and fight it out! Presently here they
come, and if a stranger had seen em, he'd a thought they were playin!
They'd jump and squat, and bend their backs, lay down and roll,
and grin like puppies. *They kept gittin nearer and nearer,* and it were
gittin dark, and I know'd I must let drive at the old *he* 'afore it got
so dark I couldent see my sights; so I jest dropped on one knee to
make sure, and when I raised my gun I were all in a trimble! I know'd
that wouldent do and *ris!*

"You are witched, Chunkey, sure and sartin," said I. Arter bracin
myself I raised up agin and *fired!* One on em sprung into the air and
gin a yell, and the other bounded towards me like a streak! Lightin
close to me, it squatted to the ground and commenced creepin
towards me—its years laid back, its eyes turnin green and sorter
swimmin round like, and the end of its tail twistin like a snake.
I felt light as a cork and strong as a buffalo. I seen her commence
slippin her legs under her and knew she were gwine to spring. I
throw'd back my gun to gin it to her as she come; the lick I aimed
at her head struck across the shoulders and back without doing any
harm, and *she had me!* Rip, rip, rip—and 'way went my blanket,
coat, and britches. She sunk her teeth into my shoulder, her green
eyes were close to mine, and the froth from her mouth were flyin in
my face!! *Moses!* how fast she *did* fight! I felt the warm blood runnin
down my side—I seen she were arter *my* throat! and with that I
grabbed *hern* and commenced pourin it into her side with my fist,
like cats a-fightin!—Rip, rip, rip, she'd take me—diff, slam, bang,
I'd gin it to her—she fightin for her *supper*, I fightin for my *life!* Why,

in course, it war an onequal fight but she ris it! Well, we had it round
and round, sometimes one and then yother on top, she a-growlin
and I a-gruntin! We had both commenced gittin mighty tired, and
presently she made a spring *tryin to git away!* Arter *that* thar warn't
no mortal chance for her! Cause why, she were whipped! I'd sorter
been thinkin about sayin, "Now I lay me down to sleep," but I
knowed if I commenced it would put her in heart and she'd riddle
me in a minit, and when she hollered *nuff,* I were glad to my shoes
soles and had sich confidence in whippin in the fight that *I offered
two to one on Chunkey,* but no takers!

"On, dam you," says I, hittin her a lick every time I spoke, "you
are willin to quit even and divide stakes, are you?" and then round
and round we went agin! You could have hearn us blow a quarter,
but presently she made *a big struggle* and broke my hold! I fell one
way and she the other! She darted into the cane, and that's the last
time I ever hearn of *that* painter!

When I sorter come to myself I war struttin and *thunderin* like a
big he-gobler, and then I commenced examinin to see what harm
she'd done me. I war bit powerful bad in the shoulder and arm—
just look at them scars!—and I were cut into solid whip strings; but
when I found thar warn't no danger of its *killin* me, I set in to cussin.
"Oh, you ain't dead yet, Chunkey!" says I, "if you are sorter worsted,
and have whipped a painter in a fair fight, and no gougin," and then
I *cock-a-doodle-doed* a spell, for joy!

When I looked round, *thar* sot the old he a-lickin the blood from
his breast! I'd shot him right through the breast but sorter slantin-
dickler breakin his shoulder blade into a perfect smash. I walked up
to him; "Howdy, painter! how do you do? how is missis painter and
the little painters? how is your consarns in general? Did you ever
hearn tell of the man they calls 'Chunkey' born in Kaintuck and
raised in Mississippi—death on a bar and *smartly* in a painter fight?
If you diddent, look, for *I'm he!* I kills bars, whips painters in a fair
fight; I walks the water, I out-bellers the thunder, and when I gets
hot the Mississippi hides itself! I—I—oh, you thought you *had* me,
did you?—dam you! But you are a gone sucker, now. I'll have your
melt, if I never gits home, so—"

Look out, Captin! here's the place! make the skift fast to that cypress log, take care them oars, *Abe!* Spring out and oncupple the dogs and take car they don't knock them guns overboard. Now, Captin, we will have a deer moving afore you can tell who's your daddy.

An Alligator for a Present

by "Pardon Jones" of Louisiana

§ C. M. Haile, a member of the staff of the New Orleans *Picayune*, became widely known for his humorous letters signed "Pardon Jones." A native of Rhode Island, he attended West Point for one year in 1836, came to Louisiana, and edited the *Planter's Gazette* at Plaquemine before joining the *Picayune* staff. He served as a correspondent in Mexico for the *Picayune* during the Mexican War and in the siege of Vera Cruz was commissioned first lieutenant; Copeland, *Kendall of the Picayune*, p. 158.

When Porter reprinted "Pardon Jones's" letter from the *Picayune* in the *Spirit* (XII, No. 27 [September 3, 1842], 313), he gave it this unusually long introduction: "It will be seen from the annexed correspondence which we find in the New Orleans 'Picayune' of the 19th ult., that an important addition is about to be made to our 'Cabinet of Sporting Curiosities.' The donor is no other than the celebrated Col. *Pardon Jones*, the admirable correspondent of the 'Picayune,' which announces the following: '*Arrival Extraordinary.* — Yesterday morning we received per steamer "Clipper" a "sure enough" *Live Alligator* sent to our care and designed as a present from *Pardon Jones*, to the editor of the New York "Spirit of the Time," together with a letter which will be found in another column. *Porter* may be sure of our due attention to this rare consignment. The "critter" shall be forwarded to New York by the first vessel, and in the meantime all curious enquirers may visit his alligatorship at our office.'

"Our friends of the 'Picayune,'" Porter continued, "may rely upon our giving a cordial reception to the present of the Colonel. We anticipate great things of the varmint, as it is our intention eventually to 'employ his valuable service' in the collection of subscriptions from delinquent subscribers, if sufficient inducements are offered. We shall first offer him, however, the situation of doorkeeper to our editorial sanctum. As he is an extremely 'long headed' fellow, the gentlemen loafers and the 'pickers and stealers' of our new books, prints, music, etc., will find it no easy matter to 'pull the wool over *his* eyes.' The subjoined letter, which Col. Jones has done us the honor to address to us, through the 'Picayune,' details as clear as mud the history of the capture and the subsequent adventures of this 'Creole of Louisiana'."

I GUESS you'll feel putty badly 'stonished when you receive a letter from me 'way down here in these foreign parts, but you'll 'scuse the liberty when you come to see what a putty leetle crittur I've sent to you by the *Picayune* and thank me in the bargain. This young alligator is a pure blooded annermil, and the only *cross* he's got is them yaller streeks that runs acrost his back and tail—and *they* only go to show the crittur's blood. He is a grate favorite of mine—and so is the hull race of alligators for that matter—for they are so sentimental—they sigh, and moan, and shed as many tears as a love-sick damsel—and if they could only speak I guess the tall cypress trees round their *settlements* would hear many a *long tail* of grief that would make their *knees* tremble with anguish. But I must tell you how this little feller was ketched and then close my 'pistle.

I 'spec you've heered of Grosse Tete Bay out back of Pluckmin [Plaquemine] hain't you. Wall, 'tother day I'n some friends got out our horses with our sadddlebags full of fishhooks, and lines, and bottles of wine, and salt, and corn meal, and baskets of shrimps for bait, and bread, and a fryinpan, and a pack of hounds, and guns, and huntin jackets, and horns, and tin cups. I was 'pinted *standard-bearer* and had to ride ahead and raise up the fryinpan for a *banner.* The horns blowed and the hosses started as if the devil had gin em a kick behind. I had a basket on my arm, and the fryinpan was so plaguy awkerd that I couldn't curb my hoss, and away he started full drive with the bit in his teeth! "Save the banner, save the banner!" shouted my frends. "The Curnel is goin to set away from us and have the fun all to himself—ketch him, ketch him!—but don't break the bottles!"—and after me they put! The race lasted 'bout ten miles till at last I let go the banner and got the tarnel hoss under agin. I resigned the office of *insign* tellin on em that the honor bore *tu heavy* on me and I couldn't stan' it. We all examined our saddlebags and found that nothin hadn't broke, and the horns blowed and off we started agin and rid five miles through a thick cypress swamp where at high water a hoss would a had to swum, but now it was only a little muddy. When we come to the Bay, 'fore we made enny noise, we see 'bout fifteen old alligators swimmin 'long on the water sorter sociable like, and when they heard the hounds bark, they rounded tu and come sailin tords the shore as grand as could be. The leader had got putty near to us when the fust thing *he* knowed he didn't know nothin for he got a big ounce ball 'tween his eyes out of one of our guns, and the way he kicked and flounced for about a minnet was awful to see—the blood a-spoutin out on him all the time. The rest of the alligators fell afoul on him, and when he sunk I guess he was putty well used up. The next we knowed the dogs started off after a deer, and the *next* thing the rain come pourin down on us like Noah's flud. The hosses was stripped and tied and the saddlebags opened—a fire lit up and them that didn't go scalin fish went to fishin. The weather cleared up—and then it rained agin—and you never did see nothin bite ('cept the skeeters) as them fish did! Patassas, catfish, trout, and so forth and so on—we kept whirlin on em and throwin on em at the *scalers* till they cried out, "Hold—enough." We all stopt then 'cept one young feller from New Orleans, and he'd ben pullin and yankin his line, breakin his hooks, and puttin on bait all the time, but he hadn't ketched a single fish. "I'll have him now, by jingo!" cried he, and he tied a strong line to a big cane and throwed it agin. "If I wasn't 'fraid of them tarnel alligators," says he, "I'd go furder out on this log where they bite better." "Go out," says I, "*they* won't come in sight while *you* are there," and he went out on the log that stuck out into the Bay and throwed in his hook. "He's broke three lines," says he, "and now I'll have him! I've got him!" he cried. "I've got him!" "No you hain't," says I, "but if you will pull stiddy and not *yank* so, you'll get him out." He pulled away and raised up his rod putty quick, perpendickler, and then he hollored like a loon and fell over backward into the water and swum ashore. He'd pulled this leetle alligator out, and when it slapped and kicked up in his face he was skeered near about to death. I don't 'spose the little critter was more'n a week or tu old when he ketched him, but he is now fourteen inches long, and if wal kept and properly fed he'll be fourteen *feet* long afore he dies and will make one of the best yard dogs in the world. If you've got a watermelon patch enny where's out in the field, you can tie him up to a stake in the middle on't with a long rope, and I'll be dratted if enny buddy will steal em — that is, when he gits to be four or five year old. They're (the alligators) the ony dogs the squatters uses to keep off the Injins and runaway niggers in these parts. Wall, we made the young man drink a coque of brandy after he came out of the water (though he belonged to the cold water 'siety) and then stood round the pile of fried fish and ate our dinner and washed it down with plenty of claret and got washed down ourselves by a heavy rain. The horns was blowed and the dogs called in, and off we started for hum through the woods the hosses frettin and rairin like mustangs. I brought the alligator hum in my saddlebags 'spessly to send to you. If it gets tu you safe, I hope you won't let it suffer. It will be useful to you now when it is small for a *barometer.* Just keep him in a tub with a block in the bottom for him to sun himself on, and when you see him go down into the water and shut his eyes up, you may be sure its goin to rain or storm; but soon's he comes up and rests on the block, you may look out for fair weather. There's no mistake 'bout this — wonderful, ain't it? — and still 'tis true!

I'n some of the naybors is gettin ready to go down Bayou Pluckmin and up the Chaffalyer [Atachafalaya] huntin and fishin, and if I can get my friend Pic to send you the letter, I'll give you the history on't.

Dog Days in Mississippi

by "Chips," Bayou Lafourche, Louisiana

§ Printed as "Matrimonial and Judicial Matters" in the *Spirit*, XVII, No. 33 (October 9, 1848), this story originally had a long introduction which is here omitted.

IN our village (you might infer from the superscription we had a sure-enough city here—that is not the fact; it is yet a village, christened city in anticipation of the event in the "womb of time")—in our village we have as fun-loving a set of boys as in any other diggins. They can start a saw and run it longer, I believe, than anybody else's b'hoys.[14] They have recently engaged in a little matrimonial and judicial excitement which on paper, I am afraid, will appear flat, but as acted would have excited the risibles of any laughter-hating ascetic on earth.

The chief personage in this *mellow*-drama was one James R. Jones —that is to say, at the baptismal fount he was so designated by his loving dad. But alas! the mutability of things earthly! The euphonious James has gone "glimmering through the mist of things that was;" and the significant cognomen of "Lying" has ursurped its place. Lying R. Jones is his name, beyond the possibility of change.

One word of explanation lest you may think my hero a malicious bad man. Not at all. Jones has a good fancy and with an education to match probably would have paled the high fame of Bulwer and Scott. His fancy did not run into the malicious or dishonest. Though Jones has indited a thousand fanciful histories, yet no one has ever been known to have suffered materially from them. It is true Jones had killed more "bars" and "painters" in a "fa'r fight"—had more estates in expectancy—had more women "runnin' arter him"—gave bigger prices for borrowed property, and was intimate with more

---

14. For a definition of "saw," see Section, "Jokes and Jokers," which follows. The word "b'hoys," in imitation of Irish pronunciation, is commonly used in popular humor for a group of men who are companions or friends.

big men, Generals and Colonels, than any other live man. But "there was nobody down." Inasmuch as our vicinage boasted of three other James Joneses, to avoid confusion a characteristic nickname was lashed on to each. There was "Fighting Jim," "Long Jim," "Short Jim," and our man "Lying Jim." I don't wish you to understand that our Jim wasn't, for he was "nothin else."

James is of the Toney Wellerish build; like the old Chinese junk, he has about as much beam as keel. Imagine a Cincinnati cask (sometimes familiarly called "Redhead") mounted on the forecastle of a Tennessee spinningwheel, and further suppose the said cask surmounted by a sampling keg of red cedar, and a red blanket coat over all, and you have some idea of Jim's physicals. Jim had a couple of years before retired from city life and had settled upon a forty-acre tract in the Yazoo Swamp; during these two years we saw and heard but little of him. Occasionally on the packet-boat a piece of "bar meat," flanked by a McNutt (i.e., a gallon jug) might be seen addressed to his friend Andy, which said jug was always regularly reshipped, smartly heavier than on the downward trip. And now and then some verdant land-hunter could be heard dilating on the fertility of Yazoo lands and speaking of one Mr. Jones having made seventeen bales to the hand. But a degree of fate arrested Jim's rural pleasures. Having deprived him of his better half, who, if not so in size, was certainly so in industry and economy, Jim broke up his "bottom place" a short time since and returned to town. By this move he reduced the swamp population a good deal and by his accounts left "Col. Bill, Col. Jeff, and the Judge," almost inconsolable. He brought within our corporate limits eight children and eleven dogs and hardly enough of "the root of all evil" to settle his poll tax.

Jim happened to come in at an unfortunate time for his canine retinue—the corporate authorities had been aroused from a dignified sloth of long standing—proclamations had been issued—the Dog Law was in full blast! "Four bits or death" the ordinance called for emphatically. The dog-killer with his double-barrel was on hand like a thousand o'brick, James remonstrated; he argued the "Constitution" and stoutly maintained that "nobody kudn't kill nuthin without a trial by peers" and that "bar-dogs wasn't in the law."

He pleaded poverty. He rehearsed his many misfortunes. But it all wouldn't do. "The work of blood went on": Holdfast could hold no longer; Caesar went as his great namesake did, basely immolated in the name of Liberty and Law; Brutus soon followed; and Polk, seeing the dangers by which he was encompassed, left for the quiet shades of his late residence. All the rest fell martyrs to their love for Jim and could be seen stark and stiff close about where Jim had done his "wooding."

James was stricken with much sorrow and flew to a *doggery* for relief. He drank—he imbibed immensely; his sorrows and todies finally overpowered him. He sank down on the bench before the door, appropriated to the dry and the unfortunate. He groaned— he soliloquized—"I've hearn tell o' dog days; these is em. I never know'd what they was afore. I know'd they come in August, too— umph! what a tarnal fool I was! Oh me! *What* a tarnal fool to bring em *here*. Hie! umph! poor Lege—hic—he helped me kill more'n a thousand—hic—bars; and—hic—poor Brute—wa'nt he h--l on wildcats! I tell you, Pete, a cat wa'nt nowhere where he was! Last snow him and me killed—hic—a hundred and ten cats—and 'leving painters ekal, to a hundred and ten more! umph!"

Jones about this time took a lurch to leeward and sank in a recumbent posture, and "Nature's sweet restorer" for a time obliterated his many ailments. At early dawn James was aroused by an inward monitor, which many would call conscience, but which I shall designate as thirst. Having taken a couple of fingers of "har," he departed to see his friend Dr. B---- for counsel and advice, feeling wholly unequal to meet and brave his many sorrows singly and alone.

A Wildcat Story

by Anonymous of Louisiana

§ The following tale appeared in the *Spirit*, XX, No. 13 (May 18, 1850), 148, reprinted from the New Orleans *Picayune*.

MANY years ago in the wilds of the western part of Mississippi, there lived an old hunter by the name of Rube Fox, who was as notorious in that section of country as ever Martin Scott was in the West.

One day Rube came down with a small party of friends to take a hunt on Deer Creek, and they stopped at the house of a widow, who occasionally took in travellers to stay all night. Rube was a very stout, athletic man, about six feet two inches in height, and wore his hair and beard very long. His cheeks, nose, and upper lip were deeply scarred, which gave him a very savage appearance. The widow had often "hearn tell on Rube" but had never seen him, and when he entered the room of the log house and put his rifle down in the corner, she curtsied and said, "Mr. Fox, I believe." "You believe right," said Rube; "your sarvant, marm."

After supper, which consisted of fried and stewed "bar meat," the widow, who had been listening to Rube telling hunting stories and had watched his curious countenance, was suffering all the tortures of an anxious curiosity to find out what had scarred his face. She could hold in no longer, and at last puckering up her mouth she said, "I reckon, Mr. Fox, you got them scars on your face in the canebrake."

"No, I didn't, marm," replied Rube with a scowl which was a first-rate imitation of the look of a hyena.

This sorter dampened the old lady, but the spirit of Mother Eve was too strong in her to give it up so. "If you got it in a fight," said the old lady with a sly look of malice, "I didn't mean to rile you by askin 'bout it."

"I ain't riled," said Rube, trying to smile but looking more like a man who was suddenly taken with a severe twinge of the colic.

"But it warn't in a fight, old lady," and Rube, as well as his friends, appeared to enjoy mightily the widow's curiosity.

"Well, if it warn't in a fight, and it's not imparlite to ask you," said the widow screwing up all her energy to the task, "how did you get them awful scars?" Rube shoved up his upper lip and moved it from one side to the other in a way he had while the little party could hardly keep in from laughing outright. Turning to the widow he said "Well, marm, I got these scars by lookin whar I hadn't ought to." This was too much, the widow crimsoned, and the party burst into a loud laugh.

"Come, Rube," said one of his friends, "tell the story." "It's no story," said Rube, "but an ugly fact. My neighborhood had been affected for some time in the chicken line, and their disappearance could not be accounted for until one day I got on the track of a big wildcat. As the ground was very damp I trailed up the varmint till I got nearly on him, when I brought my rifle up to my cheek—" "And it burst," cried the widow. "No, it didn't," continued Rube with another of his looks, "the blasted gun snapped and the cat sprung to a tree, which was hollow at the fork, and crept into the hole. The cunnin of the thing vexed me so I swore I'd come it over her anyhow; so I tuck to the tree and climbed up to the fork. I drew my knife to cut a limb so as to worry the cat out. As soon as I got fixed, I put my face down to the hollow of the fork to look into the hole. I saw two balls of fire and heard a growl. The blasted varmint had her young thar, and afore I could draw back my head she *nearly* grabbed me in the face with her claws. The thing took me so unawares that I let go all holds and fell about forty feet to the ground, and if you ever catch me going wildcat huntin again I wish I may be eternally and everlastingly—eh," and here Rube moved his upper lip again as his eye caught that of the widow's.

"No, I didn't either," said Rube.

"Then, how on airth was it?" asked the widow, catching a long breath and becoming so excited that she could hardly sit still.

"Well, you see, I never rightly knew," said Rube winking to the boys, "but they used to tell it that dad and mammy fit one day and she scratched him pretty badly, and I was born with the scars."

"Blowed Up" on a Possum Hunt

by "Pardon Jones" of Louisiana

§ Reprinted from the New Orleans *Picayune,* this story appeared in the *Spirit,* XIII, No. 45 (January 6, 1844), 531, under the title "Possum Hunting in Louisiana."

I'M enjoying extraordinary health, and so is Jerushy and the little one, but Capting Potter is dreadful poorly, poor old feller, and I don't know how 'twill go with him. A dredful thing befel to him 'tother night, and he's ben out of his head ever sense, and it come putty near killin me, to, but it didn't, tho,—but the dog that was along with us, nothin hain't been heard of him sense, and I'm sorry nuff 'bout that, too, for he was a darned fine dog, and I wouldn't a took five dollars for him; I was offered four dollars for him the day before and wouldn't take it, and I'm most sorry now I didn't take it, sense it turned out as it did; but there ain't no use in crying over spill't milk; *main ravenous a notre mouton,*[15] or rather to Capting Potter, as the French says.

Four nights ago, I'n the Capting got ready and went out possum huntin a-horseback. The Capting kerried matches and a candle and lantern, a little flask full of conyack, some bread and cheese, and his pipe and tobacker. I kerried a gun and ammynishun and my cob pipe and tobacker, and the nigger kerried an axe and a bag to bring the possum home in, and off we started with old Gum the possum dog taggin 'long behind. Poor old Gum, he little thought that was goin to be his last hunt, but it was, tho'. Well, we hunted round the woods a spell and treed tew or three raccoons that got away from us, and everything went on as nice and comfortable as could be till we come to a big ditch that somebody had been diggin thro' the woods (the legislature ought to pass a law preventing people from diggin ditches in the woods, enny how), and there we come up all stannin.

15. *Mais revenons à notre mouton:* "Let's return to our sheep," that is, get back to the point.

The nigger said at the ditch warn't more'n a foot deep 'cause he know'd it warn't done and that we could walk our horses right thru it. It was 'bout twelve foot wide, and I didn't like the looks on't, but the nigger stuck a stick into it, and sure nuff it didn't seem's if 'twas very deep, so Capting gin his hoss a lick with his cane and tried to make him go in, but the hoss snorted and hung back. "Look here, Jack," says the Capting, says he, tu the nigger, "now du you cum up tu the ditch, and then du you gin him a sudden push agin the rump, for as soon's he once gits into the ditch he'll wade rite thru' reddy 'nuff, I'll warrant." Wall, Jack did as he was told, and as soon's the hoss was on the ege of the ditch he gin him a push behind, and in he went head over heels where the water was as much as five foot deep, and the Capting fell under, and the hoss jammed him down head and ears into the mud, and the nigger slipped up and come putty near fallin in tu, but he didn't. That was a putty category for a man to be in! How to get him out was more'n I know'd, but afore I could get down the hoss began to flounce about and got up, and the nigger jumped in and pulled the Capting's head above the water, and we got him out. The old man choked and spouted out mud and water, and 'twas some time afore he could ketch his breath, but he did ketch it at last, and the fust thing he did was to pull out his flask and put it to his lips, and he didn't stop suckin on't till 'twas putty near gone. I took a suck at it, then, to sooth my nerves, and then gin it to Jack, and he finished it.

While we was doin all that, old Gum had ben barkin away, as hard as he could tu a cypress log close by us. He'd treed a possum in there. The Capting begin to laff as soon's he'd got the stiff'ner down, and said it was a fust rate joke, but his teeth begin to chatter, and he said we must build a fire tu warm up and see to cut the possum out by. The matches was all wet, so I stuck a light with my gun, and Jack broke up some dry lims and we made a fire in the eend of the log next to the stump. I took off my powder horn and shotbag and put em into the holler of the stump and set about cuttin a pole to puggle out the possum with, and Jack he begin to make fires along the log and then to chop into the top eend. He'd cut holes, and I'd puggle thro' em into the holler and punch a firebrand in to make the possum move back, and old Gum he'd dig and bark, and the Capting he sot up on the holler stump a-warming himself by the fire.

We got the possum clean down most to the butt eend of the log, and I split the eend of my pole and stuck a blazin brand into it and poked it in at him, and Jack hild the dog to keep him from ketchin the crittur when it came out and spilin his meat by bitin and bruisin on it. Wall, I puggled away and putty soon out he come, and as I went to jump over the log to kick him and make him curl up, my foot ketched in a vine and I fell over, and the possum run into the stump, under the Capting. The old man sot there a-laffin away as good natured as could be. Jack went round 'tother side of the stump with the dog, and I took about a peck of live coals and burnin chunks to throw under the roots of the stump to start the possum out. "Now," says I, "Jack, when I throw in the fire, du you let go the dog and let him ketch the possum, and as soon as he ketches him, du you choke him right off and not let him bite much." Well, I throwed in the fire, and the possum run up the inside of the stump to the top, and old Gum he lit upon him like a cat on a mouse, and I jumped to ketch the dog, but afore I got tu him I didn't know no more; I can jest remember seein a good deal of fire flyin up, and that is all for I was knocked down and stunded, and the nigger says I laid there five minutes as dead as a mackerel.

My powder horn that I'd put into the stump and forgot all about had ketched afire and gone off. There was about a pound and a half of powder in it! Soon's I come tu, the nigger told me what had happened but said that the Capting and the dog and the possum had all ben blowed clean over the tops of the trees and had gone he didn't know where! He pinted at a big sickymore tree and said he'd seen the Capting go clean over the top of that with his breeches all afire; but the nigger lied, for when we come to look round we found the poor old man layin 'bout a rod off in a briar patch where he'd ben blowed by the powder. I thought he was dead for a good while arter we'd pulled him out, and I couldn't help cryin like a baby over him. His breeches where he'd ben settin on the stump was all blowed off, and he was burnt terrible bad all up and down his back; but he soon began to come to, and then he begin tu laff as hard as he could as soon's he could make enny noise at all! He was out of his head and hain't had his senses sense. He lays all day long a-hollorin out every minit or tew, "That's fust-rate, Parding!—fine duckin warn't it? Puggle him out, Parding; puggle him out!—Don't let old Gum go, Jack!—don't let him bite the possum!—Ha, ha, ha!"

Oh, it is a dredful site to hear him and see him go on so, but the doctor says he'll soon be better when the information leaves the backbone. Hopin next time I write to tell you good news of him.

Fun and Frolic

The word "frolic" to describe a community gathering has been in use since about 1775. Though such gatherings in the North were usually called "bees," in the South meetings to boil down salt, make cartridges or candles, chop or roll logs, make cider, catch fish, grub stumps, shuck corn, pick lint from cottonseed, sew or quilt, raise cabins, or harvest crops usually ended with a dance that was commonly called a frolic.[1]

The most popular form of group entertainment in the Southern backcountry was the dance which might be held either in the daytime or at night and invariably on holidays. In the early days when dances were held in the clearing outside the small log cabin, such a dance was called a "bran dance" (later corrupted into "barn dance") because the ground was smoothed and sprinkled with corn bran to keep down the dust and to make the earth elastic. Otherwise, the dance was held in the typical double log cabin, composed of two rooms joined by a "dog trot," all of the furnishings having been removed from one room for the dancing. Guests sometimes arrived early in the morning, and visiting and swapping of opinions about crops and weather went on until the noon meal was served on temporary tables set up under a tree in the yard. Dancing started in the afternoon and often lasted all night. Though the one-night frolic was usual, in Tennessee in 1788 when John Sevier and his Indian fighters returned from a long campaign, the frolic that followed lasted for a week. Among special days celebrated with a frolic was January 8, the anniversary of the Battle of New Orleans.

1. For much of the material that follows I am indebted to Everett Dick, *The Dixie Frontier: A Social History of the Southern Frontier from the First Transmontane Beginnings to the Civil War* (New York: Alfred A. Knopf, 1948).

The wedding frolic was by far the most elaborate—and often the most boisterous—of frontier dances. In the early days on the fringes of the frontier, visitors brought the newly married such practical gifts as a powder horn, a shotpouch, or tinder box for the groom, and a trencher, gourd vessel, buckskin moccasins, or mittens for the bride. A supper of wild game preceded the dance. In the older settlements wedding dances were more elaborate and uproarous. The groom's friends might "ambush" the wedding party with fireworks; a bottle of whiskey, decorated with ribbons, was hung on a limb, and two young men raced for it over an obstacle course through the woods. After the wedding supper, the dancing began, and early in the evening the bride's friends "stole her away," took her up in the loft, and put her to bed; the groom's friends brought him up, put him in bed beside his bride, withdrew, and the dancing continued below.

At all dances the fiddler, sometimes a transient, was of great importance. Usually in the South the fiddler was a Negro. He played "by ear," and his reward for playing all night was the traditional extra swig each time the whiskey bottle went around. His fondness for whiskey became so proverbial that "as drunk as a fiddler" was a common frontier expression. His fiddle might well be an improvised gourd with a single thong of deer gut on which he sawed with a hickory bow. Fiddles brought from the old country were tenderly carried on the migrations over the mountains into the Old Southwest; like trusted rifles, such fiddles sometimes had names. The fiddler's repertoire might well be limited to a breakdown and a reel or two, but that was no handicap since rhythm was the most important element. The tunes, adapted from folk airs, were named for frontier occupations, patriotism, humor, and fantasy.[2] An Irish dance tune called "Money Mush" was corrupted into "Monkey Mush." As a hoedown "Soldier's Joy" (probably derived from some ballad about some war) competed with "The Eighth of January," commemorating the Battle of New Orleans. Other breakdowns recalled the hunt—"Leather Britches," (probably the same tune later called "Hell Among the Yearlings" and "Buckskin Britches") "Buffalo Girls," "Possum Up a Gum Stump," and "Rally in the Canebrake"; some reflected occupations— "Jim Crack Corn" and "Waggoner"; some, memorable local or national characters—"Old Dan Tucker," "Old Zip Coon," "Sally Goodin," "Old Van Buring," and even "Scolding Wife"; some, famous and infamous places—"Forked Deer" (a creek), "Sandy River," "Natchez-under-the-Hill," "Roaring River," "Happy Hollow," "Sourwood Mountain," and "Billy in the Low Ground"; some, mere fantasy—"Turkey in the Straw," "Sich a Gittin' Upstairs," "The Devil's Dream," and "Cluck Old Hen." Usually the fiddler alone furnished the music, though a rhythmic accompaniment might be added—a frying pan struck with the knuckles of the hand or knife, a clevis struck with its pin, or a jug partly filled with water and struck with a stick. A strong current of rhythm was furnished by the thump of the dancers' feet, even if bare.

Like the tunes, the dances were adapted from traditional English, Scottish, and Irish folk dances. The "Kentucky running set," ancestor

2. These names have been gathered over the years from many sources.

of the square dance, stemmed from an English folk dance and was popular because it required fewer dancers than the reel, which was of Scottish origin. The reel, a contra dance (often corrupted into "country dance"),
required two rows of dancers, partners in opposition, and was especially suited for the exhibition of individual steps. Of reels, the Virginia Reel was the most widely known.

Descriptions of frontier dances, especially the wedding frolic, became a tradition in the humor of the Old Southwest with the publication of Longstreet's *Georgia Scenes* in 1835 in which he included "The Dance," an account of a country dance in backwoods Georgia; the setting is described; dialogue is given, sometimes between the narrator and local people; a humorous account of the dancing is included; and some dramatic elements are worked in. Following Longstreet, accounts of wedding frolics became a staple in newspaper humor, and the *Spirit of the Times* published such sketches from almost every section of the nation. Some of the sketches, such as "A Wedding Frolic in Arkansas," are surprisingly realistic in view of Porter's repeated warnings to his contributors about submitting material that was, as he called it, "too spicy." For a long time he rejected such sketches (along with controversial pieces dealing with religion and politics) with a sentence or so in his "To Readers" column. In 1850, however, he made one of his rare editorial appearances (XX, No. 25 [Aug. 10, 1850], 294) in reply to a letter he printed from "Subscriber," Madison County, Miss. The writer of the letter criticized Porter for not printing sketches he had sent in. Porter replied, in part:

Of the two communications referred to, we think the first one was an account of a singing master who taught school in the winter and kept a stallion in the summer. The success of both man and horse was highly flattering, but the details were quite too spicy for our columns.

Porter went on to say that he had fifty or more unprintable sketches that he was circulating among acquaintances. He then repeated his policy of printing only articles that the writers "would venture to read to a company of ladies and gentlemen...if the subject is neither religious nor political." Evidently Porter thought his women readers less affected by Victorian prudery than one of his correspondents who two years before had complained of "the exalted tastes of the Miss Nannyites, who dress the legs of their tables in frilled pantelettes and faint over a nude cherub." That writer, by the way, wrote "Fire in the Rear" (included in this section) which along with "Ducks in Summer" exhibits a healthy interest in nudity.

The humorous sketches about the fun and frolic of the backcountry were evidently written by older men, many of them probably with country backgrounds. Thus they often sound, as Longstreet did, a note of nostalgia, a yearning for a lost youth, and a healthy interest in life and the continuation of it. Even those sketches written by outsiders who laugh at country manners and customs reveal gusto, love of fun, enjoyment of repartee, and admiration for the countryman's tenacity, wit, and healthy vigor—a vigor which matched the youth and optimism of the new Republic.

A Surprise Wedding in Georgia

by "Uncle Solon" of Georgia

§ Rowland E. Robinson, who used the pen name "Uncle Solon," was a local-color writer that "caught the dry comedy of Vermont," according to Blair (*Native American Humor*, p. 140). Yates (*Porter and the Spirit*, p. 27) says that Solon Robinson, "the agricultural pioneer...contributed many factual articles on scientific farming as well as some local-color sketches of unscientific farmer-squatters...."

In an introductory paragraph to the following story, Robinson says that he had the tale from a woman in Athens, Georgia. He goes on to say that Longstreet's *Georgia Scenes* and Thompson's *Courtship of Major Jones* "fell very short of exhausting the supply" of stories about Georgia "Crackers." Robinson's own description of "Crackers" appeared in the *Spirit*, XXI, No. 7 (April 5, 1851), 79, under the heading "Sketches of Piney Woods Characters" with the subtitle, "Music on That Long Thing."

READER, did you ever see a *raal* specimen of a piney woods chap who had travelled enough to give him confidence and make him feel at ease upon a Turkey carpet? If not, just imagine the appearance of the present one as he stalks into the parlor of Col. Jones, whom he called upon to sell a "right smart chunk of a critter beast." His bushy head of undefinable colored hair was full six feet above his immense cowhide understandings, the lower half of the intermediate space being covered with a sort of homegrown and homespun dirty-looking Georgia nankin-colored fabric, not quite as coarse as the fellow's shirt, which he said was warped of grapevines, filled with oven-wood, and wove in a ladder. His coat was of the same sort, only a little more so, being ornamented with a stripe of redoak brown and another of hickory-bark yellow; but the vest was "just the article of dry goods to take the rag off the bush." The cut and set of the whole suit was enough to give a tailor fits, and that was more than was ever given to the clothes.

The way he walked into the parlor was a caution to old folks; taking a seat on a divan, he began diving his hands into the inmost recesses of the aforesaid yaller trousers, because he did not know where else to put such useless appendages which were in his way powerful. His hat he hung upon one of the arms of a branch candlestick on the mantle, and his whip he spread out upon the center table.

The entrance of Miss Lizzie cost him a desperate effort at politeness, but as the Colonel would not be in for an hour he had to fill up the time with conversation. Looking about him he discovered a piano which he knew by sight as well as the boy did the letter A, but dod rot him if he could call the varmint by name. So he made bold to ax the gal if she ever fiddled songs on that long thing in the corner, cause he'd hearn old Sykes' gal make um go like thunder, that's a fact, Miss; she's a raal screamer—enough to knock the hind sights right off a feller what's got no old woman of his own.

Not liking to be outdone by old Sykes' gal, Miss Lizzie kindly consented to entertain the gentleman until her "dad" should return.

Piney yellow plush was mightily taken, but didn't think it quite equal to the music at his wedding. This announcement entirely knocked up all of Miss Lizzie's music, since it would be a vain effort to capture, although she might win her polite beau.

"Ah, how was that, do tell me? I do like to hear about a wedding, and everything connected with it—do tell me. If you will, I will try and sing you one of the sweetest songs in the world about a wedding, and here comes my two sisters who will be delighted to hear about yours, and what you had for supper, and all about it, for I must tell you, one of them is thinking about her own wedding."

After a succession of the politest crookings of the back in honor of the newcomers, and after a little more urging, he spread himself and began to cut loose.

"Well, you see, gals, I and Jule—that's my old woman as is now— she was miserable good looking then—had done a heap of courting off and on, but nobody thought we was as mighty nigh getting coupled, when old Missus Wade—that's Jule's mother like—made up a quiltin, one of the real old fashun sort, you never seed the like on't, I'll bet my pile.

"Well, old Missus Wade is jist the *oncontankerest* best hand to get up a quiltin supper as ever trotted round a stump in them parts— but, Lord help you! she'd no idea me and Jule had any notion of splicing—that is, doubling teams you know—joining giblets—or what d'ye call it—that arternoon; but me and Jule had talked the thing over a powerful heap of times and had just fixed things up just ready to take em all in a heap on the last quarter stretch. So she sorter put the old woman up to have the quiltin, and the way she coaxed to go for the feed would astonish any them sort of things now-a-days I reckon.

"Well, I went over t'other side of Little Muddy Clear Big Creek on the Dry Fork of Rapid Run and told old Parson Roberts if he would come over and just make me and Jule one, I would give him two days' work next corn shucking time; and he said he would if the water got down in Dry Fork, so he could get his critter over, case he had got a *ramfoozleifycation* in one of his dog-kickers so he couldn't walk no way it could be fixed. Well, when I told the old hoss how Jule and the old woman had been poking in the sugar 'mong the flour, he 'lowed he'd come anyhow, if he had to go round the big swamp and cross over Jones' Bridge by the new Zion Ebenezer meetinghouse.

"So when the day came, the way the gals did shell out of them parts couldn't be beat, I tell you; and some of them were all-killfired smart to look at, mind I tell you.

"Well, when they all got a going it, I rode up sorter accidental like, and says I, 'Hello there, house!'

"'Hello yourself, Jim Billings,' says the old woman; 'light and come in—there's none but your friends here I reckon.'

"'Why, what on airth,' says I, 'is the doings here?'

"Never letting on as though I knowed the first thing about the gathering; and then the gals they all jined in and 'lowed I mought as well hang my critter to a swinging limb and come and string needles for 'em till the rest of the fellers come anyhow. And so I pretended as though I didn't think of coming at all, only as I was going by on my way down to Smalley's store to see what would be the chance of getting some seed taters up from Augusta next week, and seeing a right smart gathering there, I thought I'd just see what they were all up to, but I couldn't think of stepping in, for I wa'nt fixed for't no how. But arter a while I concluded I might see some of the fellers up from about Smalley's coming to the dance the gals said they were going to have arter the quilt was out, and so I could find what the chance was for taters, maybe as how. I concluded I'd stop, if they'd say nothing about my having my everyday dry goods on.

"So I tied my critter out and came in, and the way I did string them needles and talk pritty is one of the most onaccountablest hug-um-easy spreadifications I ever made. I jist crooked my eye over to Jule not to notice my crankums, and she took the hint and led off the beautifulest of anything I ever seed.

"Well, about the time we'd rolled the thing for the last pull, some-body sung out down by the bars, 'Who keeps the house?'

"I knowed right straight it was Parson Roberts, and I sorter looked over to Jule, on the sly, as much as to say, 'My filly, I'll be hugging you powerful 'fore long, or I ain't Jim Billings no way you can fix it!'

"And when the gals seed who it was, I said mighty innocent like, 'I'll bet a peck of goubers, ready roasted, the old Parson is going over to see Aunt Sally Wilden's old man, for he is mighty nigh going off with one of them old turns that come nigh upon't upsetting his applecart last spring.' So says I, 'Parson, you're on your way to see old man Wilden, ha? Well, light, Parson and come in a while, and I'll go over with you.'

"'Oh, yes! do get him in,' says all the gals, 'and we'll get up a ceremony.'

"'I'll act the feller and marry any gal what'll have me,' says Mehit-able Ann Eliza Jones Baily.

"'So will I,' says I.

"'I should like to see you try it!' says about six of em at once.

"'Well, I reckon you would,' thinks I; 'but there's only one gal in this crowd will git that offer.'

"Well, the Parson he tied his critter and come in, and almost the first thing he ax'd Marm Wade was if she had a pack of keerds— 'cause, you must know, he was jist one of the powerfullest preachers in Georgia, and he could jist beat anything that ever wore a shirt at Yuker [euchre], and he knowed I could take a hand 'bout equal to the next feller.

"Arter a while the fellers began to gather, and 'fore long the gals finished the quilt, and such a shaking and pulling, and howling, as you never seed no how, I reckon. Old Marm Wade declared if any of them gals, seeing Parson Roberts was there and all ready, would get married she would give em that quilt, sure as grease. So at that I gin Jule a wink and she slipt out and got in the smokehouse to put on her calico fixins, and I tuk my saddlebags and made for the fodder stacks to git my Sunday rig on. And I tell you what 'tis, Miss, I reckon you never seed a couple of chaps look much slicker than me and Jule by moonlight. So I tuk Jule by the hand and walked right in among all the gals and fellers, just as they'd began to wonder what on yearth had become of Jim and Jule, and I tell you she did look mighty sweet, that's a fact, and they all seed right off that something was going to happen, case we was fixed up slick, that ar a fact.

"So says I, 'Marm Wade, I should just like to have that quilt for mine and Jule's, if you are willing.'

"At that, I never seed anybody in my life so mightily knocked up all of a heap, since I know'd myself. She know'd something was come round, for I was dressed up rather more than when I first stopt in, and Jule had on her best, I tell you, with a string of blue diamond beeds on her neck that shined like stars; and she'd got shoes and stockings on, and that the old woman know'd well 'nuff she wouldn't do at home, 'cept on some extra 'casion, and so says she, arter looking at us about a minute, good, says she, 'Jim Billings, are you in downright yearnest? and do you want to marry my Jule for keeps? cause if you do, you may jist do it right now; but if you're going to fool her, you'd better make your will 'fore you go out of this house.'

"Me and Jule both answered at once that we'd just made it up to have the quilting to get the gals and fellers there without letting on anything about the wedding, and we was in right down yearnest about it.

"'Now,' says I, 'Parson, cut loose, and let us have it over.'

"He went at it like a day's work, and, Lord bless you, it didn't take him no time hardly to make old folks on us, and then such a hugging and kissing, and pulling and howling, and jawing, you never seed, for you see they all liked Jule mightily.

"Soon as they'd got sorter over this heat, the old woman told them they mought as well trot themselves into t'other room and get a feed. Well, I never did eat in any of the big houses — 'cause when we goes down to Augusta, we always carries grub along with us — but I should like to know if they ever have any better feed than that was."

"Oh, do tell us what you had, and how it was made," Miss Lizzie said. "I assure you, I have no doubt it was at least equal to any other in anybody's house, big or little. Pray describe it."

"Well, you see, Miss, the old lady had spread herself to have a heap of good things. First there was a biled pig stuffed with taters, and it was so tender that you could just eat it without a knife, just as easy as falling off a log. And there was a sight of fried chickens and gravy enough to eat with a spoon, and just as much bacon and greens as anybody could put under their belts, and there was tater-coffee and store-coffee — you could have as much as you could pour into your funnel. But the pies and cakes, they was all killing nice, I tell you; they had some cake they called plum cake, though 'twant plums, but it was full of black-looking sweet things they tried to make me believe was raisins, but 'twant equal to the real huckleberry cake. And they had tater pies and peach pies; I reckon you'd jist like to know how to make 'em?"

"Certainly; do tell us — I am very fond of good pies."

"So am I, and Jule can beat the nation making them sort. Now, to make tater pies, you stretch a piece of dough 'cross a plate, and then smear biled tater over it, with some milk and sugar, and it can't be beat. And peach pie, you take a piece of dough and stretch across a plate and pour some biled peaches in it, and then you stretch another piece of dough over it for a kiver, and when it's baked you can't tell what it's made on 'less you peck a hole in it; and that's the way we had to do that night, cause there were lots of all sorts of pies with kivers to em. I reckon every gal and feller there eat nigh upon as much that night as they knew how to put under their dry goods, and arter supper the way they did dance was enough to make the fur fly in a tall coon hunt. Jule she tried a while with her stompers on, but she couldn't stand it, case every now and then she'd tread on some feller's toes, and then he'd cuss, and so she went down on one knee and then t'other and had em off in less than no time, while she and her feller was waitin' for a chance to cut in, and so t'other gals seeing how she did they all come down on their marrow bones as they come round and when they had all got rid of their shoes and stockings, the way they put in the double licks beat anything I ever saw afore in Georgia. And would you believe it, Miss, there was only three gallons of licker drank there that night; but mind I tell you, there was a right sweet chance of courting done 'fore morning. I do 'spect Bill Fisher would have tied up to his gal that night, but when he got her in the notion, come to look round, d--n me if old Parson Roberts—the old fox—hadn't cut out and gone, clear as mud; and 'fore next week, what do you think she done? why, she just nater'ly turned in and died—she did, as true as my name is Jim Billings—and Bill he jist took to drink and ain't been worth a dog's runnet ever since."

A Wedding in Mississippi

by "The Turkey Runner," Vicksburg, Mississippi

§ Another in the series of tales about Chunkey and Jim, the following
story appeared in the *Spirit*, XIV, No. 30 (September 21, 1844), 349,
with the title "Catching Buffalo with a Gig: With a Wedding Night
Scene in the Backwoods of Mississippi." The first part concerns "The
Turkey's Runner's" misunderstanding about a hunt on which they
were to catch *buffalo fish*, not hunt bison. Only the last part of the
story is printed here.

JIM had just returned from a trip to the northern part of the
state in company with a very distinguished gentleman—a Democratic elector. Jim was filled with wonder at the appearance of the
country and habits of the people—no lakes, bayous, mosquitoes,
no swamps nor alligators. "I and the Squire," said Jim, "had a great
time in Itawauba county, a place whar the people enjoy as much
freedom as on any part of the living globe. One night we jist lumbered, at least, the Squire did. We expected to camp as it were gettin
mighty nigh night, and we could find no settlement; we were ridin
long jokin each other about it and pityin our hosses mightily when
I discovered lots of tracks in the road, folks tracks and hoss tracks,
some with shoes and some barefooted, all gwine one way. 'We're
safe,' said I, and on we went in mighty big spirits. After gwine a
short distance the tracks all turned off into a little path. 'A quiltin
or bran dance,' said I, and sure enough we hadn't gone a quarter
afore we heard the sound of a fiddle and then the clatterin of feet
to the chune of

Dance, dance, de boatman dance

" 'In town with a pocketfull of dornicks,' said Barbecue, and 'a good
bed,' said the Squire. 'Plenty of whiskey, I hopes, dancin and
wimmin.'

"As we rode up to the fence a feller come out in his shirt sleeves
and said, 'Light strangers! Light and hang your horses to a tree—
walk in—we'll spare you some licker and gin you something to gnaw
on. We're pretty thick about here now, and some on us is sorter

gwine to marry each other. I'm gwine to hang myself to that red haired gal in the corner thar soon as the squire comes, so jist dart in make yourselves at home, it's free doins—every man for hisself and the gals for us all!'

"In we went and the Squire commenced bowin to em all looking mighty serious, and the wimmin sittin with their hands crossed on their laps lookin down on the floor, and the gals sittin up in the corner sorter giglin—but Lord, that just sooted the Squire; he can jest sweeten sich a crowd as that quick as any man livin. He shook hands with all the old wimmin, (some on em he'd gin a double shake), the younger wimmin and children, drank whiskey with the men, and called an old nigger woman 'Aunty.' He can jist stand up and talk the har off a man's head, and you'd jist better believe it warn't long afore he went to work on em. Thar he stood at the water bucket in the passage with a gourd of water in one hand and a glass of licker in the yother, givin a perfect cord of news. Presently the fiddle stopped and out come the fiddler, a little lame, red-faced critter what makes his livin by fiddlin at frolicks and playin short cards at quarter races. He took a drink and then walked round and round the Squire, jist like you would round a hoss you were gwine to buy. He then walked up, and says he—

"'Look here, Squire! Ain't you Squire Joe M————ws of Marshall!'

"'Yes, my friend, that's my name. Howdy!'

"The fiddler shouted it out and everything on the ground flocked round him—the men, the wimmin, the gals, and the old nigger 'oman, and sich a shakin of hands agin and sich a 'howdyin' you never seed. Then he had to tell the news over agin. Some on em wanted to hear all about the Governor—what he was doin and when he was gwine to commence doin somethin for em. Most all the wimmin were mighty petickler about him, and one—a sorter old gal and a mighty good lookin one at that, sorter tall and active made with light har and a heap of fine fixins on her—she jist parted the crowd and come in; she wanted *all* the news about the old he. When the Squire told her I lived with him, she darted at me, her eyes bright as diamonds, and she all over in a swivet. She invited me to the yether room, and thar we both sot down on a bed, and she let in on me. After gettin through she jumped up and ran outdoors and come in with a good chunk of a boy, a sorter chumpy and bright-eyed boy and a perfect pictur.

"'How old is your boy, Miss?'

"'He'll be six years old in the spring.'

"'And what's his name, marm?'

"'I calls him arter his — *the Governor*!!'

"'Did the Governor stay here much them times?'

"'I reckon he did,' said she, sorter tossin her head. 'He used to stay a month at a time — with Uncle Josh.'

"'Well,' said I, 'if this don't beat Repudiation into fits. I'm d————d.'

"When I went back into the passage, the Squire was still lettin in on em about old Jackson and the last war. Some on em had been with the old General at the Enuckfaw, the Taladega, and New Orleans; and when he alluded to them fights, the men shouted and the old wimmin said, 'Yes, Lord.' Some of em asked the Squire who'd be the next President?

"'My friend,' said he, sorter straightenin himself up, 'my friend, Col. Polk of Tennessee will be the next President. I'm gwine through the country to let you know all about it, and I want every man and woman to go to the election and vote for Polk. If you don't,' said he, and then he turned in and abused Clay and praised Old Hickory and Young Hickory. He said, 'Young Hickory was a chip off the old block,' winkin at the wimmin, and then he worked round to Orleans agin and got to shoutin mighty. Jist then that feller what met us at the still walked up and said. 'If you ain't no objection, I'd like you to jine I and Sal Brown.'

"'I would with pleasure, my friend, but I ain't got no authority.'

"'What's the reason? I'd like to see the man what says you ain't — I'd snatch him afore you could say "who's who".'

"The Squire then turned in and explained his want of authority and the consequences of acting without it. While he were makin these explanations, the real sure enough Squire came in. He was in his shirt sleeves but made himself easy. He shook hands with the crowd, took three or four drinks, and then told Bill to git his gal and stand up. He pulled out a little piece of paper about big as your hand and sorter read and spelled it over, and then said somethin I couldn't understand; then said he, 'If any of you is got anything to say agin William Jones and Sally Brown, now's your time—if you don't call it out now thar ain't no use sayin anything about it hereafter. I now pronounce you man and wife. If anybody fools with Bill or Sally arter this—durn em—Sally-ute your bride, and let's all go and take something.'

"Arter the ceremony were over, every man took a 'oman and hand in hand we went to the spring to get supper, and if you'll believe this child, thar was a level cord to eat. Thar were turkey and deer meat, mutton and hog meat, and lots of sweet truck. Afore we sat down the Squire made a short talk, and then the benches were filled in a minnit. But to cut a long story short, as Jones says, we all got through and went back to the house; the fiddler set to grindin and the dancin commenced to the chune of

> *I had a wife and she wouldn't stay,*
> *I brought her back, and then run away.*

"You see, I and the Squire were tired and concluded we'd go to bed. They took him into the room and put him on one of the only two beds thar were on the place, and me they put up stars on some deerskins. The noise of the music and the lumberin of the dancin kept me awake a long time, in fact, until the bride slipt into the room whar the Squire was and went to bed, too—*I hearn her.* Arter a while in comes Bill; he fooled round her a little; but she wanted him to come to bed, and not drink any more; but Bill wouldn't. She then got mad and cut up a power of rustys, and Bill said if she cut up any more shines darned if he wouldn't drink a gallon and wouldn't come to bed no how! He then bursted out and commenced dancin, kissin the gals, and cuttin up all sorts of fixins. She got up and crept to the door and pulled the counterpane aside and popped out. She seen something she couldn't stand—she didn't take time to think, I reckon, 'cause she bulged right out on the gallery and clinched one of the gals, and the way her tongue went was a caution. After a while she sorter run down and then commenced sobbin and cryin. Some on the old wimmin led her back to bed, and you could hear Bill a-lettin off steam; he said he'd be darned to darnation if he didn't like Becky Martin better nor she anyhow, and he'd be cussed if he ever did go to bed. After a while it got sorter quiet, and the last thing I recollect was hearing Bill a-hiccuppin. Just about the crack of day I waked up and hearn somebody talkin downstairs mighty *low* and *fast*. I listened and it were the Squire; says he, 'It was all fun, you know—I were jist playin with her. We'd determined to be revenged on you for behavin so bad last night.'

"'Yes, but darn my sister's cat if I like sich fun,' said somebody, what I knowed was Bill. 'It's too easy to make it rale.'

"'Oh, I've got you plagued,' said the Squire laffin. 'I and Sally thought we'd fix your flint. But come, let's go and get a little some-thin. It's mighty nigh day, I reckon, and I must be gwine.' Bill didn't say anything but went along. I thought Bill was reasonable—*some*."

A Wedding Frolic in Arkansas

by "Skyscraper" of Iowa

§ No information could be found to identify "Skyscraper," author of the following sketch, which appeared in the *Spirit*, XVIII, No. 21 (July 15, 1848), 247.

IN the latter part of last August I happened to be travelling one sultry afternoon through a picturesque country not more than twenty miles from Hot Springs, and becoming tired, sick, or lazy, I has just spread myself on the grass in the shade of a tree when my ears were saluted with a strange combination of sounds which I thought might possibly be intended for singing. The melody was a sort of crossbreed between the jaybird and owl—mixed up with a little wolf howl and buffalo bellow; somewhat startled I turned over and beheld three of the sovereign people mounted on scrub ponies without saddles charging full speed down on me. "I arose!" as Jake said when telling about finding a snake in his bed and calmly inquired if "H–ll had busted or the Milennium commenced?" but found it neither, only a wedding to come off some three miles farther on and nothing would do but I must go along. "No excuse, stranger," said one. "Jim Wilkin's going to be put to Sal Jones! Jim's a hoss! H–ll, stranger, you're bound to see the fun or fight. Gobs of honey, lots of licker, and the finest gals, oh hush!

> *Go way, white man, don't come a nigh me!*
> *Hip, hip, hurrah for Jim! He's some."*

Well, seeing I had to go or fight and not caring to fight, I went. After riding some three miles down a dark hollow, we came so suddenly on a little log cabin that my horse nearly tripped over it.

This was the place—a yell brought about forty hounds and as many girls around us. They seemed to come from every place; the woods, the house, the bushes, were filled with them. I was introduced: "Stranger, our gals! Circulate!" And perhaps I did. After a while the Parson rode up and we broke for the house. Across one corner of the room a sheet and bearskin were hung and behind there was the bride's chamber. After resting a while and drinking several times, the preacher rose and said, "Let the candidates come forward at once," cos he was "bound to be five miles from there in an hour to judge a hoss race between his son Bill and a nigger!" At this there was considerable fuss outside, and presently appeared two men leading or rather holding back a tall, slim, barefoot "son of a gun" with a shocky head of red hair; he was the groom; he came a-pawing and sqeeling and nickering and snorting like a four year old. His grooms had hold one on each arm and were obliged to dig their heels in the dirt floor to hold him in, he was such a snorter.

The preacher ordered him to "stop acting the fool" and not to go cavortin that way or he'd see them ten feet under the mud hills before he'd marry them. Marriage was a holy sacrifice, and he wouldn't allow anyone to get in that-a-way. When the bride appeared the groom was worse than ever. At length they got him quieted enough to stand alone, and the ceremony proceeded—but now and then he would look sidewise at the bride and squeal.

As soon as "Amen" was heard, he seized his newly-made wife under his arm and at one jump disappeared with her under the bearskin. Further, deponent sayeth not, but about four months after, I happened to pass the same place and stopped and found him father—or she the mother—of a pair of twins. The squealing lover followed me to the fence and said, "Stranger, ain't I some pumpkins? Twins and all alive! Git married, stranger, git married, and see if you can beat that!"

Commemoration Ball in Bates, Missouri

by J. N. M. Harding of Missouri

§ Most authors of backwoods tales printed in the *Spirit* used pen names. Although the author of the following story used what appears to be a real name, further biographical information is missing. The story was reprinted from the St. Louis *Reveille* in the *Spirit*, XVII, No. 1 (February 27, 1847), 2.

BATES County is situated very pleasantly on the map of Missouri, nothing but the prairie intervening between it and sunset. The following is a veritable account of the last *Commemoration Ball* on the 8th of January. We will begin by giving the "Notice." It ran in this wise:

Notiss too ull peepeel.
too ull on mi naboars an' freens greeten—thee affturmeenshun squir in bats Counto inteens hooldin a baulld of Thee memorasun on Thee wictoree on new orleens By generelle jacsoon!—wood Bee Gladde Iff ull on mi naboars an' freens Giv mee thar compeene an Patruneege to Thee casun Thee Eevnin on Thee aigh Instans—

justees Jude esq—

"Naboars an freens" all went—babies and all—to the full number of three score—yes, all! fathers, mothers, sons, daughters, belles, beaux, *babies!*—all to be jammed into two cabins ten by fifteen each with an open entry between. By ten o'clock, a.m. (we always go about this hour to *evening* parties in this country), we were all on the spot, all except the fiddler (he, being a parson and horse-racer, too, had "other fish to fry" that morning). But he came in time to "noon" on good venison and dodgers. Up to five o'clock, p.m., the only music we had was—*"in the gourd"*—"guggle, guggle, guggle"—"yor good shine"—"squaker-ack-u-ack"—"hush-sh-sh, my baby"—"squak-u-ack-u-ack—squak-u-ack-u-ack"—"thuth-thu-thu-thu-"—from just nineteen points.

All was preparing—ten fires blazing in the yard—shuffling ground swept off—babies put to bed or, rather, put into the corncrib among

147

the shucks—coats off—fiddler tuning—partners selected—there they stood, with a half-ague jig. Clunk, clunk, clunk—cling, cling, cling—up went "Hogs Are in the Corn Field!"

"Set to pardner!"

Off they went. Good hookey! you would have thought that a volley of first-rate thunder was mingling with some ninety-nine score of giant drumsticks in a *reveille!*

"Jim, by the catemount! dosen't Suze fling a hoof to the whole compass!"

"Wal, she doz, essentially! Bob!"

"Gosh! I'll larn that triang'lar top, Bob—that I will, sartin. Murdar! look at that! she whizzes on her heel jist 'zactly like that cretar them peeple call a 'bullune'."

"'Zactly, Jim—one of them we seed strutin itself clean off the arth."

"I'll jist tap her on the shoulder and say, 'Miss Oglesbushy, whar on arth did you larn that whize?'"

Good as his word, Jim Squizzlebrief tapped Suze on the arm and put his question.

"Why, Jim, it wur fotch in a nuzepaper clean from the continent of Fillerdelfee—it's wot them folks thar calls the *'polecat!'*

Just then Mr. Ned Cookingsbee, Suze's partner, gave Jim *one* in the region of his eyes laying him flat in the yard just as Suze was making one of her whizzes! Her calico flaunted over Jim's head. Up sprang Jim, half blinded, and taking Suzie to be the knocker-down he bestowed upon her a return blow which put an end to her *polka* suddenly.

"What was to be done?" Justice Jude, Esq., was put into his chair official. The fair client stated the case while Jim was going his nine-by-the-hour across the prairies, bareheaded, for another country.

"He must be cotch!" says the Squire.

"How'll you fix it to cotch him?"

"Why, my unfortunate Miss Oglesbushy, I'll put out a writ of *hogmentorun:* The officer kin then take him as well war he *ain't* as war he *is!*" So the writ was issued, and all were ready to go on again.

But before the fiddler struck up "Hogs Are in the Corn Field" again, the Squire stepped out by the crib. He came running back whispering, "Boys, we'll have some spare ribs now, by coonskins, we will!"

"How are you going to fix it, Squire?"

"Follow Squire Jude—he'll larn you."

The Squire led a band of young men to the crib door whispering, "Listen! don't you hear the pigs sleepin in the shucks?"

"Yes, by baldface, I do!" and into the crib they rushed among the babies.

"Har, Squire, here's one fine feller!" handing out a babe hanging by one leg.

"Har's a par on em more."

By this time the fathers and mothers heard the squeaking. Out they rushed falling on the pig party, knocking suddenly the idea of spareribs out of their hands. Mars never saw the like before! Babies screaming—clubs cracking—mothers yelling—fathers cursing—the knocked-down calling for help—a rich scene, as may be supposed, and this broke up the *"baulld."*

Pretty Gals and Snuff

by "Joel Darlin" of Louisiana

§ Reprinted from the New Orleans *Delta*, the sketch which follows appeared in the *Spirit*, XVII, No. 37 (November 6, 1847), 433.

PERHAPS you've never been to a quiltin frolic, tho' it's as like as not you have; most everybody in their young days goes to sich jolifications—I mean in the country places and not in towns and big cities whar thar is the theater and the balls and the like— but here in the settlements we hain't so much light doins in the way of entertainment, only a quiltin once in a while, or a fishfry, or a log rollin. I've had my sheer of those last kind of frolics, and if it wan't for the name of it as a sort of public gatherin, I'd never go to 'nother log rollin as long as I live. There ere heavy lifts are mighty tryin to the narves and sinners of a feller's back, I tell you.

But 'bout this quiltin—that's the kind of place for young folks to gather in at; they had one in the piney woods back of our settlement a week ago; I tho't I'd telld you 'bout it afore; I don't see how I forgot it. I jist happened out thar and dropt in 'mong em sort o' onawars and seed enuff to tell you a little 'bout it and kinder make you remember your own young days. It sarved me that-a-way.

O it's a wonderful thing to be young and frisky, chuck full of life and overrunin with love. It's astonishin how these gals and boys fancy one 'nother. I've often tho't 'bout it and wonder'd how 'twas that a couple of folks—strangers so, jist a-meetin kinder by axident— find somethin in one 'nother that draws like loadstone and sticks like shoemaker's wax. But it ain't wonderful neither, if a body only looks at it the right way. Natur has fill'd the world all full of bewtiful things besides wimmen: thars the flowers in the garding and the green trees in the woods out thar; and jist look too at them cypresses a-hangin so full o' long moss a-wavin 'bout in the wind o' nights in the moonshine; them's natur's productions, and they're pretty; but what's prettyer than a bewtiful crittur of a woman when she's youngish and sweet temper'd and modist and nice?

150

O la! now I've got to thinkin about it, consarning this party doins and so many young chaps and young gals, I can't but remember my own boy's days what's past by, however. It's mighty strange a feller's feellins should underwent sich changes. Why, I remember the time when a small bunch of gals, may be only one on em, fill'd me fuller of rale heart-gladness than enything has ever done since. I like to make money these days, and it takes hard knocks to do it, too; but all the fresh feelins of a grown boy is clean gone, and now a-days a gal in my eyes is a gal; tain't as it use to was for I once thought em to be sort o' angels in them ere days as I talk of.

Well, 'bout the quiltin—thar was quite a 'sortment of young folks thar, and, in course, they seemed to enjoy themselves mightily. Thar was more gals than you could shake a stick at; all the woods, settlements, and naberhood round seemed to a been stirr'd up and gathered together like butter in a churn. Ater dinner—for you see the boys didn't gether in much till tords night—ater dinner thar was a mighty collection of all the young gals round a desperate ugly, black-lookin snuff bottle, and I'm dreadful sorry to say it but they went into it jist as if it was the daintiest morsel of sweetness in natur.

Did you ever see a passel of gals a-dippin snuff? Well, if you did, I'll be bound you never had sich a poor consate of tobaccer in your born days. I'm sure I whist all the snuff mills in Halifax afore they ground up the nasty weed sich as our nice gals spile their pretty mouths with a-usin of it. As I was sayin, they got the old ooman's snuff bottle, and they hunted up all the old bits o' sticks they could find—some that had been used afore and some that hadn't—and at it they went. I whist I hadn't a-seed em—rale, revrend, Scotch snuff, enuff to choke a body to smell and set him a-sneezin to think on. Yes, these nice pretty looking gals with their smilin mouth all gaumd up with snuff and a-spittin like a deck-hand on a steamboat!

As I sot thar and seed em dippin that ar snuff, I growd oneasy and began to feel restless. It was the nateral loveliness of woman, that what grows so on a man and fetches him clean down into the condition of a worshipin slave—a sort of fanciful idear as a body mout say—it was that that was a-leavin of me, and all the angel in em that I could see was clean gone. I took the chaw o' tobaccer out o' my own mouth, went to the door and flung it as far as I could send it, and declared to myself I wouldn't touch 'nother bit o' the trash. I kept my promise all that day.

I'm used to tobacker, and somehow or 'nother can't git 'long well without it—I s'pose I could tho' if I was to try—but it don't signify. I'm a man, a sort of a coarse, two-fisted woodchopper, and it don't make no odds with me no how what I do with my mouth so's I don't tell lies with it and slander my nabers. Why should it? I'd like to know. Who keers for a man's looks what they be, so's he's got a heart of nateral goodness under his jacket? But with the gals it's different— O, it's monstrous different—it's another matter altogether. With them looks is a heap—good looks and sweet looks and sweet ways is everything. When I seed em at that ar nasty snuff bottle, I declar to gracious that all the notions I ever did have of likenin a woman to an angel and thinkin her mouth and lips was sweeter than honey and the honeycomb either, all felt flat as a dishrag.

As I'm an honest man, it's a fact I have jist tell'd you and I couldn't help it. The consate we have for woman is fancy and our fancy leadin us in the way of sweetness and purity, you see this here nasty snuff that was all defilin their sweet mouths so was to my notion the very likeness of anything but what was pretty and sweet and nice and pure. As I said afore, my young days is gone—the kitten-time of a feller's life when he hain't got his eyes open yet—those days is past, and I can see things with my eyes. I can't say adzactly what I would a-thought in my young days of sich a sight as a passel o' gals at a snuff bottle; I say, when I was young and lively and sort o' blind like the rest o' the boys maybe I could a-stood it without flinchin and still a-fancied the wimmen critters so pure and so nice and so loveable in their ways and could still a-thought em a sort of angels in the shape of a human. But I tell you, now I've my doubts whether I could or not; it don't seem to stand to reason that I could, seein as how the main prop of their loveliness was throwed down and every grain o' sweetness got lost when that ar snuff bottle was found.

If you'll lissen, I'll jest read you a bit out of an old book what's in my cabin and what's in pint I think—it won't take long and I'll spell all the hard words. The man's a-speakin of how lovely a woman is and how keerful she ort to be to keep herself so. Natur, says he, has laid out all her art in the bewtifying of her pretty face; she has touched it with vermillyun; planted it with a double row of ivery; made it the seat o' smiles and blushes; lighted it up and made it blessed with the brightness o' the eyes; hung it on each side with queerious organs of sense (them's her ears, you see); and then has give to it (still meaning a woman's pretty face) sich airs and graces that can't be described; and put round it what Solomon or David calls her chief ornament, that is, her long flowing hair, and altogether has made it jist sich a piece of finishin bewty as the eyes of a human loves to look at and his heart within him loves to regard. That's pretty isn't it, and it's naterally true, too. Then to think of how all the brightness and blessedness of sich a bein should be sacreefizd by ugly habits and ways and oftentimes by their tempers gettin spiled and onmanageable—but this I ain't goin to talk on no how, for everybody knows as that lovliness and sweetness becomes a woman in her habits and ways, so a bad disposition and a bad temper, bein of the natur of the devil, nobody can allow it and a sweet woman to occupy the same head and shoulders by no manner of means in the world.

Them are my notions anyhow. I hope I havn't hurt any nice gal's nice feelin in what I have writ for it's jist the rale truth; it's the tobaccer that's to blame—the nasty, hateful weed. I would call it all sorts o' hard names if I thought it would do any good in inducin of the lovely gals from defilin their sweet mouths with it.

Ducks in Summer

by "Stahl" of Tennessee

§ "Stahl" was the pen name of George Michael Wharton, according to Blair (*Native American Humor*, p. 567). Wharton published two books — *New Orleans Sketch Book. By "Stahl"* (Philadelphia, 1845) and *The Portfolio of a Southern Medical Student* (Philadelphia, 1851 and 1872). The following anecdote was printed in the *Spirit*, XVIII, No. 15 (June 3, 1848), 169.

AARON was a tall, strappin, good-looking fellow, near seventeen. You never saw a more susceptible youth; the girls were as easily smitten with him. They used to flock out to the country on Friday evenings and stay till Monday mornings. Talk of a colt! There's no such romp as a town girl turned loose in the country. She races, she jumps, she climbs the trees, shaking the wild cherries down upon the timorous beau beneath her. Oh, she is the most beautiful, winning, delightful creature in the world.

Moses was much younger than his cousin. He knew that Aaron was taking on about that naughty lass May Stelton. And May was in love with Aaron. May, and Troup, and Sue, and Polly, all came out one Friday evening with Moses' sister, Angeline. Mose went off Saturday early to let Aaron know. Aaron was for running over to his aunt's.

"No," says Mose. "Bring the gun. The woods are full of squirrels. We might kill a dozen walking the two miles."

The road led along the creek bank. Aaron was in a brown study, thinking of May. Mose was looking up in the treetops and among the bushes, anxious for a pop at something. It was the shadiest and the quietest of places. So far, no game.

"Let's leave the road a bit and go to the bend of the creek," said Mose; "it's so out of the way nobody ever disturbs it. We'll see something there." And they did. Let it be dated — July 25.

"Sh!" hissed Mose through his teeth.

"What is it?" asked Aaron, roused a little.

Mose put his hand to his ear. "Ducks, the biggest kind!"

"This time o' year?"

"I see em!"

"Give me the gun!"

"No — couldn't think of it!"

Klick-Klack!

"Well, blaze away! they'll fly if you go nearer."

"The bushes are in the way," says Mose, bringing the piece down from his shoulder.

"Shoot anyhow!" insisted Aaron impatiently.

"Oh, Lord! oh, Lord!" cried Mose, turning pale as death and dropping the gun on the ground.

"What's the matter?" said Aaron, running up.

"It's *the girls in a-swimming!*"

They sat down still as snowflakes. They were white as the petti-coats strewn on the pebbly beach. Their teeth chattered. A long silence. At last Aaron looked slowly round at Mose with the mean-est sort of countenance. As he returned the glance, Mose's face was a regular sheep-killing one.

"Can they find it out?"

"I reckon not, if we're sly."

"Let's climb up the tree; it leans right over them."

They crept along like snakes. They reached the tree. Mose, being the lightest, gave the gun to Aaron and climbed out on a branch over the creek and got into a squirrel's nest. Aaron wasn't quite so high.

It was a pretty sight, in course. You've read about nymphs, sirens, and so forth? They couldn't compare. Hair loose and floating on the waves; arms, etc., etc., glistening in the water. Polly was white as snow. Sue was plump as a partridge in pea-time and sat in the waves like a bird in its nest. Troup was slim all over, except the upper works. Aaron promised not to look at Angeline if Mose wouldn't wink at May. Impossible! Angeline sported gracefully like a native of the element, and May was a black-eyed houri, *couleur de rose* from toe to brow. They splashed, and paddled, and chatted like mad.

The tree began to shake. Aaron had a terrible buck-ague, and little

Mose began to smoke and burn, commencing at the ears. There was a louder noise than usual among the unconscious bathing beauties. Aaron stretched his already elongated neck, at the same time hitching the gun forward. Unfortunately, the trigger caught in a vine, and the gun went off with a more deafening report, it seemed to the parties, than ever echoed from a cannon's mouth. It was the climax of the adventure. Mose tumbled, from excitement, plump into the creek between Sue and Polly. The gals! they dove madly, strangled, and put up the bank, their white backs gazed at by the watery eyes of the fishhawk that had pounced among them. They were robed in a twinkling but not one with her right dress on. Aaron dashed into the woods. There was a terrible scream as he ran right into their midst.

All split in different directions and came dropping in one after another at Mose's mother's. The boys took a long turn into the woods and did not get back before night. They said they had been deer hunting and hadn't seen the creek. *The girls appeared to believe them!*

Fire in the Rear

by "Megatherium" of Louisiana

§ The only hint of the identity of the author of the following tale is an introductory note by an editor of the New Orleans *Delta* in which the story first appeared. He said that it came from "a country friend to the N.O. 'Delta'" and that it "is too good to be lost," though its "raciness may not accord with the exalted tastes of the Miss Nannyites, who dress the legs of their tables in frilled pantalettes and faint over a nude cherub." With obvious pleasure, Porter reprinted the tale in the *Spirit*, XXI, No. 12 (May 10, 1851), 136.

OLD Squire Parish was an hospitable old soul. Every Friday evening it was the delight of the girls of the Academy and the boys of the Schools and College to go out to old Squire Parish's farm about six miles from town and stroll in the woods, bathe in the creek, search the orchard and the hen nests, and turn everything about the premises upside down. And old Squire Parish would sit in his chimney corner, pipe in mouth, and tell them stories about the first settlement of the country and how "Old Hickory" whipped the Indians—for the old Squire had been in Jackson's army—and never let the boys off without at least one story about the "old man," as the Squire delighted to call the General.

One Saturday, about the middle of the afternoon, Bill Jones, a wild harum-scarum young fellow of some sixteen winters, rode up to the Squire's door and hailed the house. His summons was answered by that black young rascal Josh, who told Jones that the boys were gone squirrel hunting, "but you better believe, Mass Bill," continued Josh, "that the gals is carrying on high. Why, Mass Bill, you can hear em squealing clean up here." Jones soon learned that the girls had gone to their usual bathing place which was at the foot of a high precipice and only approached on that side by a solitary footpath, which was guarded by Dinah. On the other side of the creek lay a broad sand bank so that no one could approach it without being seen. Jones had been to the Squire's house so often that he knew all his stories by heart, and as it was almost impossible to find the boys in the woods, he determined to have some fun out of the girls. About a quarter of a mile up the creek lived Old Aunt Judy, and there Jones and his attendant, Josh, immediately proceeded. While Josh went to the old woman and for a fo'pence purchased the largest gourd in her possession, Jones slipped behind the garden and threw off his clothes, then cutting off enough of the handle-end of the gourd to admit his head and making two holes for his eyes, he slipped it on his head and jumped into the stream. So soon as the gourd reached the point above the bathing place, it commenced floating towards the shore until within a few yards of the bathers, when it drifted against a limb which overhung the stream and lodged. If Jones had looked through the loopholes (he swears he didn't) he would have seen a sight that would have made the gourd itself blush. On one rock were three or four swimmers, alternately squatting down and rising up on their heels, and imitating the cry of the bullfrog, and when one would say "chug!" they would all plunge into the water, frog fashion. At another place they were striving to duck each other; while a third party was leading by force into the water a coy damsel, who had been too modest to undress before so many folks. But Jones's gourd did not long remain un- noticed in the water, and the damsel who espied it, sailed up to it, seized it, and with slight resistance it came off and disclosed the curly head of Bill Jones! Miss Betsy screamed and Bill Jones yelled! Miss Betsy and the other bathers rushed up the bank, and Jones, in his fright and confusion, followed them. Here the girls turned on him, seized him and threw him on his face, twined his arms around a sapling, and bound his hands with a kerchief; Jones lay defenseless in the power of his captors. The girls now leisurely dressed themselves, and then each provided herself with a trim birch or willow rod, and, without further ceremony, began applying them to the back, sides, and legs of poor Jones. Jones twisted and Jones writhed; he drew himself up and he spread himself out; he begged and he prayed. But in vain. His captors were insensible to pity until their arms were fatigued and their rods frayed into ribbons.

Alas, for poor Jones; he was not yet to escape. His tormentors provided themselves with fresh instruments and stationed themselves in a row along the footpath from Jones's tree to the water's edge. On the rock from which he was to plunge was posted a stout country lass whose strength he had often tried in a wrestle and whose endurance he had often tested in a bran dance. At last he was released and told that he was to run the gauntlet. He could not but comply. Straightening himself up and drawing a long breath, he started at full speed, as he thought; but at every step something touched him that accelerated his motions, and, as he was about to take the last, final leap, such a blow fell upon his rear that the sparks flew out of his eyes, and he bounded half across the stream at one leap. This rock has been known as "Jones's Leap" ever since.

Without stopping to see any more of his fair friends, Jones hastened to Aunt Judy's cottage, dressed himself, gave Josh a thorough kicking, borrowed a sheepskin from Aunt Judy, mounted his horse, and rode slowly back into town. And, from that day to this, Bill Jones has never shown his face, nor any other part of him, in good old Squire Parish's house, nor the stream that runs by its door.

The Singing Teacher of Snake Hollow

by "Rial Owen" of Arkansas

§ The unidentified author of the following story may have been from Virginia, because his tale pretends to be a communication to a relative back home. It was printed under the title "Rial Owen to Uncle Peter in Virginia" in the *Spirit,* XXIV, No. 28 (August 26, 1854), 326.

EVERY chap in our parts who pretends to any larning 'lows as how that Snake Hollow is the greatest clerin in the hul state of Arkansaw. The nicest, rompinest, purtiest lot of gals that ever a fellow seed in his life time, always ready for a frolic or a dance, right away. The chaps for five miles round always comed to Snake Hollow for a shindy, for the old folks themselves was perhaps about the jolliest parcel of old stumps that ever got together in sich a small place.

Now one day a chap, a smart sight the querriest looking fellow I ever seed, rid into Snake Hollow, and, in course, everybody wanted to know who he was and where he come from. He rid a little black, short-tail pony which seemed for all the world as if he wished to say something to a fellow, he held down his head so meek and looked so implorin, while the chap set on him as if he was cold, and darn me if his nose didn't turn up as if he smelt something not so rottin nice. The fellow in ginerally tuk with him a long narrow book under his left arm, and we all thort he was sure nuf of a sombody, tho we 'lowd anyhow that Uncle Doe (Durastus was his name—we called him Doe for short) had as much larning and could lam his very socks off on the fiddle. Howsomever, the chap turned out to be a fellow that guessed he could teach the folks how to sing some. He was right *bran new* from away down yonder somewhere 'bout a place he called *Cunecticut,* and mabe he didn't know a red ingon from anything that looked monstrous like it—he did that for sure, and guessed agin that he could do something past common in the way of a song. After squirming round a few days and times, he stuck out his plank with "Singing tort moderate hear, by Mr.

160

Thea. Small, from 'Cunecticut','' painted in big black letters right down the middle. No quicker was his sign up than every gal in the place wanted to know how to sing — such an accomplishment! — la, what a chance! — how nice! — now's the time to learn something! and, darn my daddy, if every gal in the hul place didn't go, as sure as shot. Why, sich a devil of dust did this chap cut up in Snake Hollow that a Methodist preacher who had been down in our parts afore couldn't hold a candle to him. He turned all the gals heads right round — his voice was so sweet — his manners so nice — and his whiskers so pretty — and all this and that and tother that I really thort the gals would eat the chap up, whether or no. In fact, the boys haden't had a dance for the longest sort of a spell; everything was turned to singing while the hul place was kept awake of nights by the fellow. *Do ra me — Fal, da la,* and all sorts of screeching sounds as them. Mr. Theodore Small, for that were the chap's appellation, was jist the thing; a fellow stood no more chance long of them gals with Mr. Thea. Small than a rat in a steeltrap. When the gals wan't at singing-school, Mr. Small was either at their house, or they were practising, as they called it, so that the boys in Snake Hollow felt real oneasy and looked awful folone. Mr. Thea. Small wored on his nose a pair of spectacles with four green pieces of glass in them, two in front and two at the side, while he sported a blue coat with the shinest parcel of buttons on it I ever seed, which tickled the gals' fancy considerable.

Now the boys bout there spected that Mr. Small, after he had teached the gals how to sing, would cut out, but Mr. Small had no sich notion, for he hung on like a loafer to a grog shop and kept the gals in a fuss the hul time he stayed. Howsomever, Mr. Small, tho' considerable at a song, couldn't come it over the boys in that slick sort of style nohow. So they vowed that Mr. Thea. Small must quit the clerin by the fust boat, sure. Now Sam Nixon's youngest gal, Rose, was perhaps the gamest and nicest gal in the place — anyhow, the boys thort so — so did Mr. Small, for he was eternally there with his confounded songs; so the chaps swored that Mr. Small must be put adrift in spite of every gal in Snake Hollow and Rose Nixon to boot.

Every Friday night Mr. Small held school at Sam Nixon's house —
I 'low bout a mile from where he staid at. Now old Mrs. Nixon was
cream and tarter to a chap she didint like and sweet as sugar to
Mr. Small. Bob Dowings and me was there one day, and Bob's dog
Watch had comed along and got under the table. Mrs. Nixon seemed
to be very good and smiling till Mr. Small rid up when says she, she
did, "Git out, you Watch, you nasty crittur; darn my liver if they
ain't more dogs here than there is at the dog maker's!" and so Bob
and me winks at each other and got up and left.

Now mabe Bob didn't bless that Mr. Small that time. Jeruselum!
he laid it down on him sure, and I was real glad for I knewed when
Bob was real riled he was a-gwine to do something sure.

Well, as I was sayin, Mr. Small held school every Friday night at
Sam Nixon's, so every chap greed to look out for Mr. Small, and so
they sot for him as he was comin to his singing school. They had
hardly got well settled fore they seed Mr. Small a-coming. "Give
him a feeler," said one of the boys, and whiz went a big stone right
side of Mr. Small's head. I reckon he drawed up his black pony pretty
short, he did, and the stones gan to fly thick as hail. "Who's that?"
sung out Mr. Small, and fore he could say another word the chaps
broke right at him. Mr. Small stood still for awhile when thinking it
no time to tarry he turned the little black and put it down in beautiful style. I reckon there wan't any singing at Sam Nixon's that
night, and the boys laughed and chuckled at the joke and thort they
had sorter set Mr. Small back some. So they went in a gang next
night to see Rose Nixon, and who should they find there but Mr.
Small, as sure as flints; he had got out his pony and give the chaps
the slip that time for he had paced all round the regular road, and
thar he was with his *Do ra me* agin. Jeruselum! how mad the boys
were, and so they come to the conclusion that it was best not to let
Mr. Small slip this time. Small sung later than ever — he was waiting
for the Snake Hollow chaps to leave and they waiting for Mr. Small
to go. He sot and they sot tu till it got so real late that Mr. Small concluded it best to make a start anyhow. So he gits up and bids em all
good night, and the Snake Hollow boys does the same. So soon as Mr.
Small had mounted the pony — and he mounted monstrous quick

for he smelt the rat sure—one of the boys tuk hold of his bridle and says he, "Smart sort of a hoss you got here, Mr. Small," and Mr. Small said, "Yes!" Just then Bob Dowings lifted up the critter's tail and slung an awful big briar under it. A chap who didn't know what was the matter would a-swore that the hoss either seed a ghost or hearn an earthquake for he pricked up his ears and screwed down his tail, and the way he kicked up behind was beautiful. "Woy! woy!" cried Mr. Small, but wouldn't do; up and down, up and down went the hoss, while Mr. Small, who had lost the stirrup, clung to his neck and cried out "woy! woy!" louder and louder. "Catch him! catch him!" screamed Mr. Small but 'twas tu late. "Hold him, Small!" cried one of the chaps, and jist at that minit the hoss turned his head away from Snake Hollow and streaked it up the road. "Go it, Thea. Small!" cried the boys, and mabe he didn't go it, too. Just as long as the boys could hear, the hoss was putting it down sweet, and Small's voice was hearn, as Uncle Doe said, high above the din, hallowing "woy." Small kept a-goin or rather his hoss did until he met some chaps on the road, who gin one scream at him till darn me if he didn't run clean into Texas.

The Professions

With tales about rivermen, hunters, and animals, stories of members of the professions of law, medicine, and the ministry appear in the humor of the Old Southwest. These professional men came in the third or fourth waves of settlement, arriving after the crossroads villages had developed into towns. As soon as local governments were formed, in county-seat towns, lawyers set up practice and rode the circuit throughout the district. Medical doctors appeared next and eventually came preachers. For example, Madison Parish in northeast Louisiana was organized in 1839 and by 1842 had a district court.[1] Another year passed before the first itinerant minister is mentioned in the local newspaper; several years went by before a church was built. Meanwhile, three or four medical doctors had started practices.

Of the representatives of the professions, lawyers enjoyed more popular interest, both as authors and subjects in the newspaper humor of the time. Called "the gentlemen of the green bag" because of the green baize satchels they carried, lawyers were among the civilizing forces on the frontier. The typical lawyer of the time was young, born and educated in an older state, and was likely the younger son of a planter or the elder son of a tradesman. Finding his profession crowded at home, he sought his fortune in the new states or territories where the shortage of men trained in the law might soon elevate him to a judgeship or state representative and in time even the governorship. Equally as often he became the son-in-law of a wealthy planter. Though few lawyers in the Old Southwest achieved the

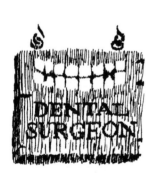

1. *Richmond Compiler*, III (May 10, 1844), 27. Richmond, La., parish seat of Madison Parish, in the northeast corner of the state opposite Vicksburg, was destroyed during the Civil War and was never rebuilt.

heights of a Sergeant S. Prentiss or an
Alexander G. McNutt,[2] almost all were highly
regarded citizens, especially in the county-seat
towns on court days when they displayed their
oratorical power for planters, farmers, bear
hunters, peddlers, slave traders, and adventurers
—all gathered for trading, buying and selling,
and listening to trials; lawyers were expected
to quote readily from the Bible, Shakespeare,
and the classics. Court sessions occasionally
brought unusual drama such as the trial of a
man in Richmond, Louisiana, who had shot and
killed another with a double-barreled shotgun.
Defended by five lawyers—among them the
famous Henry S. Foote of Mississippi—the
accused was the center of a legal battle which
the local editor compared to the grappling
of giants.[3]

But the entertainment function of "the
gentlemen of the green bag" was not finished at
the end of the day in court, for they gathered
at the taverns in the evening and swapped stories
they had gathered on the circuit. Lawyers were
among the chief purveyors of tales, many of
which found their way into print, as Philip
Paxton in 1853 indicated:

These gentlemen, living as they do in the thinly
inhabited portions of our land, and among a class of
persons generally very far their inferiors in point
of education...are apt to seek for amusement in
listening to the droll stories and odd things always to
be heard at the country store or bar-room. Every
new expression and queer tale is treasured up, and
new ones manufactured against the happy time when
they shall meet their *brothers-in-law* at the approaching
term of the district court.... Each one empties and
distributes his well filled budget of wit and oddities,

2. Brief biographies of Prentiss,
McNutt, and other early lawyers
are given by Frank E. Everett,
Jr., in "Vicksburg Was Center
for Famous Lawyers," *Vicksburg
Evening Post*, p. 6, "A City Is
Born," Anniversary ed., July
1, 1963.
3. *Richmond Compiler*, III (May
24, 1844), 29.

receiving ample payment in like coin, which he
pouches, to again disseminate at his earliest
opportunity.[4]

Perhaps never again will members of the legal
profession enjoy the popularity these frontier
lawyers did.

Doctors and preachers are less evident in
the humor of the Old Southwest because their
ministrations to the bodies and souls of people
were more serious matters than court-day speech
making and tavern entertainment.

The doctor's role and his experiences in
frontier communities are best illustrated in
Henry Clay Lewis's *Odd Leaves from the Life of a
Louisiana Swamp Doctor* (1850). Apprenticed
to a medical doctor, he studied books in the
office, helped with calls, and attended medical
school for two years (the usual period at that
time)—all before he was twenty-one. His first
practice in a backwoods community provided
unusual patients and experiences about which he
wrote humorous sketches. The apprenticeship
system which brought mere youths as dispensers
of medicine to the attention of people was a
source of amusement. Furthermore, there were
violent controversies in the medical schools
over treatments and medicines—the cold-water
treatment, steam treatment, bleeding, use of
herbs, use of calomel as a cure-all. Quarrels
between doctors were aired in newspapers;
sometimes doctors even fought duels. Arthur P.
Hudson has pointed out that doctors and their
mysterious methods were long before that time
objects of satire and ridicule and that medical
science until comparatively recent times was
considered a pseudo-science, "lending itself to
infinite quackery and skullduggery."[5]

4. As cited in Blair, *Native
American Humor*, p. 73.
5. *Humor of the Old Deep South*,
pp. 16-17.

Although religion was a hotly debated subject on the frontier, most newspaper editors were reluctant to become embroiled in such controversy. Fewer humorous sketches about preachers appear in Editor Porter's *Spirit of the Times* because he repeatedly warned contributors that he would not print material about religion and politics. He was not consistent in this position, however, as some pieces in the following section show.

As a rule, organized religion came late to a town or community compared with the arrival of saloon keepers, merchants, lawyers, and doctors. Church buildings were among the last establishments to appear, and an educated ministry came only after communities were well established. Writers of popular humor usually represented the more conservative religious denominations and naturally did not write about their own kind. Rather they concentrated on what they considered the extravagancies of such evangelistic sects as the "Hard Shell" Baptists and "Shouting" Methodists; in the 1840s much ridicule was heaped upon the Millerites whose leader predicted the end of the world in 1843 or 1844; called "Resurrectionists" because reportedly they put on ascension robes and waited in cemeteries, they received a great deal of attention in the public press. The uneducated backwoods preacher who knew Scriptures only from hearing sermons and who confused texts and doctrine is the usual subject of humorous sketches about preachers. "The Harp of a Thousand Strings" is an excellent example. So popular were these parodies that a series called "Dow's Patented Sermons" ran regularly in newspapers. Newspaper editors, known for their skepticism and lack of piety, could not resist publishing such an item as this:

> At a campmeeting near Jonesborough, Tennessee, on the 16th ult., several persons were killed and others injured by lightning. The text of the morning was 'Meditate on these things,' followed by another 'But the thunder of his power who can understand'; and at night as follows: 'And the rains descended, and the floods came, and the winds blew.' The destructive storm immediately succeeded the last sermon, which was preached by the Rev. Mr. Milbur, who had preached in the same pulpit for the two preceding years and was on each occasion interrupted by severe storms.[6]

The item may well be an example of a favored form of journalistic amusement of the time, the hoax—startling information printed as serious news in order to deceive other newspapers who might so reprint it.

The affinity of the backwoods preachers for liquor and horse racing gave rise to much popular humor. For instance, in 1844 the *Spirit* reprinted from the New Orleans *Picayune* an account of a religious service in northwest Louisiana during which the preacher announced,

> immediately after the service this evening, there will be a race just back of the church, two mile heats, for a purse of three hundred dollars—two nags entered and some hopes of another. I trust you will be there.[7]

As is true of tales about hunters and rivermen, the humor of the Old Southwest exaggerates the practices and experiences of lawyers, doctors, and preachers, much to the amusement evidently of newspaper readers of the time.

6. *Richmond Compiler,* II (September 27, 1842), 2.
7. *Spirit,* XIV, No. 3 (March 16, 1844), 31.

Primitive Courts in the Southwest

by "Amite," Vicksburg, Mississippi

§ "Amite," who may have taken his pen name from the Amite River in Mississippi, contributed several sketches to the *Spirit* from different locations. This story, which indicates that he may have been a lawyer, was printed in the *Spirit*, XIX, No. 41 (December 1, 1849), 482.

'TWAS a glorious day in the autumn of 182- when I was called upon to go to the then new County of ---- in this state.

I took one of the crafts of that time with several others alike destined; we were put out during the night upon the banks of the river and there left to meditate till daylight should give us shelter and food.

Judge Z---- (as we will call him) was going to hold his first court in this county, and as is frequently the case in new counties no courthouse had been built. The house of a planter near the intended site of the courthouse is generally chosen when this is the case. We were much gratified, therefore, to find ourselves when daylight came near a large, comfortable-looking log house, a perfect daguerreotype of neatness.

Most of our party were in the arms of Morpheus, having wrapped themselves in their bearskins and coats and taken to the ground during the night, and among the rest was the Judge. Now the Judge was a talkative, lively, good-souled man, who was fond of life and his bitters before breakfast. If he did not possess real dignity, he managed to assume enough of it to answer the purpose of the court. Notwithstanding his social qualities, it appears all were not friends to the Judge in the County of ----, and the owner of the neat log house was not even known to keep his temper when the Judge's name was mentioned.

Mr. S---- (a clever man and lawyer, by-the-bye) was not aware of this fact and waking up before the rest of the party determined to make out to the log cabin and apply for leave to hold the court there. We thought of an early breakfast with its occupant. As we

171

neared the cabin, we descried the old man leaning on the gate apparently waiting for our coming, and I know that an inward congratulation at least possessed me, as I saw his good-natured countenance, that we had fallen in good hands.

Introducing Mr. S----- and myself to him, we told him of whom our company was made up and of the intended honor we had in store for him of holding the first court of ---- County at his house. The old man looked at me steadily, and I noticed that the good-humored look was passing away very rapidly.

"Perhaps, you don't know, gentlemen, and perhaps you *do*, but it's better for you that perhaps you *don't*," at length spoke the old man, "that Judge Z---- ain't no friend of *mine*, and I therefore excuse you for speaking of him to me. And as for holding *his* court here or anywhere about this clearing, I'll see him hung first, and then he shouldn't do it! And stranger," he continued, "the less I see or hear of Judge Z----, or any of his traps, the better it will be for all concerned."

The old man had turned away ere his sentence was finished, and as we retraced our steps, the vision of "corn dodger and pullet fixings" came not with us but hovered still near the log cabin which first created the illusion.

The preceding day, so beautiful and Indian summer-like, was to be succeeded by its very antipodes, and already big drops of rain and gusts of damp, chilling winds warned us to seek protection. Seated on a log awaiting our return, our original party had been augmented by the arrival of the Sheriff and a posse of jurors. And such a *crowd!* Having stated to the Judge how the matter stood, we proposed that the Sheriff should find a place to hold the court and at the same time shelter us from the impending storm. A deserted blacksmith's shop some half mile distant was the only place according to his knowledge in "them parts," and so to the shop we trudged.

Just imagine yourself in a small shop, one story high with one window and a door and like all windows and doors in blacksmith shops very large. The rafters were covered with boards, making an apology for a garret to the building. The Sheriff deputed two of the jurors to kindle a fire in the old forge, and they were busily engaged in putting damp wood on it and blowing the wheezing bellows, filling the house with smoke. But as it was a choice of two evils, we preferred the smoke in the tenement to the cold chilling storm which already raged with violence outside.

Seated on a tool box turned edgewise with his back against the chimney was "his honor" Judge Z----, looking the very counterpart of enduring philosophy. At his feet and around the fire were the "limbs of the law," their few statute books protecting them from the damp earth upon which they would else have been obliged to sit. The officers, jurors, and all others concerned were scattered through the building.

Having myself given the Sheriff a private lesson under the river bank upon the manner of opening the court, he, with great solemnity, proceeded to do so upon the Judge's order.

Now, it must be borne in mind that a little party of the jurors had, by the Sheriff's permission, gone aloft on the rafters to have a sociable game of cards, they reciprocating the favor by a promise to let him in the game as soon as he had opened the court; meanwhile Sam L--- (who was in the Sheriff's custody for various misdemeanors and awaiting his trial) was to play his hand.

The Sheriff had only cried, "Oh! yes! – oh! yes!" when down came Sam through the opening above with his cards in one hand and his other doubled into a mallet.

"Go it, Sheriff!" cried Sam – "pitch into em! Give it to em in the plural. Where's the man? Jest *tell* me, where's the man? (looking significantly at the Judge), and I'll do the rough work! Do tell me, Sheriff, who's to fight?"

Sam evidently was in error and mistook the opening of the court for the opening of a fight, and it was not until he was assured and re-assured that he went up aloft to resume his hand with the boys.

Silence being restored, the court was finally opened, but the noise above having increased the Judge told the Sheriff to quiet it. He proceeded to do so by going up the ladder after the fashion of Sam and probably thought it his duty to remain there as he did not return again.

Several small cases had been rapidly disposed of to the apparent satisfaction of all parties, as after each case the court, counsel, and jurors were invited by one or both parties to "imbibe." The court had kept within bounds, but part of the jurors had already begun to feel their independence and asserted it by quarrelling about an old fight down in the swamp and to which party the victory belonged. 'Twas in vain that the Judge ordered silence.

The case before the court was a dispute over a tract of meadow and upland which the plaintiff claimed to have entered some time before the defendant knew who his father was.

"Silence!" cried the Judge, as one of the jurors brought his neighbors a "back lick."

"'Taint worth a d--n, Judge, that land, no how!" cried a "reserved" juror from the top rung of the ladder where he had "located" that he might know all that was going on above and below. "I tell you, Judge, you ought to *see* that land. Why, Bunkum County in the Old North State is a garden spot to it!—See him two and a half better, Sheriff," raising his head above the rafters.—"Why, Judge, that land—"

"Silence!" thundered the Judge. "Now, Mr. W----, you can continue, but let me repeat that your assumption a few moments since is entirely incorrect and will not be allowed by the court. True, this is but *my* opinion, as you remarked, but, sir, *my* opinion is the opinion of a court; and as you further knowingly suggested, you differ only from me by entertaining different sentiments. But this difference of opinion as you are aware originally created the necessity for courts of law and gave rise, too, to the interesting practice of horse racing."

Leaving the Judge and Mr. W---- to expatiate upon this and kindred topics, we will take a view aloft.

On a keg of "old rye" was placed a broad plank around which was clustered the card party, and at the time we look in the Sheriff and Sam, the prisoner, were "bluffing."

"'Taint no use, Sheriff, to play agin science," said Sam, "specially, Sheriff, when I've got the spots agin you, too. Show your hand, old feller—that's mine!! And they allers *did* win!" And sure enough, he had the "old feller." "Now," continued Sam, "let's pull the cob out of that keg, take a pull, and go down below, for I hear that big-mouthed deputy of yours calling for me to come before the court. And, fellers, I'd just say that I've got all the small change there is in *this* crowd, and if I ain't cleared afore sundown, I'll *keep* it, too, for I won't play when I can't walk off with the winnings!"

The jury cleared Sam without leaving their seats that day.

Towards sundown, most of the cases had been disposed of—summarily, 'tis true.

Upon Sam's suggestion to the Judge that as "that ere sort of doings" were a new thing in them parts and that he hadn't better run it into the ground right at the start, the Judge concluded he wouldn't, and so adjourned the court of ———— County.

The clouds had been fast breaking away, and here and there upon their fantastic wreaths and columns appeared golden tints, and finally from a dark cloud emerged "old Sol" in all his splendor. I would not but contrast the day with its coming in and going out with law and its execution in its primitiveness and strength and power of it in after years, when custom and understanding of it made it appreciated.

And almost alone I have lived to see the bright sunlight of justice and equity shower its life-giving beams even over the County of ————, and judges and jurors now deal their even-handed justice—the just pride and boast of our institutions.

Storming an Arkansas Courthouse

by "Falconbridge"

§ This story, reprinted from *The Forest Garland,* appeared in the *Spirit,*
XXII, No. 51 (February 4, 1854), 604, under the title "Having a Crack
at 'Em, Or, Storming an Arkansas Courthouse."

THE State of Arkansas is not exactly what it used to was;
civilization, schoolmasters, colporteurs, and common sense have
quite changed the general aspect of affairs, political, legal, agricultural, and domestic. And hence, the never ending Arkansaw stories
of the "ancient regime" become the more vivid, thrilling or ludi-
crous, contrasted with the present order of things in that part of
Uncle Sam's farm.

Some years ago in one of the newly laid out counties of Arkansas,
quite an intestinal war broke out among the people relative to a
courthouse. One party would have the county seat here and another
party there. The one side insisted the courthouse should be located
here and built so; "the other half" persisted in building a courthouse thus and there and no way nor no how else. The democratic
or dominant party went to work, made *a clearin,* and up went a
spacious log edifice in which justice should hold her court and legal
affairs of the new and not overly populous county be dispensed
according to the statutes, Blackstone, Coke and Littleton, etc. The
court being ready to begin business, the judge proceeded to organize
juries, grand juries, and swear them and the officers of the court.
Upon reaching the courthouse, the judge found a very considerable
gathering of the people; he felt proud to have such a grand opening,
and feeling his oats and knowing all Wild Cat County had their
eyes stretched to that auspicious epoch, with the weight of his official robes and the dignity of the State of Arkansas resting upon his
broad shoulders, he determined that the glory of the one should not
be tarnished nor the ponderosity of the other shrank from. Hitching
his horse to the rick in rear of the courthouse, the Judge took off his
mittens and saluted the crowd that began to assemble around him.

"Well, gentlemen," he began, when a coarse voice interrupted the Judge with,

"Look here, old hoss, none o' your palaver now."

"Sir!" the Judge responds in some amazement.

"Yes, sir-ee, old hossfly, you ain't comin none o' your big locks over this crowd, nohow," says another.

"Why, gentlemen," stammers the Judge, "what's all this mean?"

"Mean? Why it means, Judge, you can't come no sich a load o' poles over us, well you can't."

"But, I, a gentleman—"

"Gentlemen be _____, you'll find us *men* 'round yer," bawls one of the crowd, now hemming in the bewildered lawyer.

"Well," continues the Judge, "really this is without precedent. I am astonished—"

"And ye'll be more 'stonished yet, Judge, if you open a court in these diggins!"

"It can't be did, ole hoss!" cries another.

Now the Judge was a whole team himself when aroused; he had lived too long in the woods to be frightened at ground hogs or garter snakes; his courtesy and good humor were threadbare, he was growing red about the gills, his hair bristled upon his capacious head, and it was very evident an explosion was on hand.

"Look here," says the Judge, "I've come here to open court; if the court is ready, I'm ready for court; if there's any cases on the docket I'll try them; if there's any nigger-stealers, horse thieves, counterfeiters, or_____rascals of any description, I'll put them through a course of sprouts, or my name's not Judge Buzzard, of Wild Cat County, State of Arkansas!"

"Hurrah! Hurrah!" bawls the crowd.

"Three cheers for the ole hoss, he's raising steam!"

"And," continues the Judge, "I will further state, for your general and several good, and respective information—"

"Go it bob-tail!" cries one.

"Silence, darn ye!" echoes another.

"If any man attempts to show any contempt for my court, I'll clap the screws on him quicker than lightning; if any man, with

malice aforethought, dares to molest me, I'll throw down the dignity
of my official station and wattle the skunk until his onry hide won't
hold corn shucks!"

"Put em through, Judge!"

"Go in! Give em goss!"

"Three cheers for the Judge, hurrah! whoo-o-oop!"

And the Judge started for the courthouse door, his saddlebags on
his arm, the air resounding with a full yell and chorus of the crowd.
There were the jurors, the lawyers, the cases, the plaintiffs, defend-
ants, witnesses, sheriff and officials, and persons necessarily connected with a temple of justice. It was very evident, however, that
a row was brewing; it was in vain that the crier cried order or that
the Judge ordered the disorderly out. His eloquence, his dignity,
his common sense, all failed to restore "order" or oganize the court.

"I would like to know," said he, as soon as partial quiet was
restored, "what this cabal means, who are the disorderly, and what
they are after?"

"Well, Judge," says a tall, gaunt, wolfish fellow, rising above the
crowd, "you see we folks up above Rattlesnake Fork of Possum
Creek and the jinin neighborhood are agin this yer court."

"You are?" exclaims the Judge, "who are you, sir?"

"That'll 'pear Judge when I git through my argyin," continued the
Demosthenes of Rattlesnake Fork of Possum Creek. "We 'posed the
idee since the county lines were drawn, we 'posed this yer location
for gineral court; we 'posed it then, we 'pose it now, and I stand yer,
Bill M'Cracken of Rattlesnake Fork of Possum Creek, I stand yer to
defend our 'pinion, defend the universal rights and sacred liberties,
and the justis of the country! That's who I am, yes sir-ee!"

One grand and indiscriminate yell of approbation followed Bill
M'Cracken's sublime peroration. Now the Judge rose, he twitched
down his sheepskin vest, he fumbled nervously about his wrist-
bands, he looked warm and wolfish all over.

"I perceive," said the Judge with the strongest possible effort to
keep cool, "that there is a determination on the part of sundry
evil-disposed individuals to interfere with and obstruct the duties,
dignity, and responsibilities of this court. And (waxing warmer!) I

should hold myself recreant, (raising his voice!) cowardly, and contemptible, (steam up!) to a degree utterly and continently beneath the character of a sheep-stealing *boy*, if I did not put it down!"

"Give it to em, Judge! Go in ole firefly!" is the chorus.

"And," continued the Judge, wiping the perspiration now freely percolating through the cuticle of his massive and fury-stamped brow, "I'll put it down, and the friends of order now in court will lend a hand to the sheriff and officers of the court to clear these rapscallions and peace-breakers—clean out of these precincts. Sheriff, clear the court; men lend a hand, and we'll show the Bill M'Crackenites that we are not to be impeded, insulted, or mobbed in no such way. Sheriff, do your duty; friends of law and order assist!"

"Then I'm in!" cries Bill M'Cracken, rushing forward. "Judge, you and I've got to lock horns, whoo-o-oop!"

With yells, hurrahs, and all sorts of cross-butting, pitching and tearing, gouging, biting, rough and tumble, they went at it. The war raged inside and out. Sometimes the Judge and his followers drove out the M'Crackenites; sometimes the M'Crackenites drove out the Judge and court. The fight not only spread all over the neighborhood but lasted with unabated fury for two entire days and nights. They fought and *fit*, fit and *fought*, up trees, on top of the courthouse, inside, outside, and all around the settlement. On the morning of the third day, the golden sun arose as round as a shield and bright as the winsome eye of happy maidenhood; the war was ended, the victors were there, weary and worn, and the Judge and his attaches held the court in triumph! Where was the M'Crackenites? Echo answered—*no whar!*

A horseman is seen, a lonely, solitary horseman, his steed is covered with foam, the rider with a blue blanket and dust! He has ridden far and fast; he dashed up to the courthouse; he squats down upon his saddle to get a full view of the court through the low window; he looks astonished, mortified, he speaks:

"Etarnal yearthquakes and pizend baldface! Rid thirty miles last night, all the way from Rattlesnake Fork of Possum Creek to have a hand in this yer fight, and it's all over afore I get a sight on't! Wall, *here goes to have a crack at you, ole bullet-head, anyhow!*"

The solitary horseman having thus discharged his duties and a murderous rifle at the Judge wheeled and fled as sudden and rapid as he came.

The Judge fell and they raised him up; he was but "slightly killed" and a good deal scared, an ounce ball having perforated the collar of his coat.

A Good Witness

by Maj. Kelly of Louisiana

§ Information other than his name is unavailable about this author. Porter credited this story to the *Louisiana Chronicle*, printed it in the *Spirit*, XV, No. 9 (April 26, 1845), 92, and gave it the title "Lanty Oliphant in Court" when he reprinted it in his second anthology of backwoods humor, *A Quarter Race in Kentucky*.

LAWYERS allege that there are four classes of witnesses — those who prove too much, those who prove too little, those of a totally negative character, and those of no character at all who will prove anything. We have a case in point.

Far, very far away from the tall blue mountains at a little place called Sodom, there were upon a time three neighbors called in as arbitrators to settle a point, relative to some stolen chickens, in dispute between one Lot Corson and a "hard case" called Emanuel Allen, better known thereabout as King of the Marsh.

"Mister Constable," said one of the demi-judicials, "now call the principal witness."

"Lanty Oliphant! Lanty Olip-h-a-n-t!" bawled Dogberry. "Mosey in and be swore."

In obedience to this summons, little Lanty, whose bottle had usurped the place in his affections commonly assigned to soap and water, waddled up and was qualified, deprecating by a look the necessity of such a useless ceremony among gentlemen.

"Mister Oliphant, you are now swore. Do you know the value of an oath?" asked the senior of the board.

"Doesn't I!" rejoined Lanty with a wink at a bystander. "Four bushel of weight wheat, the old score wiped off, and licker for the hul day throw'd in."

This matter-of-fact answer met a severe frown from the man with the red ribbon round his hat.

"Well, Mister Oliphant," continued the senior, "tell all you know

181

about this here case.—Bill M--k, *shoo* your dog off that d--d old sow."

Lanty here testified. "Feeling a sort of outish t'other day, ses I to the old woman, ses I, I'll jist walk over to Lot's and take a nipper or two this mornin, ses I. It'll take the wind off my stomach sorter, ses I. Then the old woman's feathers riz, they did, like a porkypine's bristles, and ses she, 'Lanty,' ses she, 'if you'd on'y airn more bread and meat and drink less whiskey, you wouldn't have wind on your stomach.' 'Suse,' ses I, 'this is one of my resarved rights, and I goes agin home industry'; ses I, sort o' laughin out o' the wrong side o' my mouth. 'Resarved rights or desarved wrongs,' ses her, 'you'r always a-drinkin and talkin politics when you orter be at work, and there's never nothin to eat in th house.' Well, as I was a-goin over to Lot's jist fernent where the fence *was*, ses I to myself, ses I, 'If there isn't the old King's critters in my cornfield, so I'll jist go and tell him on't.' When I gets there—'Good mornin, Lanty,' ses he. 'Good mornin, old hoss,' ses I—and when I went in, there was a pot on the fire a-cooking with a *great big speckled rooster* in it."

"Mister Oliphant!" here interposed one of the arbitrators. "Remember that you are on oath. How do you know that the chicken in the pot was 'a big speckled rooster'?"

"Kase I *seed the feathers at the woodpile!*" promptly responded Lanty, who then continued.

"Well, when I gits to Lot's—'Good mornin, Lot,' ses I. 'Good mornin, Lanty,' ses he. 'You didn't see nothin no where of nar' a big speckl'd rooster that didn't belong to nobody, did you?' ses he. 'Didn't I?' ses I. 'Come, Lanty,' ses he, 'let's take a nipper,' ses he; and then I up and tells him all about it.

"Had Mr. Allen no chickens of his own," asked the senior.

"Cartin," rejoined Lanty, "but there warn't a rooster in the crowd. They *was all layin hens!*"

"Well," inquired another of their referees, "how many of these hens had Mr. Allen?"

This question fairly stump'd Lanty for a moment, but he quickly answered, "Why, with what was there, and what wasn't there, counting little and big, spring chickens and all, *there was forty odd, exactly!*"

No further questions were put up to this point.

Mosquito Bait

by "Concordia" of Louisiana

§ When Porter printed the following story in the *Spirit*, he gave it the subtitle "Our Country—Her People—Their Character," because "Concordia" (who may have been Robert Patterson, editor of the *Concordia Intelligencer*, Vidalia, Louisiana) included a long introduction in which he praised the character of the American people, particularly backwoodsmen of the South and West. Though that introduction is omitted here, a portion of it is included in the section entitled "The Backcountry," as an example of the favorable opinion of the frontiersmen held by some Americans, among them Porter and Thomas Bangs Thorpe, at one time co-editor of the *Intelligencer* with Patterson.

"Mosquito Bait" may be a humorous treatment of a serious affair, the murder trial of John T. Mason in Richmond, Louisiana, in March, 1844. Mason murdered David Bradford in March and was tried in District Court in May. He was defended by five lawyers, among them the famous criminal lawyer (and later Governor) of Mississippi, Henry S. Foote. The trial attracted crowds of people. Patterson ("Concordia"), as editor of the newspaper in a neighboring parish, probably was among newsmen attending the trial. John Q. Anderson, *"The Richmond Compiler," The Louisiana Historical Quarterly*, XXXIX (October 1956), 430-431 and 437-438.

"Concordia's" "Mosquito Bait" was printed in the *Spirit*, XIV, No. 24 (August 10, 1844), 279.

THE District Court of the State of Louisiana was being holden in the village of_____, the capital of a noble parish which has been filled with population from all of the various states of the union — hardy, industrious, and enterprising citizens. Although on their first entrance into the state, they formed a mixed mass possessed of ideas of government and society varied as the communities from whence they migrated, yet by four years residence they were assimilated by that frequent interchange of sentiment common to new "settlements" and now present an interesting community, embracing some three hundred voters—their wives, daughters, and friends—comparable in all things with many other communities.

The first week of court had passed, many a civil case was disposed of, and the day was rapidly approaching for the trial of a capital offense, whose occurence some months previous had aroused to high excitement and deep interest the feelings of the friends of both parties—the living and the dead.

The day came—the trial was called, juror after juror challenged, and after hours of useless and nonsensical delay a panel was formed. The usual forms were gone through: witness after witness was examined, re-examined, called and re-called, in some instances half a dozen times upon pretenses ridiculous and inexcusable; another day and another passed, the jury being each night discharged under instruction from the court to hold conversation with no one in relation to the trial.

The third day came, and intense excitement reigned as the several pleaders for the prosecution and defense, respectfully, stated each his view of the case, the law, its application, and a thousand other matters not germane to the subject, yet, nevertheless, most liberally used by the legal gentlemen, we believe, in most instances for *humbug!* For example, we heard a fellow once interrupt a limb of the law in the midst of one of his grandiloquent strains by stopping him bluff short: "I say, stranger, you can't come the soft soder over me in that way; the man didn't steal that ar hog, and I knows it, and I ain't goin for to hear you talk about all them high falutin fixins what ain't on the *trial*—stick to the *scent, snuffle* in the breeze, and if *tha is game thar, it's bound to come! I'se hearn o' you fore today, my young sucker, but it won't do with this upland screamer!"* His Honor, taken aback—for he was himself a young'un—failed in stopping this Hercules of the hills until his speech was finished.

Well, to proceed—the third day was passed, and it was deemed prudent on the present occasion by the Judge (a most worthy and estimable man, worthy of the office, and by his dignified, yet courteous demeanor, winning the friendship of all knowing him) that the jury should be placed under the charge of the worthy sheriff. Arrangements were made with the proprietor and host of an admirable inn situated at a short distance from the courthouse to accommodate the favored, or as they deemed themselves, the *fated* twelve. They passed in solemn silence down the lane of friends formed on either side of the doorway, many with slow and dignified tread, as we have dreamed priests tread within the gloomy walls of their cloistered homes. Supper was announced, and separate and silent sat the twelve; no sign of recognition were they allowed to make; no salutation was returned by them, but deaf alike and dumb to all things save the burthen on their minds and the physical necessities before them.

'Twas a warm evening, the inn near a bayou—a perfect breeding place for mosquitoes, and in swarms and troops came they, the bloodsuckers, to prey upon those who sought the long gallery to think over the pleasant breezes that might be expected about that witching hour of eve. Bedtime came. The jurors were steady, sober men; no lovers of strong drink, no cardplayers among them; their silence for hours had unhinged them, and they were seized "of a sudden" with a wish for repose, and most remarkable, there was but one, and he a backwoods wag, who plead not guilty to a want of disposition for sleep. A large room was selected, beds of various sizes, couches, pallets, and broad, single *benches* were hastily prepared. Our friend, the deputy, who had charge of the crowd, being as clever a fellow as can be met with, busied himself much in accommodating all hands; for instance, in the double beds putting a fat subject and a lean one—a medium sized fellow and one of small size would occupy a couch—a treble bed was filled with an interesting trio, one of whom was blessed with a superabundance of the superficial; i.e., he was most unmercifully fat, heavy and dull, affected with the simples, and on ordinary occasions a slight supper would almost stupify him. Thus were seven disposed of; the other five were placed promiscuously on the pallets, benches, etc.

The deputy, having placed *his family*, as he called them, in a fair way for sleep, concluded to close the door, seat himself in the gallery upon which it opened, and luxuriate for a time in that soft, dream-like, and most fascinating state begotten by indulgence in the pleasure of a pleasant-flavored Havanna. He smoked for an hour, and another, and another, for he would even throw sleep to the stars for a good, quiet, three hours' cogitative smoke. He had translated

himself to the seventh heaven of a smoker's delight and happiness —
courts, juries, and the present responsible position occupied by him
as sentinel over the twelve upon whose impartial verdict depended
the fame, fortune, and life of the individual on trial — his fitful fancy
with fairy flight flew far and fast. The clock of the inn struck one ere
he awoke from his waking dream; suddenly jumping from his seat
he walked into his menagerie, as the joker of the jury denominated
the sleeping room, and going around respectively to each separate
bed, counted his *pets*, one by one, severally and individually, by
the touch of his hand, in the absence of a light; he counted and
recounted, missed the order of the count and counted again, and
again counted.

"What!" said he, when the truth flashed upon him, "one gone!"
With palpitating heart and blank astonishment, he left the room,
procured a light, and again went the rounds; yet still the count, all
told, found one missing. The poor fellow was distressed and knew
not what to do; his delicate sense of propriety did not allow him to
call to his aid any of those who were around him wrapped in sleep.
Setting his light upon one end of the bench and himself on the
other, he mused on the matter and endeavored to arrive at some
conclusion as to the course required by the necessities of the occasion.
While thus seated he heard a low-breathed, indistinct, and smothered
snore which appeared to proceed from beneath the floor. He started
up wild with wonder, for he knew it was impossible for any living
thing larger than a rat to get under the house. He traveled around
the room with steathly step, cautious eye, and wary glance, fearing
the pouncing upon him of some supernatural being — ghosts, goblins,
and the train of that interesting family rose in fancy before him; on
and on in lengthened line they came until at length, forgetting his
ridiculous but nevertheless most interesting position, he halloo'd
loud and long, and around him rose his *sleeping beauties* from settle,
bed, and couch in all the interesting varieties of position assumed
by men when suddenly roused from sleep.

All were awakened, and among the number, the jester, who had
caused all the difficulty. He arose, begged pardon of the deputy,
and commenced to search around the room for the lost juror, and

after much difficulty succeeded in finding him in a state of perfect nudity, stripped of everything and stretched out as one in death beneath one of the beds!

"Ah!" said he, "I thought some accident had happened to my *trap!*" And lifting up the sheet which hung down, called to the crowd, "Come, gentlemen, don't be afraid; come and look at the *prettiest Musquito Bait* you ever seed!" pointing to the round, full, pursy form of the fat man of the crowd.

The philosophy of the joker was, as there were no *bars* for more than six of the entire number, that *one* of the *six* to be exposed should, when sleep was around about them, be selected, stripped, and placed in the middle of the floor to *draw* the mosquitoes—in fact, to lay a mosquito bait. He, the hero, was to make the selection and head the committee appointed to perform this responsible office. Sleep at an early hour came upon all save him and another, and when it seemed soundest and the snoozing strongest, they picked up the fat youth as the soundest sleeper and the best fitted, in consequence of the exposure of a larger surface, for the bait.

The Louisiana Law of Cockfighting

by Thomas Bangs Thorpe

§ Thorpe wrote the following sketch while he had "a minor connection"
with the New Orleans *Tropic*, "a well-established Whig daily," according to Rickels (*Thorpe*, p. 72). Porter credited it to that paper when he
reprinted it in the *Spirit*, XIII, No. 1 (March 4, 1843), 3.

ABOUT one hundred and twenty miles from New Orleans
reposes in all rural happiness one of the pleasantest little towns in
the south that reflects itself in the mysterious waters of the Mississippi. To the extreme right of the town, looking at it from the river,
may be seen a comfortable looking little building surrounded by
China trees, just such a place as sentimental misses dream of when
they have indistinct notions of "settling in the world." This little
"urban bandbox," however, is not occupied by the airs of love nor
the airs of the lute, but by a strong limb of the law, a gnarled one too,
who knuckles down to business and digs out of the "uncertainties
of his profession" decisions, and reasons, and causes, and effects
nowhere to be met with except in the science called, par excellence,
the "perfection of human reason." Around the interior walls of this
romantic-looking place may be found an extensive library, where
are all the "statues" from Moses' time down to the present day are
ranged side by side; and in these musty books the owner revels day
and night, digesting "digests" and growing the while sallow himself
with indigestion.

On the evening-time of a fine summer's day, the sage lawyer might
have been seen walled in with books and manuscripts, his eye full
of thought and his bald, high forehead sparkling with the rays of
the setting sun, as if his genius was making itself visible to the
senses; page after page he searched, musty parchments were scanned,
the expression of care and anxiety indented themselves in the stern
features of his face, and with a sigh of despair he desisted from his
labors, uttering aloud his feelings that he feared his case was a

hopeless one. Then he renewed again his mental labor with tenfold vigor and made the very silence with which he pursued his thoughts ominous, as if a spirit were in his presence.

The door of the lawyer's office opened; there pressed forward a tall, gaunt figure of a man, a perfect model of physical power and endurance, a western flatboatman. The lawyer heeded not his presence and started as if from a dream as the harsh tone of inquiry, "Does a Squire live here?" grated upon his ears. "They call me so," was the reply, as soon as the lawyer recovered from his astonishment.

"Well, Squire," continued the intruder, "I have got a case for you, and I want jestess, if it costs the best load of produce that ever came from In-di-an."

The man of law asked what was the difficulty.

"It's this, Squire: I'm bound for Orleans and put in here for coffee and other little fixins; a chap with a face whiskered up like a prairie dog says, says he, 'Stranger, I see you have cocks on board of your boat—bring one ashore, and I'll pit one against him that'll lick his legs off in less time than you could gaff him.' Well, Squire, *I never take a dar*. Says I, 'Stranger, I'm thar at wunce,' and in twenty minutes the cocks were on the levee, like perfect saints. We chucked them together, and my cock, Squire, now mind, my cock never struck a lick, not a single blow, but tuck to his heels and run, and by thunders, puked. The stakeholder gave up the money against me, and now I want jestess; as sure as fogs, my cock was physicked, or he'd stood up to his business like a wildcat."

The lawyer heard the story with patience and flatly refused to have anything to do with the matter. "Perhaps," said the boatman, drawing out a corpulent pocketbook, "perhaps you think I can't pay—here's the money; help yourself—give me jestess and draw like an ox team."

To the astonishment of the flatboatman, the lawyer still refused, but unlike many of his profession gave his would-be client without charge some general advice about going on board his boat, shoving off for New Orleans, and abandoning the suit altogether. The flatboatman started with profound astonishment and asked the lawyer if he was "sure enough Squire." Receiving an affirmative

reply, he pressed every argument he could use to have him undertake his case and get him "jestess," but when he found his efforts
were unavailing, he quietly seated himself for the first time, put his
hat aside, crossed his legs, and looking up to the ceiling with the
expression of great patience, requested the Squire to read him "the
Louisiana laws on cockfighting."

The lawyer said he did not know of a single statute in the state
on the subject; the boatman started up as if he was shot, exclaiming,
"No laws in the state on cockfighting? No, no, Squire, you can't
possum me; give us the law." The refusal again followed; the astonishment of the boatman increased. Throwing himself in a comico-
heroic attitude, he carried his long fingers round the sides of the
room and asked, "What'r all them thar books about!"

"All about the law."

"Well then, Squire, am I to understand that not one of them thar
books contain a single law on cockfighting?"

"You are."

"And, Squire, am I to understand that thar ain't no laws in Louisiana on cockfighting?"

"You are."

"And am I to understand that you call yourself a Squire and that
you don't know anything about cockfighting?"

"You are."

The astonishment of the boatman at this reply for a moment was
unbounded and then suddenly ceased; the awe with which he
looked upon "the Squire" also ceased. Resuming his natural awkward and familiar carriage, he took up his hat, walked to the door,
and with a broad grin of supreme contempt in his face, he observed,
"A Squire that don't know the laws of cockfighting, in my opinion,
is distinctly a dam fool."

Dental Surgery

by "Amite," Vicksburg, Mississippi

§ The story which follows was printed in the *Spirit*, XX, No. 1 (February 23, 1850), 1.

WILL you be kind enough, good reader, to locate this scene "in and around and about" a clearing in some parish or district in some state in the Southwest? "All set," are you? Well, I had hung out my sign, all gilded and set off with

Dr._____

Dental Surgeon

with a row of teeth capping the whole, in the clearing aforesaid, in a parish or district in some state. I had been recommended to settle in this strange settlement by a friend who clearly proved to me that it would be a good opening from the fact that a portion, and a good portion, too, of the year was devoted to frolics of various kinds, and at such times there was a universal gouging out of eyes, pulling of hair, and best of all, a breaking off and knocking out of teeth. I suppose there had been no frolics, or if there had, the people thought, as one of them upon whom I desired to practice my profession told me, "There warn't no use to have em put in at an expense to be knocked out free gratis for nothing!"

Wearied with the monotony of such a life, I not unfrequently went to bed at any early hour to sleep off time. I was awakened one night — a cold unpleasant night it was, too — in March by a thundering noise outside of my cabin and "office." Putting my head out of the window, I desired to know the cause of the disturbance.

"Well, Mister," answered a gruff voice, "I should think you wasn't troubled with laying awake o' nights, nor nothing of that kind! But I want you right now, if you're Dr._____, so peg about, for I reckon thar's no time to be lost."

"Wouldn't the morning answer just as well?" I inquired, feeling a damp blast through the window.

"*Morning!* Well, that is *some* for a doctor! Why, mister, you're

191

wanted *right now!* and I should suppose the worst sort."

I gathered my clothing about me, and half asleep and vexed with the inauspicious opening of my practice, I followed my man to his cabin some four miles down the clearing. There were only two rooms in the house, into one of which I was ushered. There was a good deal of bustle in the room adjoining, but being drowsy I did not take much note of what was passing. In the course of an hour, I was called into the other room, my friend asking me if I had any objection to his coming along, "as there warn't no white persons about the place but him." I, of course, assented, wondering what he was "driving at."

Entering the room, I found the woman in bed. "Ah, Madame," (I introduced myself with) "must be in a good deal of pain—had to go to bed, eh? Perhaps it is what we call the Tic Dolereaux!" I heard my friend mutter something about his being "d——— before *he'd* call it Dick!" but paid no attention to him and turned to his wife.

"Now, Madam," said I, in my blandest tone, "will you please open your mouth, and I will pull it out in a sec————"

"H——l and scissors, stranger!" exclaimed my friend on the other side of the bed. "What *are* you going to *do!* Do you know what my wife wants of you?"

"Why, yes, sir—I *suppose* she wants a tooth pulled, as that is my calling."

"Oh, the goodness to gracious! *only* a tooth, doctor! Sally right here, and so bad off! Me right here, and dono what to do; and *you* right here a d——— tooth doctor, and, I suppose, dono what to do no more nor I do!"

It was too late to send for the physician who resided some miles distant, and so we had to use our wits to a successful *issue* of the affair. By the assistance of the black nurse this was happily accomplished.

"Stranger," said the backwoodsman, as I mounted my horse to return, "you must excuse me for the trouble I've put you to, but the fault is mostly your own for hanging out that sign. In these parts we dono much about big words, and I thought your 'Dental Surgeon' was a sure enough doctor, and I'd a swore that what you meant for a picture of a row of teeth was just like what Sal's sister sent here from New Orleans, and *she* called it an *abominable supporter*—and d---- me if *that* was for any *head* fixing!"

I left—I did.

Uncle Johnny's Tooth Pulling Story

by "Obe Oilstone" of Mississippi

§ Phillip B. January, who wrote under the pseudonym "Obe Oilstone," probably met Porter when that New York editor made his Southern tour in 1838. January became a contributer to the *Spirit* shortly thereafter. He is referred to simply as "a country gentleman from Mississippi"; further biographical details are missing.

January's "Uncle Johnny," who narrates the following story, is considered by Yates (*Porter and the Spirit,* pp. 35 and 71) one of the best characters in Southwestern humor. The tale appeared in the *Spirit,* XIV, No. 51 (February 15, 1845), 607.

ELECTION day is a day out here in the woods; and notwithstanding we have precincts scattered throughout the counties, yet the county seat is the place at which most do congregate for the triple purpose of voting, spreeing, and lastly, for the peculiar pleasure of witnessing the beginning—aye "the opening of the ball"—of the "Fall Fighting Campaign," which interesting event is usually postponed to that exciting period when party excitement and individual misunderstanding leave a man very little hesitancy to "pitch" into his neighbor; this comes not oftener than two years—often enough, however, for "regular work."

Having the common anxiety to see the first "regular dispatch," I arrived early at Fayette (our county seat) on the 4th of November, last, when and where I had the good luck to see the campaign open; the anxiety among the numerous spectators to continue the sport was really commendable. Both claimed the victory, but the ring declared "a dead match"; another heat was promised by the defendant—I immediately staked a hat on him "what got gouged."

Whilst in the crowd a well known voice addressed me, "Hello, boy! come over here! How are you? I say it's your treat now, *certain.* Come in, men."

"Certainly, Uncle Johnny," said I, "pleasure always to treat you."

"Me? I'm_____if you don't treat the whole crowd! Rosser, tell *all* them men to come in! *Hyena's breakin chains and things!* Eh! You thot I'd never see a paper, did you? Well, well, I don't care a cuss about it myself, but the fact is, "Old Iron's" in town now, and he says when he sees you that'll be another dog fite;[8] so if you see him gittin anyways high, *whar's your hoss?* Well, well, jist keep out'n his way. Is you seen Wills sence them fellers was a-pullin his tooth!"

"What fellows?" was the immediate inquiry.

"Oh, ho! and so, my boy, you ain't said nothin about it, eh! Well, that is rich—fond of *ritin* stories but never *tells* em, eh! Well, I'll—"

"Uncle Johnny, don't tell tales out of school, if you please. Recollect you should do unto others as—"

"I *am* done by, that's a fact, by gracious, so I'll jist out with it":

You see 'twas the night after the big dinner up here, and Wade got a crowd of youngsters to go home with him for some *fun*. Jist afore they gits to Wade's they overtake me, and I took him up at his first offer to go by, too,—he keeps good licker, Wade does. Well, after supper I seen the boys was in for a frolic. I took two or three hands with em at cards and after punishin sum of the old stuff, I lays down. Well, I spose it wanted about two hours to day when I was roused with the wakenest noise I ever riz to. I can't hardly tell how they was all fixed in that room, but thar lay Wills flat on his back on the floor, a big nigger aholt of each hand, holdin him spred out—the Doctor in his shirttail setting straddle of his breast with a pair of bullet moles in his hands trying to pull out one of his teeth! Then thar sat Henry B––nes from Claiborne County at his head holdin the candle, and every now and then he would reach one hand over and hyst Wills's upper lip for the Doctor to get the moles onto his tooth. Henry had a big pair of goat locks under his chin, and in peepin over at the operation he'd git em right over the candle and they'd swinge. I see him keep turning up his nose like he smelt something a-burnin, but he never dreamed it was his whiskers. Wills was a-gruntin powerful, and what between gruntin and the hiccups I thort he'd strangle. Major Bob was thar, too, and he had on a wonderful short shirt for a big fat man. He swore he could beat

8. A reference to January's most widely known sketch, "That Big Dog Fight at Myers's," printed elsewhere in this volume.

that Doctor a-pullin teeth, and he was hollerin for his "insterment" (a hammer and nail) to knock it out! They got the nail and as they couldn't find a hammer, in they fetched a pair of shoemaker's pinchers that's got a sort of hammer on one side. The Doctor dropt the moles for he found out that every time he'd *jerk* they'd *slip;* so he sings out for the pinchers—swore they were his favorite insterments—always used em—beat pullicans, too by_____! Well, you never did see a drunken set so busy about a serious job! Everyone was in ded ernest tryin to help Wills, and he was takin on wonderful, that's a fact! The Doctor set to work with the pinchers, and there set Henry with the pleasinest countenance (and when he gits three sheets spred and is tryin to unfarl the fourth, he can jist out laugh the universe, or I'll borrow a hat to go home with!). There sot Henry reddy to hist Wills's upper lip when the Doctor would stagger that way, he got reddy; Henry histed his lip, and after two or three false jerks he found the hammer was on the wrong side of the pinchers for *that* tooth; so he turns in and asks Wills on which side the akin tooth *was?* He said he didn't know!—So he fastens em onto a sound tooth on tother side, but the major had got impatient, so he riz— pulled his shirt as low as he could git it (and then it didn't hide nothin) picks up the tongs, walks around, and puts one foot on Wills's brest before the Doctor, and says he, "Doctor, you've been set cross that man for three hours! You can't pull no tooth, nor never could! Git up, man, git up! I can jist take *these tongs* and pull his tooth in half the time." But he hadn't a chance to try, for Henry, who had been leanin over to Wills's lip, puts his chin right over the candle and before he knowed it his whiskers was in a big blaze! He drops the candle with a "hooze" right into Wills's face—nigger let go and jumpt—Bob and the Doctor fell in a lump, tongs and all. Wills rize to his all fours and made for the gallery with the stranglinest hiccups I ever heard! I follered the man out—I raly thort he was strangling to deth—but he had rize up by the gallery post and was a-heavin and settin! It beat all tooth pullins I ever seen. Says I, "Curnel, what's you doin?" Says he, "trying to throw up (hic) that d———— tooth! I think I muster *swallered* it!"

Well, I looks around for this boy, and not seein him I enquires, but they had bin so busy they hadn't missed him. Thinks I, I'll take a turn around and see if I cant find him a-holdin up the fence somewhar! Well, as soon as I got out of the noise in the house, I hear somebody hollerin and there he was, sure enough, huggin a red oak, three feet thru. "Well," says I, "What are you doin here?" "Uncle Johnny, come here — for God sake, come here," says he, "and put a rail up agin this tree! I'm mighty tired," says he, "it's right easy now, but *when the wind blows* Lord J————— its mity heavy—hurrah, here it comes," says he; and he spread himself to it as if he'd bin holdin up the universe! Ha! Ha! twas rich to see him surgin up agin that tree to hold it up and beggin me to prop it up with a rail. I gits a rail and leans it agin the tree. "Uncle Johnny," says he, "hadn't you better git another! It's a mity big tree and ruff at that." "Let go," says I, "'twon't fall—these rails 'll hold it—let go." Soon as he let go, slam bang he went agin the pickets—knocked some off and went clean thru!—"G—— *durn* them pickets! they bin tryin to run over me all night," says he pickin himself up mity awkward. I couldn't hold in, he talked so natural—"Why," says I, "you run over *them!*" "Oh no," says he, "what with holdin that tree up and gittin round on tother side at the *same* time to git out in the pickets' way is nily took all the flesh off'n my arms—that's proof ain't it." Well, I couldn't begin to lead him to the house, so I jist got behind and pushed him. He's a little man, but you ort'er bin thar if you ain't never seen a man walk *tall*—every time he stept his legs went out at right angles—I say how's your arms got?"

"That'll do now, Uncle Johnny—treat, won't you!"

"Now you hit me—come in men, what'll you pull your tooth with?"

Irregular Practice of a Regular Practitioner

by Anonymous, New Orleans, Louisiana

§ Credited to the New Orleans *Picayune,* the following story appeared in the *Spirit,* XXI (August 16, 1851), 305.

THE members of the medical faculty, here and elsewhere, are great sticklers for what they term "the regular practice." Many of them indeed, carry this feeling so far that they would prefer killing a patient by a prescription administered in the regular way to curing him by recourse to a simple but unprofessional remedy for his disease. There are exceptions, however, to this general rule, and one notable instance we are about to relate.

In the summer of 1848 about the period of the close of the Mexican War, one of the officers of our army, an amateur zoologist, returning home from the scenes of his perils and his glory brought with him a number of rare insects and animals indigenous to Mexico. He put up for some time at the St. Charles Hotel, where his cabinet of natural curiosities attracted much attention. Among them was a living ichneumon fly, a repulsive looking animal of the most destructive instincts that would destroy and devour ants and other insects with the most sanguinary rapacity. A gentleman, whom for the nonce we shall call Jones, was at the time stopping in the St. Charles, and he formed for the ichneumon a strong dislike; indeed, having once seen it, he could not bear again to look at it. He was a man of kindly nature and generous qualities. His mind was genial and sociable to a fault, and this sometimes led him into convivial excesses which tended to cloud a mind and confuse an understanding that were otherwise strong and comprehensive.

About the time we speak of, he indulged to such an extent in a debauch that *mania-a-potu* followed. He was no sooner seized with this disease than the ichneumon seized upon his distempered imagination. The single obnoxious animal multiplied into ten thousand.

198

They covered his body, he thought, and like so many vampires were sucking his life's blood from him. He looked out in the room and saw them engaged in a most deadly conflict with grotesque red and blue monkeys, and they were drawn up in solid column all around the mosquito bar to prevent his escape. His nerves were unstrung, his brain was fevered, and his distress of mind could not have been greater if his apprehensions had been founded on reality instead of being—as they were—the emanations of a disordered imagination. Under the circumstances, his friends concluded to send for Dr. _____, one of our most eminent city physicians, with the view of his prescribing something to allay the nervous irritability of the patient. They did send for him, and soon after the Doctor arrived, smoking his cigar, caring nothing about the antics of ichneumons or the pranks of red monkeys. As he entered the room, he found the patient engaged in a vigorous conflict with some imaginary enemy beneath the mosquito bar, acting, more, however, it would seem on the defensive than the offensive. Now he would slap his hand across his face as if to drive something off his nose; now he would draw his knee and make a spasmodic kick towards the foot of the bed; now he would make his open hand resound on his shoulder and now again on his thigh. The odds against him seemed to be overpowering, yet he battled manfully. The Doctor saw at once what his disease was, and at once he resolved to resort to a quick remedy for its cure.

"Don't you think, Doctor," said a friend of the patient—who, by the way was a regular practitioner too—"don't you think phlebotomy would have an excellent effect in his case?"

"Don't think it would be worth a d--n," said the Doctor.

"I am sure," said the nurse, who believed that hydropathy was a cure for all diseases, "I'm sure that if he got a cold bath and has his temples bathed with ice, it would afford him great relief."

"Fiddlesticks," said the Doctor, puffing his cigar as unconcernedly as before.

"I have seen a man laboring under a similar malady," said the barkeeper of the establishment (who felt a strong friendship for the patient and who was present at this quasi-medical consultation), "and gentle purgatives gave him immediate relief."

"You did, did you?" said the Doctor.

"I did," said the barkeeper.

"What a pity," said the Doctor, "that you did not publish the fact in the columns of the *Medical Journal!*"

While this conversation was going on, poor Jones, who had taken lessons in boxing from Roper, was availing himself of his knowledge of the art of self-defense to beat off the hideous enemy. The doctor approached the bed, saying, when he got there, "Halloo, Jones"— they were on terms of familiar intimacy with one another—"Halloo Jones, what are you about? What are you driving at?"

"Oh, Doctor!" said poor Jones, the perspiration running down his face and fear seated in his eyes. "Oh, Doctor, can't you drive off those ichneumons? There, there!" (here he gave his ear a crack). "That fellow was striving to get in my ear."

"So you are troubled with ichneumons, are you?" said the Doctor.

"Troubled with them!" said Jones. "I'm tortured—I'm maddened to death with them."

"Well, I must see and relieve you," said the Doctor; and laying his cigar on the table, he took up a bootjack that lay before him, and just as Jones had turned over to have a tussle with an imaginary ichneumon, the doctor gave him a lusty crack with the bootjack on the posterior that made him bounce in the bed, which bounce made the bed shake.

"Halloo, Doctor!" said Jones, "what are you about?"

"Just chasing off the ichneumons," said the Doctor, and he gave Jones another lick with the bootjack, striking in the same place.

"Murder, murder!" said Jones; "you are killing me, Doctor—you'll kill me!"

"No," said the doctor, repeating the blow, "but I'll kill the ichneumons," and poor Jones received another lick with the bootjack, well laid on.

"Murder, murder, save me—save me," said Jones, jumping out of bed, running around the room, followed by the Doctor, plying the bootjack all the time.

"Oh, enough! enough, Doctor," said Jones, getting behind a rocking chair to shield himself from the bootjack.

"Then you cry enough, do you?" said the Doctor.

"Too much—altogether too much," said Jones.

"Do you see any ichneumons now?" said the Doctor.

"Not a d––n one," said Jones.

"I thought not," said the Doctor. "Get to bed now."

And Jones, his thighs covered over with red blotches, the imprints of the bootjack, quietly went to bed.

"Now, take this," said the Doctor, filling out a pint bottle of London porter, in which he put an opiate; and Jones, as submissive as a child, swallowed it as ordered. He soon fell asleep, and after a long and refreshing one, awoke well.

Poor fellow! he is since dead, but as long as he lived, he never again saw an ichneumon.

The Harp of a Thousand Strings

by William Penn Brannan

§ The authorship of this classic burlesque sermon has been in dispute for more than a hundred years. George Kummer in "Who Wrote 'The Harp of a Thousand Strings'?" *Ohio Historical Quarterly*, LXVII (July 1958), 221-231, shows that the sermon was delivered, according to tradition, by an old flatboat captain who was also a Hard-Shell Baptist preacher at Waterproof, Louisiana (then Mississippi), in the early 1850s. It soon appeared in newspapers all over the nation. It was printed in the *Ohio State Journal* in July 1855, in the New Orleans *Daily Crescent* in September 1855, and was reprinted in the *Spirit* that same month. The earliest appearance in book form, Kummer says, was Thomas Powell's *Chit-Chat of Humor, Wit, and Anecdote*, 1857; William E. Burton included it in his *Cyclopaedia of Wit and Humor*, 1858. Henry Watterson printed it in the first edition of *Oddities in Southern Life* (Boston: Houghton Mifflin, 1883), and Edward W. Cole in *Cole's Fun Doctor: The Funniest Book in the World* (London and Melbourne, Australia: 1886.)

As early as 1879, A. J. Frantz, editor of the Brandon, Mississippi, *Republican*, attributed the sermon to the Rev. Henry T. Lewis (1823-1870), Methodist minister and temperance lecturer. Mrs. Anne Roberts, Lewis's daughter, included a lengthier version in her *Harp of a Thousand Strings, With Waifs of Wit and Pathos*, 1907, with a citation from the Louisville *Courier-Journal* dated 1881 claiming Lewis's authorship. Some twentieth century anthologists have accepted this identification. However, Jay B. Hubbel in *The South in American Literature* (Durham: Duke University Press, 1954) attributes the piece to William Penn Brannan.

Kummer's investigation shows that Brannan, an itinerant portrait painter and journalist from Cincinnati, was in the vicinity of Waterproof in the summer of 1851, as noted by the *Port Gibson Herald* in which he published a poem under his own name and a burlesque novel under the pen name "Bill Easel." In 1856 Brannan had a studio in Louisville and contributed to the Louisville *Courier* under both names. In January of that year he published "Brother Crafford's Farewell Sermon" (included in this volume as "Farewell, Brother Crafford!" pp. 209-211), the opening sentence of which reads, "During my sojourn in Mississippi (shortly after I heard the great sermon which was played on a harp of a thousand strings), I had occasion to visit a friend in the neighborhood of Port Gibson." In connection with the story of Brother Crafford, the editor of the *Courier* referred to Brannan as the author of "The Harp of a Thousand Strings." Later in 1856 Joshua S. Morris, editor of the *Port Gibson* (Mississippi) *Reveille*, claimed to be the author of "The Harp." "Maulstick" answered him in the Louisville *Daily Democrat* and cited Brannan as the author. Brannan's obituary in the *Cincinnati Commercial*, August 10, 1866, claims the piece for him. Kummer concludes that Lewis probably used the sermon in his temperance lectures and thus gave the impression that he wrote it, but that Brannan's claim to authorship is much stronger than Lewis's.

The following version of "The Harp" is from Watterson's *Oddities of Southern Life and Character* (Boston: Houghton Mifflin, 1900).

"I MAY say to you, my brethering, that I am not an educated man, an I am not one o' them that beleeves education is necessary for a gospel minister, fur I beleeve the Lord edecates his preachers jest as he wants em to be educated; and although I say it that oughtn't to say it, yet in the State of Indianny, whar I live, thar's no man as gits a bigger congregation nor what I gits.

"Thar may be some here today, my brethering, as don't know what persuasion I am uv. Well, I may say to you, my brethering, that I am a Hard Shell Baptist. Thar's some folks as don't like the Hard Shell Baptists, but I'd rather hev a hard shell as no shell at all. You see me here today, my brethering, dressed up in fine close; you mout think I was proud, but I am not proud, my brethering; and although I've been a preacher uv the gospel for twenty years and although I'm capting uv that flatboat that lies at your landing, I'm not proud, my brethering.

"I'm not gwine ter tell you *edzackly* whar my tex may be found; suffice it tu say, it's in the leds of the Bible, and you'll find it somewhar 'tween the fust chapter of the book of Generation and the last chapter of the book of Revolutions, and if you'll go and sarch the Scriptures, you'll not only find my tex thar but a great many other texes will do you good to read; and my tex, when you shill find it, you shill find it to read thus:

And he played on a harp uv a thousand strings—sperits of just men made perfect.

"My tex, brethern, leads me to speak uv sperits. Now thar's a great many kind of sperits in the world. In the fust place, thar's the sperit as som folks call ghosts; then thar's the sperits uv turpen*time;* and then thar's the sperits as some folks call liquor, and I've got as good artikel uv them kind uv sperits on my flatboat as ever was fotched down the Mississippi River; but thar's a great many other kind of sperits, for the tex says: 'He played on a harp uv a thou-*sand* strings — sperits of just men made perfeck.'

"But I'll tell you the kind of sperits as is ment in the tex; it's *fire.* That is the kind of sperits as is ment in the tex, my brethering. Now thar's a great many kinds of fire in the world. In the fust place, thar's the common sort uv fire you light a segar or pipe with, and thar's camfire, fire before you're ready to fall back, and many other kinds uv fire, for the tex ses: 'He played on a harp uv a *thou*-sand strings — sperits uv just men made perfeck.'

"But I'll tell you the kind of fire as is ment in the tex, my brethering — it's *hell-fire!* an that's the kind of fire as a great many of you'll come to, ef you don't do better nor what you have bin doin — for 'He played on a harp uv a *thou*-sand strings — sperits of just men made perfeck.'

"Now, the different sorts uv fire in the world may be likened unto the different persuasions in the world. In the first place, we have the 'Piscapalions, and they are a high salin and a highfalutin set, and they may be likened unto a turkey buzzard that flies up into the air, and he goes up and up till he looks no bigger than your fingernail, and the fust thing you know he cums down and down and is a-fillin himself on the karkiss of a dead hoss by the side uv the road — and 'He played on a harp of a *thou*-sand strings — sperits of just men made perfeck.'

"And then, thar's the Methodis, and they may be likened unto the squirrel runnin up into a tree, for the Methodis believes in gwine on from one degree uv grace to another and finally on to perfecshun; and the squirrel goes up and up, and he jumps from lim to lim, and branch to branch, and the fust thing you know, he falls, and down he comes kerflummux; and that's like the Methodis, for they is allers fallin from grace, ah! And 'He played on a harp of a *thou*-sand strings — sperits of just men made perfeck.'

"And then, my brethering, thar's the Baptist, ah! and they hev bin likened unto a possum on a 'simmon tree, and the thunders may roll, and then the earth may quake, but that possum clings there still, ah! And you may shake one foot loose, and the other's thar; and you may shake all feet loose, and he laps his tail around the lim, and he clings furever—for 'He played on a harp of a *thou*-sand strings—sperits of just men made perfeck.'"

Daddy Donk and the Spirits

by "Number Eight" of Alabama

§ In the first part of the following tale as it was printed in the *Spirit*, XXIII, No. 29 (September 3, 1853), 337, the unidentified author takes issue with another correspondent about woodcock hunting. That introduction is omitted.

O N recurring to the manuscript of the "pious" friend who took notes on the sermon of "Father Donk" (the "Two-Seed divine"), I see that only the peroration of that memorable discourse has been preserved. Future generations must remain ignorant of the text. What has been preserved, however, by the hand of my friend, I proceed to give you:

"My breethren," continued Father Donk, "thar's a thing been on my mind all the time I've been talkin to you this mornin. Looks like the Lord has been callin all day for me to *talk it right out!* But my breethren"—here the parson's voice faltered and he wiped his eyes with the tail of his hunting shirt—"I nately hate to say the word, be-kase it's consarnin givin up the church here on Timber-Gut Creek, whar I've sowed the good seed—glory to the Lord—and whar it sprouted and brought forth fruit, some fifty and some an hundred fold. Breethren, the Lord knows I love you Timber-Gutters; but, my breethren, the Church and me seems to be a-defferin (differing) on some p'ints o' faith, and I reckon I'd better go. Yea, Lord, thy will be done, but Timber-Gut is dear to the heart of old Daddy Donk! Here I've striv and here I've rastled, and here I've snake-poled Satan as far as the Lord has given me strength. Praise the Lord, I've give the old varmint's hide some mighty tight dressins, but he's a-gettin the upper hand of old Daddy Donk now!

"You breethren"—here the speaker warmed up evidently—"you that lives a way down here on Timber-Gut don't know what's a doin a-way up yonder to Jacksonville; but I'll tell you, breethren! Yes, I'll raise my voice and tell it so loud that there shan't be a man, nor a woman, nor a child on all Timber-Gut but shall hear it—*Satan has had another flirt with the old strumpet of Babylon*—and what d'ye reckon she's brought forth? I say, *what* has the old slut of Babylon brought forth? Why, *Sons-o'-Temperance!*

"Yes, breethren, and 'fore you know, you'll have a cross of the same stock down here on Timber-Gut! I see it a-comin! And right here, breethren, this fetches me up to the p'int I was aimin at a while ago. Bless God, breethren, you all know that when old Daddy Donk fust come down on Timber-Gut about a year ago there warn't but two or three breethren of the Two-Seed faith on all Timber-Gut! But your old Daddy preached and he prayed in the neighbors' housen, and by and by the Lord begun to move, and 'many were added to the church!' And by and by, breethren, we got up a 'scription to build a house to the Lord, and the breethren was liberal, and we built this nice house — and breethren, we had seven dollars and a half over and above buildin the House of the Lord! And the Lord prospered the Church on Timber-Gut on every hand; and we took the money that was over and above the buildin of the meetin house, and we laid it out in *fifteen gallons of mighty good corn whiskey,* for the breethren to use on meetin days! Oh, glory to the Lord, *them* was the days when the church on Timber-Gut was like a green bay tree! *Then* you might a seed the breethren a-flockin in of a Sunday mornin! *Then* was the time your old Daddy Donk went down into the water with somebody or another every meetin day! And breethren" — here the speaker sobbed between his words — "there was added to the church *ondurin the time we had that good sperrits, forty-five members!*

"Praise God! it was just adzactly *three to the gallon, breethren!*

"But now, breethren," continued the venerable Donk with a trembling, plaintive intonation, "but now, breethren, them sperrits has been out for two meetins. Your old Daddy comes down every month to see you, and preach for you, and pray for you, and fight Satan for you, and thar's not a drap in the kag. The Church, too, is lukewarm, and Satan seems to be a-gittin it all his own way. Breethren, I hope the Lord will bless the Church on Timber-Gut, but the way things is fixed, breethren, your old Daddy Donk is satisfied in his own mind that the Lord is about to call somebody else to take charge of the Church on Timber-Gut, for your old Daddy do not feel willin to rastle for souls with Satan *and give him all under holt!*"

It is but justice to the highly intelligent congregation of Parson

Donk to state that a committee was raised immediately upon the conclusion of the Parson's discourse, that a sufficient sum was raised to
procure a suitable supply of munitions of war, and that the venerable
pastor consented to continue his ministrations on Timber-Gut, where,
I doubt not, the devil will get some confounded hard falls, now that
Daddy Donk has in a (tin) measure deprived him of his "under holt."

"Farewell, Brother Crafford!"

by William Penn Brannan

§ This story of Brannan's appeared under the pen name "Bill Easel" in the *Spirit*, XXVI, No. 6 (March 22, 1856), 65, reprinted from the Louisville *Daily Courier*. The opening sentence refers to "The Harp of a Thousand Strings."

DURING my sojourn in Mississippi (shortly after I heard the great sermon which was played on a harp of a thousand strings), I had occasion to visit a friend in the neighborhood of Port Gibson. The next day being the Sabbath, I accompanied him to Zion Chapel. A new minister had been called to that neighborhood, and this was to be his salutatory sermon. Zion Chapel was some hundred yards from the main road and surrounded by forest trees. Having arrived rather too early for the service, my friend and I sauntered about the woods rather actively employed in brushing away the cloud of mosquitoes that surrounded us. At length a strange specimen of *genus homo* made his appearance on horseback; it was Brother Crafford.

His dress was decidedly peculiar. On his head he wore an old-fashioned, bell-crown beaver several sizes too large. To remedy this defect, a cotton bandana handkerchief was stuffed between the hat and forehead. His coat was of a most ancient pattern—blue, with brass buttons, short waist, and long swallow-tail; the collar came within an inch of hiding the back part of his head. His vest was extremely long, and his pants ditto short. The latter were held down by a leather strap passed under a huge pair of brogans of an untanned leather color. Altogether, his presence strongly suggested Dan Marble in his Yankee character of Jonathan Homespun. But to the sermon— or at least a portion of it—for it was utterly impossible to report the whole.

The congregation was large as it had been "norated" abroad that a new minister was to make his debut at Zion. Brother Crafford slunk into the pulpit with more than ordinary humility, and after devoting a few moments to silent prayer he rose. Gingerly pushing up the sleeve of his *store coat,* he displayed a pair of large, long, bony hands of a beet-red color; he grasped the handle of an earthen pitcher and poured into a tin cup a draught of water which he drank with inimitable gusto. His appearance in the pulpit was a study for an artist. His face was long and lank, eyes pale gray, nose aquiline, complexion sandy, hair grayish sandy, head bald on top with the exception of a small patch on the organ of reverence (as if to shade it). He began apologetically, as follows:

"You don't see me today in the dress I allers wear; I come among you as a stranger, and I am now tricked out in my store clothes; I am not a proud man, but I thought it would be more becoming before strangers." After this he raised a hymn in which the congregation joined. Then he began his sermon:

"My dear breethern and sisters, first and foremost, I'm gwine to tell you about the affecting partin I had with my congregation at Bethel Chapel. Arter I had got through with my farewell sarmont, as I come down outen the pulpit, the old gray-headed breethern and sisters who had listened to my voice for twenty years crowded around me and with sobbing voices and tearful eyes said, 'Farewell, Brother Crafford!'

"As I walked down the aisle, the young ladies — tricked out in their finery of brass jewelry, geegaws, jimcracks, paint, and flounces — looked up with their bright eyes and pronounced with their rosy lips, 'Farewell, Brother Crafford!'

"The young men in their tight patent leather boots, high collars, and flashy waistcoats — smelling of pomatum and cigar smoke — with their Shanghai coats and striped zebra pants — they, too, said, 'Farewell, Brother Crafford!'

"The little children — lambs in the field — lifted up their tiny hands and small voices and with one accord said, 'Farewell, Brother Crafford!'

"The colored breethern of the congregation now came forward (black sheep who had been admitted to the fold under my ministry) with tears rolling down their sable cheeks — they, too, said, 'Farewell, Brother Crafford!'

"As I got on my horse and bade adieu to my congregation forever, I turned to take a last look at the old church where I had preached the unsarchable riches of religion for mor'n twenty years, and as I gazed at its dilapidated walls and moss-covered roof, it, too, seemed to say, 'Farewell, Brother Crafford!'

"As I rode down through the village, the people who poked their heads outen the winders and the servants who lent on their brooms —all seemed to say, 'Farewell, Brother Crafford!'

"Crossing a little creek that was gurgling and singing over its pebbly bed as it rejoiced on its way to the great ocean of eternity—it, too, seemed to say, 'Farewell, Brother Crafford!'

"As I rode along down a hot, dusty lane, an old sow that was asleep in a fence corner jumped out of a suddent with a loud broo-oo, broo-oo—she, too, seemed to say, 'Farewell, Brother Crafford!'

"My horse, he got frightened and jumped from under me, and as he curled his tail over his back, kicked up his heels and ran off—he, too, seemed to say, 'Farewell, Brother Crafford!'"

Shifting the Responsibility

by Anonymous of Alabama

§ Though it appeared anonymously, this tale was written by J. J. Hooper, according to W. Stanley Hoole, *Alias Simon Suggs: the Life and Times of Johnson Jones Hooper* (University, Ala.: University of Alabama Press, 1952), p. 75. It seems strange that Porter did not recognize the story as Hooper's when he printed it in the *Spirit*, XXI, No. 7 (April 7, 1851), 74, and introduce it with a puff for the author as he usually did Hooper's work. "Shifting the Responsibility" appeared first in the *Chambers* (Alabama) *Tribune* (which Hooper edited), was reprinted in the *Spirit*, and again in *Polly Peablossom's Wedding, And Other Tales* (Philadelphia, n.d.), Thomas A. Burke, ed.

WHILE attending Court recently in the adjoining county of Randolph, a friend who is fond of jokes of all sorts and who relates them almost as humorously as "His Honor," gave us the following, vouching for the substantial, sublunar existence of the parties and their present residence "in the county aforesaid":

Brethren Crump and Noel were both members of the Primitive Baptist Church and both clever, honest men who paid their taxes and debts as the same annually accrued with regularity at once Christian and commendable. If when settling day came round Brother Noel was "short," Brother Crump was sure to be in funds; and, on the other hand, it almost seemed providential how, if Brother Crump fell "behind," Brother Noel always had a surplus. Thus borrowing from and lending to each other, worshipping at the same church, and living only a mile apart, they developed an intimacy that gradually ripened; so that at last they did not hesitate to speak in the freest and most familiar manner to each other, even in regard to their respective foibles.

Now it came to pass that Brother Crump during the liveliest period of the cotton season drove into Wetumpka and disposed of his "crap" of ten bales at the fair price of twelve and a half cents per pound. It was more than he expected, and as the world was easy with him he determined to invest and did actually invest a portion of the proceeds of the sale of his cotton in a barrel of Western whiskey, paying for it at the rate of precisely two pounds of middling cotton for one gallon of "ditto" whiskey.

Of course it was "norated in the settlement" that old man Crump had bought a whole barrel, and after a few weeks people began to observe that his nose grew redder and his eye more moist. The idea that Brother Crump was "drinking too much" diffused itself in the neighborhood until, as one might say, it became epidemical. People talked and talked, more especially "what few" of other denominations of Christians dwelt thereabouts.

Brother Noel was "sore troubled" at the scandal which circulated about his brother and friend, and especially regretted the injury it brought to the "ciety" at Sharon. So, one morning he stepped over to Brother Crump's and found the old man in a half-doze on his little porch.

"Won't you take a drink?" asked Brother Crump, as soon as he was aware of the presence of his neighbor.

"Why, yes, I'm not agin a dram when a body wants it."

Brother Crump got his bottle, and the friends took a dram apiece.

"Don't you think, Brother Noel," said Crump, "that sperits is a blessin."

"Y-e-s!" responded Noel; "sperits is a blessin, but accordin to my notion, it's a blessin that some of us abuses."

"Well, now, Brother Noel, *who* do you think abuses the blessin?"

"Well, it's hard to say—but people talk—don't you think *you* drink too much, Brother Crump?"

"It's hard to say—it's hard to say!" returned Crump. "Sometimes I've thought I *was* a-drinkin too much—then agin, I'd think *maybe not!* What is man? A weak *wurrum* of the dust! What the Lord saith, that shall be done! So I left it to the Lord to say whether I was goin too fur in sperits. I put the whole *'sponsiblity on him!* I prayed to him, ef I was drinkin too much, *to take away my appetite for sperits!"*

Here Brother Noel groaned piously and asked, "What then, Brother Crump?"

"And," replied Crump, "I've prayed that prayer three times, and HE HAIN'T DONE IT! So I'm clear of the 'sponsibility, anyway!"

"The Lord's will be done," ejaculated Noel, and after taking another dram he went home, thinking all the way how cleverly Brother Crump had *shifted the responsibility.*

How to Draw the Sinners

by "Subscriber," St. Louis, Missouri

§ Credited to the Cincinnati *Nonpariel,* the following anecdote appeared in the *Spirit,* XXI (July 5, 1851), 240.

SEVERAL years ago we were a resident of northwestern Louisiana, near the confines of Texas. The people there, as a general thing, were not given to religion. A young itinerant preacher happened along in the neighboring district during this dearth of religion and set about repairing the walls of Zion in good earnest. But his success was poor. Not over half a dozen could be got together at his Sunday meetings. Determined, however, to create an interest before leaving the neighborhood, he procured printed handbills and had them posted up in every conspicious place in the district, which read to the following effect:

"RELIGIOUS NOTICE—The Rev. Mr. Blaney will preach next Sunday in Dempsey's Grove, at ten o'clock, a.m., and at four o'clock, p.m., Providence permitting. Between the services, the preacher will run his sorrel mare, Julia, against any nag that can be trotted out in this region, for a purse of five hundred dollars!"

This had the desired effect. People flocked from all quarters, and the anxiety to see the singular preacher was even greater than the excitement following the challenge. He preached an elegant sermon in the morning, and after dinner he brought out his mare for the race. The purse was made up by five or six of the planters and an opposing nag produced. The preacher rode his little sorrel and won the day amid the deafening shouts, screams, and yells of the delighted people. The congregation all remained for the afternoon service, and at its close, more than two hundred joined the church: some from motives of sincerity, some for the novelty of the thing, some from excitement, and some because the preacher—in the unrefined language of the country—was a "d---d good fellow!" The finale of the affair was as flourishing a society as can be found in the whole region thereabouts.

The Good Shepherd

Anonymous of Louisiana

§ The following story appeared in the *Richmond Compiler* II (March 14, 1843), 1, Richmond, Louisiana, where it was reprinted from the *Louisiana Chronicle.*

THERE dwelt in a certain parish of this State, not above a thousand years ago, an individual who followed the sacred calling of expounding the "scripters" to poor benighted sinners on the Sabbath and sometimes on a week-day, when he could gather the wicked to listen to the words of warning that fell like molten lead from his reverend lips. Fearfully did he depict the terrors of the "sulphurous" abode to which all evil doers would certainly be consigned, unless they repented of the error of their ways, and supplicated for mercy. It was wholesome and edifying to sit within the sound of his voice and hear him tell how the bones of the d––-d would scorch and crackle in the great fire that ever burns in the bottomless pit and how they would cry aloud for something to drink but "couldn't get a drap."

Much the people marvelled at the parson's self-denying piety, but more did they wonder at the profound learning which enabled him to tell, within a fraction of a fraction, how much brimstone and cordwood it took to keep up this everlasting blaze, upon the grim horrors of which he did most lustily descant. In the psalm-singing line, too, our man of grace outstripped all competitors. He was unapproached and unapproachable in that spiritual twang which no amateur may ever hope to acquire, and many good gossips yielded ready credence to the belief that his nasal organ had been especially constructed as an auxiliary to his throttle in this "David Gamut" exercise. All his psalmody–all his exhortations–all his eloquence–even the terrors of Tophet–had no effect, however, upon the hearts of stone which congregated to hear but not heed these divine outpourings. Had the ghost of Whitefield risen from the tomb and told of the wrath to come, it would have been to no more purpose, for the people were encompassed about with unrighteousness, and they grew apace in sin. Occasionally a precious few would assemble at some house in the village or country to take counsel and comfort each other, and it was then that the sore spirits of the foul made clean would groan in very agony that their neighbors had been called but would not come, had been bidden but would not enter. At such times, mighty was the wrestling of the good man with the Evil One, and frequently it was not until the perspiration rolled from his head in drops as large as blue beans that the victory fell to the side of the church. Often when night had thrown its sombre veil over the earth would a voice be heard in the vast wilderness of tall pine trees that surrounded G_____, calling upon the faithful to remain steadfast and the heathen to repent until it became the settled conviction of many good people that the spirit of Lorenzo Dow walked abroad in the piny woods to terrify sinners and evict Satan.

Thus matters stood, until it fell out that Parson W————— discovered one evening in the only grocery of the place a parcel of the Devil's chosen ones, upon whom much labor and counsel had been expended, putting "poison into their mouths to steal away" what brains nature had given them. Verily, they were graceless scamps and what with shouting, singing, tearing, and swearing, it was such a sight as made our spiritual man sore amazed and exceedingly indignant. Therefore, buckling on the armor of reproof, with fire in his eye and scorching words upon his tongue, did he rush into this den of vipers, and vehemently did he exhort the revellers to desist from such practice; but they had already steeped their senses too deeply in "blue ruin" to pay any attention to the wrath-denouncing parson. He might as well have addressed himself to a whiskey barrel that stood near by, for the only answer he received were vociferous invitations to "stand treat round" or "if he hadn't the times" to take a horn any how. Exasperated beyond endurance by this perverseness and seeing the utter uselessness of longer continuing the combat against sin in that quarter, he raised his voice in agony, and thus spoke to the crowd:

"Fellow sinners, I have preached to you, I have prayed for you, and often exhorted you to flee from the wrath to come; but notwithstanding all this, here you now are as drunk as Billy be d———d. If you are determined to go to h--ll head foremost, I am too good a shepherd to desert my flock in the hour of danger, and therefore will go with you. Landlord, give us something to drink! Come up boys!"

When our informant left, the hero of this true tale was on a billiard table patting "Juba".

Jokes and Jokers

Twentieth-century readers may find it difficult to understand why American men in the first half of the nineteenth century devoted so much time to playing practical jokes, "running saws," befooling and bemusing strangers, and perpertrating deviltry that is now thought to be characteristic of high school students, boys at summer camp, fraternity brotherhoods, and some kinds of day laborers. As Yates in *Porter and the Spirit*, pp. 143, 146, says of sketches in the *Spirit* devoted to this kind of humor, "the note sounded may have been merry or boisterous to the devotees of the magazine but seems discordant enough to us." Noting that the practical joke was "played in ways that are as rough as they are ingenious and varied," he concludes, "Yes, practical joking was an art and a science to the hard-handed humorists of the 1840's and 1850's."

Deception for amusement is only part of the great body of folk literature devoted to deception generally; almost every primitive culture has folktales in which a trickster deceives, either maliciously or in good fun, the high and the low. Sometimes he gulls the proud to make them humble; sometimes he deceives the rich for the benefit of the poor; sometimes he deceives merely to amuse himself or others. Then, ironically, the trickster himself is sometimes tricked, often by one who appears to be far less shrewd than he—just to redress the balance. At all stages of civilization, it seems, man has loved his jokes and enjoyed the role of joker, but to be the butt of the joke is an entirely different matter.

In the humor of the Old Southwest jokers and joking may for convenience be divided into two categories: deception of the stranger or member of the out-group and deception of a member of the in-group. Jargon words used to describe this deception are "selling," "being sold," "running a saw," and "sawing," terms which seem to have these meanings: A "sell" was a hoax or joke in which the person being deceived was led to believe something opposite to what the truth was; hence he was embarrassed mentally or verbally. The "sell" also might be of the type called practical joke; in this case the victim was led to *do* something which resulted in physical embarrassment. In either instance the butt of the joke is "sold." A "saw" seems to have been roughly equivalent to a "sell." "Running a saw," then, was about the same thing as "selling." In both instances, the joke might be nothing more than a quick-witted or unexpected reply to a question or series of questions, the intent being to mislead or squelch. On the other hand, "running a saw" sometimes required time and elaborate preparation. For example, "Ruff Sam" carefully plans a practical joke that will show up his braggart neighbors and make them a laughingstock. Sometimes the "saw" depended entirely on the eccentricities of local characters. Uncle C., for instance, was such a confirmed horse trader that he would trade anywhere, any time. Taking advantage of his widely advertised peculiarity, the prankster ran a double "saw" on him by trading him a *saw horse* for a real horse. Exposing pretense was also greatly enjoyed, such as the local boys who drove away the European fortune hunters in "Fortunes in Prospect." The shrewd backwoodsman who outwits the townsman, as in "An Arkansas 'Sell,'" reversed the usual yokel-city dweller situation. Tricksters who maliciously deceived innocent and helpless victims were apparently not greatly admired even by the fun-loving jokers of the Old Southwest; few sketches deal with such swindlers, large or small, such as are seen in "An Egg-straordinary Act" and "Getting a Railroad Subscription."

Practical joking and other forms of fun-making in the early part of the nineteenth century may have resulted from the aggressive American faith in the democratic experiment. The pursuit of this kind of amusement was characterized by the same gusto and youthful vigor that is evident in other activities during the early days of the Republic.

Fortunes in Prospect

by "Jersey," Natchez, Mississippi

§ Perhaps a businessman or traveler from New Jersey, the author introduced his story with a note to Porter as follows: "You are a treasure to
a man waiting for a steamboat. What a crowd of subscribers you could
get on the bank of the Styx—weary souls that know no pastime—how
like them is the still incarnate mortal who is tied to a steamboat landing
waiting for the next boat." Porter printed the tale in the *Spirit*, XVIII,
No. 27 (August 26, 1848), 313.

NATCHEZ is the prettiest and best shaded village this far
South. It is buried in china trees, the foliage of which is nearly black
and so dense that the sun cannot penetrate it. There is but one hotel;
of an evening a knot of gentry sit at the corner and the stranger may
sit near enough to hear what is public. Here is about the center of
cotton growing; out of cotton in the days when the staple was of
more value than at present enormous private fortunes have been
accumulated.

There is a higher "game" more ardently hunted than the feathered
and finny tribes, and this place has been and still is a "hunting
ground" to be noted. "Is that a *swan* I see?" To be sure. Was there
ever an heiress that was not a beauty, or if not a beauty her wit is
sparkling, or her step majestic, or she has the intellectual brow of her
father. At all events, the gilded frame attracts. Consequently, at the
proper season when all the "pretty birds" are wintering at home, it is
not astonishing that many nice young men have business at Natchez.

I have amused myself with looking over the register at the "Man-
sion House," and with some of the names there is a story. For instance, here are Captain Beerom and Baron Blucher, distinguished
travellers, who stopped to see the country with some thoughts of
making investments in cotton planting. And gallant looking men they
were, such as seem sent into the world expressly to storm a battery or
the fortification of a woman's heart. The Captain was tall, muscular,
erect, with a soldier-like bearing, and was said to hold a commission
in some European mounted regiment. But the Baron, with his pink

cheeks and raven moustache, was perfection to look upon. The way he broke his English was distinguished.

They bought no plantations, notwithstanding they passed a winter here. Very soon after their arrival, however, it was apparent that they had made a selection of "the properties" they desired to own. How the acquaintance was made, I have not heard (which is the more to be regretted as it is the only part of my story which might be of use to future "followers of the sport"). Not much time elapsed before they became the constant cavaliers of two of the wealthiest, if not the love-liest, of the natives. To and from their morning calls, they charged up and down the decorous streets of the town with a desperate horse-manship—which the Major had to put a stop to. And if of an after-noon you should lose your way upon a crossroad or shady lane, it was not improbable that you would meet one or the other couples on their horses with all their company.

The nerves of a small town are easily jarred, and the antics of these strangers—jumping their horses over drains, wheelbarrows, and such small obstacles—looked like an attempt to astonish. This, in a country where one of the first things a boy learns is how to ride, was, you must admit, a little unsafe. I need not tell you what a Southern boy and his horse will dare attempt, and they will do it, too, if neither gets his neck broken—which sometimes happens.

Alas for the Captain and the Baron! Puffed up with the fame they had secured by frightening the citizens and bewitching the ladies, they were one day heard to lament that there was no fox hunting to be had. In Germany it was their favorite sport, and deprived as they were of the old familiar sound of hound and horn, there was danger of their manhood becoming rusty.

"No fox hunting!" said an accidental hearer amongst the ladies; "why, gentlemen, we have plenty of young men who do nothing else at this season. My cousin runs a pack every other morning, and I'm sure he would be delighted that you should join him." And accord-ingly the cousin waited upon the gentlemen, and arrangements were made for a start the ensuing morning as soon as possible after day-break.

"I say, Sam," said one of the regular huntsmen, "I will make you two bets: one, that neither of those chaps will attend, the other, that one out of the two gets his neck broken, or thereabouts."

Between daybreak and sunrise the next morning the valley of the Saint Catherine echoed with the cry of the pack; hot and fast spurred the riders whose healthful whoop disturbed the slumbers of many a fair pair of eyelids; after due time the "varmint's" brush was taken, but the expected guests had not appeared.

As the hunters returned to the place of meeting with occasional comments not much to the advantage of the absent strangers, the Captain, to his credit be it said, loomed up in the distance with a party of city friends. With many graceful apologies for mistaking the hour of meeting and regrets that the Baron was suffering from a head-ache, he hoped it would not be impossible to get up another start.

This was at length assented to, after a short time allowed for the horses and dogs to blow. The ground was changed, and after a brief delay a well-known veteran fox, an ancient customer, which many a time before had led the pack, was up and away. With many a joyous whoop giving new life to the thoroughbreds which had already done a morning's work and with hasty adieus to the city spectators, off they went; the old fox, as was expected, took the most villainous course which the face of the country presented.

"I say, Sam, I want to see those toes go through the grapevines. Do you think Lucy can clear the bayou this time?" (Bayous are ravines or rain-gullies of any width and depth, and in a field grown up in sedge grass, they cannot be seen by a rider until he is upon them). On dashed the crowd; the Captain on his fresh horse rode on his stirrups, toes out (Is that German fashion?), going for speed and leading the way. Mile after mile was passed, over fallen timber and fence gaps and through treacherous bottoms abounding in dangerous sinkholes; and still horses and riders were right side up. And now the course lay through an old cotton field thrown out and grown up in sedge grass, sloping on the far side towards the creek.

"Better let me lead, Captain. Look out for the bayous."

But alas for the unbeliever! While the shout of warning was still ringing upon the air, the martingaled head of the Captain's mare mounted towards the sky — a yawning chasm was before her and she checked her speed—a leap alone could save her—one moment of doubt and in that moment the treacherous bank crumbled beneath her—horse and rider seemed to melt into the earth. "The rude sons of the hamlet" took the bayou flying, showing to the fallen a *shower of horseshoes* but generally forbearing to fall in on top; and when the old fox as usual had placed an impassable canebrake as a stopper, "the guest" was carefully dug out of the soft bottom and returned to his admiring friends.

The Baron was never in health for a fox chase, and the Captain probably wondered with Lord Chesterfield, if ever people "hunted twice." Their fair acquaintances looked lightning at "those coarse young men," but "the accident" somehow sullied the bloom of the foreigners' chivalry. Then one fair spring morning the illustrious visitors disappeared—unwedded and alone.

A Snake Story

by "Ruff Sam" of Mississippi

§ This is one of three dialect letters which "Ruff Sam" contributed to the *Spirit*. Another is included in the section "Masculine Amusements," which follows. This snake story appeared in the *Spirit*, XVIII, No. 19 (July 1, 1848), 217-218.

I RECKON it's a'most time for me to let the folks know what's a kum on me agin; and as I played a rite good joke on the boys the yether day, I mite as well tell you bout it.

I've sed monstrous leetle bout what sorter people populates these parts, no more'n I ain't menshuned old Squire Duballs and his boys, what lives round here. The Squire's the only law man we've got here, and what he sez is jest as good as the Bible. He's a tremendous slim man, and what ails him he keeps on a-gittin slimmer. He's afeered he'll melt this kummin summer, so he's inventid a instrument which he says is to cool him. I like to laffed myself to deth to see him the yether day a-layin flat on his back, 'thout a yarthly thing on him 'cepen his sheert, in a leetle room he's got fixed up, his hans and feet stuck into rings, and the rings tide on to pulleys to move a rale course lookin sorter fan made outen clapboards. I axed him what ailed him, and he told me he was a-koolin himself; but ef you hear me speek, he was in a delugin swet. I thoed a bucket er water on him and opened the winders, or he'd a-bin a-runnin steam in less on a minit.

The Squire's got a cupple of powerful smart boys. Zeek's like his daddy, sorter slimish, and jest knows a lettle more'n any live man you kin pick up—he knows everything afore you tell him and ollers did. Then thar's Abe—everybody knows Abe—he's been everwhar and kilt every bar that ever klum a tree and every buffalo that ever didn't klum a tree and kin do a'most anything. I kum in the yether day and tole the boys ef they'd kum along with me, I'd show em one of the most ondashus big rattlesnakes they'd ever seen, what I'd jest kilt, and as I'd sprained my back, I couldn't fetch him in, but that they might tote him together. Zeek jest ups and sez he know'd whar his hole was—he'd seen him the day afore—and then he wanted to know whar 'bouts I'd seen him—what his kuller was—and how long he was. But I knowed Zeek would talk. Abe sed he was the man that could pack him plum home 'thout takin a long breath and that he could a-kilt him with his fist.

I whistled up Boss, and we was in the woods shortly. We'd gone 'bout a mile when we hern sumthin in the bushes. Zeek asked Abe ef he didn't know what that was and then tole him 'twas a owl. Abe he sed, "Yes, it is a owl." And so they kep a-jokin of each other, as they always is, twill we got to the snake what was lyin on the groun as stret as a log.

"Ke-ristopher!" sez Zeek, "that's the dustiest lookin rope I ever didn't see!"

"It's a reg'lar hoss, sir," sez Abe, a-gettin smart.

'Twas most nite, and they couldn't see rite good.

"Well," sez I, "he's stiff by this time. Whar's the man what's feer'd to help carry him home?"

"Ke-ristopher!" said Zeek, "whar's his tail! I'll lift that eend. He's a'most twenty feet long. Whar does he put up at o'nites! Well, I never did—"

"Yes, but our Joe ever did," sez Abe, a-laffin. "I'll take hole of his tail, too, and we kin drag him."

"Oh, no," sez I, "that'll spile his skin. If one kan't ketch holt of one eend and the yether the yether, you mout as well leave him."

They thoed up for the tail eend, and Zeek won. 'Twas so dark I had to tell em which was the tail eend, as I had kilt it. "Bout face! shoulder arms!" sez I, a-seizen holt with them and a-histen it up on ther shoulders. "For'ad march!" and away we went, me a-leadin the way and Boss a-follerin in the rair, as ef thar wan't a snake in the whole country.

"Corderoys and trowsers! Did you hear that?" sez Zeek. "Ef he didn't rattle *then*, I ain't got no snake on my shoulder, that's all!"

"I've bin a-watchin him pokin his tung outen this end all 'long," sez Abe a-rollin his eyes round.

"Hole on for what?" sez I, a-seein em stop. "He's so stiff he can't turn his head to bite, and it's four feet clar of your shoulder any how."

"Oh, Moses!" sez Abe, "his head's as big as a alligator's—looks like a nat'ral knot. Thar! didn't you feel him squirm, Zeek!"

"Yes, I think I did," said Zeek, a-wipin the swet offen his for'ed with his elbow and a-smellin his hans to see ef thar was any pisen on em. "He must be a monstrous tuff snake," sez Zeek, a-goin on; "his skin feels as ruff as the bark of a persimmon; ef he's the reg'lar cheeze, dad'll use him for the rumatiz."

"I'm goin to stuff his hide with sawduss and sell him to the mewsum," sez Abe.

"Well, ef you does, I'll have his rattles," sez Zeek. "I've jest kounted em and thar's aty-three!"

I didn't say nuthin, 'cause I know'd I'd have a laff when I got home.

"Why don't you kum nyer and talk sum, Sam," sez Abe. "I believe you're gittin skeerd."

"I am sorter that way," sez I, "but we're most home, now, and thar kums the nabers to meet us; they've got wind of it sum way."

"Hurrey!" they shouted, "whar's the snake?"

"Stan back!" sez I, "You shall all have a look at him when we gits him in the yard. Clar the way! You Ned, open the gate wide! Gabe, you fool, hole that torch up hyer, or you'll have the boys bit here afore you know it! Stan aside, I tell you ! Keerful now—heeve away!"

Down kum the snake, ke-smash, and roun tore the boys to see the varmint.

"Hello!" sez they, all in a breth, "you calls this a *snake*, does you? I want to know! Well, ef it ain't a pure poplar pole, it ain't nuthin else! Well, I do say this *is* a joke! How-de-doo, Mr. Snake-hunters? Ha, ha, ha! ha! Ho!! Whar's Sam? Ef he ain't fooled you sum, *I* wouldn't menshun it!"

Abe and Zeek wanted to tare my very internals out, but after they got kool, I tole em 'twas only a leetle of my fun and that I'd gin a blow out next Saturday kum for thar benefit, and so we shucked hans. But ef you doesn't want to see thar backs up, you musn't menshun "snake" in thar hearin.

Catching a Weasel Asleep

by Anonymous, New Orleans, Louisiana

§ This example of a gag appeared originally in the New Orleans *Crescent*, a newspaper established in 1848 by Alexander H. Hayes and J. E. "Sam" McClure, both formerly with the *Picayune* and *Delta*, according to Copeland (*Kendall of the Picayune*, pp. 141-142). The story was reprinted in the *Spirit*, XIX, No. 10 (April 28, 1849), 113.

AN individual as well known around ———— as the guide-board at the crossroads, your ABC's at school, or the church steeple, once toted into the village inn on one of his customary horse-trading errands. Old C. was a "hoss," if not "half alligator," in all kinds of matters having the slightest affinity to horseflesh. He could see through a beast as well as you can through the bars of a gridiron. *"Veni, vidi,"* was his motto; and he decided just as quickly as a wink could be made, or the fire from the limestone *some where* scorched a feather. He never would allow the chance of a trade to slip through his fingers like a greased pig but would jump at one as readily as a trout will at a fly. I solemnly aver that had he, by some providence or other, happened to live in the days of Alexander, he would have attempted to "come it over" that great "b'hoy" and swopped him a miserable creature for his Bucephalus; *ditto*, had it been his fortune to fall in with Don Quixote, ten to one he would have "struck a trade" with the valiant knight and obtained the far-famed Rosinante as an equivalent for some "bishoped" affair. In fine, reader, C.'s fame was as renowned as his white neckcloth, *a la* parson, and other clerical eccentricities were well known for miles around.

Very well C., we were saying, once tottered into the village tavern. At his appearance a stranger might have mistaken him for a fallen deacon or an itinerant temperance lecturer bearding the "crater" in its den: he looked a little like both, only more like the former than t'other by reason of a well-dyed nose and other marks which king 'cohol is apt to leave as mementoes of his favor upon the features of his proselytes.

"Who wants to trade today?" he exclaimed, emptying the tumbler of "sling" which the attentive Boniface knew was *de regle* with C. and had consequently concocted on his entrance. "Got an all-fired putty hoss tew hum," he continued, "fresh from 'Hio — slick as a new dollar — smart as young lightnin after a spankin — and will trot it like a bull-gine down a greased sunstroke."

"Considerable kind of a critter, I should expect," remarked one of the would-be bloods of the village, calmly whiffing his long nine, and a smile of incredulity crept quietly over his sharp wag-like countenance.

"He's nothin else, Sam," assured the old man, seating himself beside the "young 'un" and producing a jackknife which had assisted him in the perfection of scores of trades.

"Well, Uncle C.," drawled out Sam, "seein you're sorter anxious to trade, 'sposin we talk it over a leetle; I've got a hoss I jest got I should like mighty well to swop off."

"That's the talk, Sam," exclaimed C., rubbing his hands with delight, for he was about plunging in his element. "What sort of critter is he, Sam?"

"Nothin very alarmin, I guess, Uncle C., but sound as a dime, though."

"Considerable old, I reckon," says Uncle C.

"Not very; and what mought be yourn's age, Uncle C.?"

"Four, comin five next grass, Sam. An all-killin fine colt, Sam, ef I say it."

"I ain't seen him, Uncle C., and you ain't seen mine, as I know on; now let's do the thing up in short meter. What d'ye say to swoppin without seeing, Uncle?"

"Don't care a hoecake, Sam — soon trade blindfold as not — no use my bein with eyes wide open, 'kase you'd cheat me of my eye teeth ef so be I had all the specs in creation to help me!"

"Sho! Uncle C., you're poking fun into me when you say that — me, green as thunder, think to take advantage on you?" And he laughed at the idea.

"Well, Sam, that's for talk's sake. Shall we leave it out to judges, Sam?"

"Jest as you mind to have it, Uncle C."

"Who d'ye take, Sam?—I take Seth, cause Seth's honorable," and he called up a tricky looking soap-lock who was known as Uncle C.'s standing referee.

"Wal, Jake," and Sam winked to a roguish fellow and whispered a word or two in his ear.

The referees chose the third judge, a very simple-minded individual, and all were about leaving for the respective domiciles of the traders where the horses were said to be, when Jake remarked:

"I 'spose we've got to bring in our award, whatsomever's the horses we're going to see."

"Sartin, Jake, sartin," simultaneously replied the two jockeys.

The trio were absent about twenty minutes and stated that the result of their "chatting" was that Sam should pay Uncle C. fifteen dollars to boot. The hat was held out and both dropped in a cent in token of their satisfaction with the decision. Sam produced his sheep-skin, ponied up the rhino, saying as Uncle C. counted the cash:

"All right, I expect, Capting?"

"I guess so, Sam," replied the venerable jockey. "Now let's go and deliver the property."

An inkling of the probable result of the affair had got rumored about the room, and the spectators followed the traders to enjoy the finale.

"Let's go to my place first," said Sam, and thither they went. Uncle C. directed Seth to run to his stable and lead out his hoss.

The party arrived at Sam's house. He led them to his yard and pointed to a very useful domestic contrivance known as a *sawhorse.* "There's the hoss, Uncle C."

"Hoss be d————d!" roared Uncle C. Then turning to Seth, who was approaching with a pretty decent animal in the lead, he cried, "You tarnel fool, *you*! Didn't you know nuff to tell me on this afore I cum here?"

"I thought it 'twas 'greed you should trade no matter what kind of a *hoss* 'twas," doggedly replied the fellow.

"And my colt's worth thirty-five dollars; so you've brought in this consarned sawhoss worth twenty, eh? you natral fool!" And Uncle C. fairly shook with rage.

"I baulked on that, Capting," observed Seth in self-justification; "but that 'ar tonguey cuss, Jake, thar, talked into old Bill (the third judge) as how a sawhoss was equal to a twenty-dollar bill, and so I was overruled."

"Consarn the critters," growled Uncle C. "Well, it can't be helped, Sam; you've got into me fair this time, but won't you let me off, though?"

"Ef you'll stand treat all round, Uncle—jest to obleege you," quickly answered the mischievous wag.

Uncle C. *did* treat all round and does it again when reminded of the trade.

The Beautiful Widow of Shirttail Bend

by "Falconbridge"

§ Ossian E. Dodge (1820-1876), the central figure of the following story, was a popular singer and entertainer. At the height of his career, he organized a troop that gave musical programs concentrating on humor and politics. He himself specialized in Whig campaign songs. Later he owned a music store in Cleveland. In 1862 he settled in St. Paul, Minnesota, and prospered in land speculation. He died in London.

"Falconbridge's" (Jonathan F. Kelley) account of this "Episode in the Life of a Showman" was printed in the *Spirit*, XX, No. 16 (June 8, 1850), 183.

SEVERAL readers may have some indifferent recollections of an elbow of the Mississippi bearing a very unharmonious *patois* in the unrefined of times past. I've seen some queer *tableaux* formed by ladies and gents who, in quest of information respecting the various "bends," as they glided down by them on the Mississippi when the blunt pilot or "bully" mate named this peculiar bend. Dodge, the comic nightingale, tells a little joke of his adventures on the "big drink" some years ago. On a trip to New Orleans on the *Ben Sherrod* —afterwards lost by fire—Dodge fell in with a beautiful woman in widow's weeds and was completely *knocked* by her musical talents, beauty, etc., etc. The captain saw how things were and thought he'd run a small "cross cut" on the old joker; he told Dodge the lady was a widow, rich as cream and up for "Cowes and a market." "She's got five children," says the Captain, "but then she's got 500 acres and as many niggers."

"Well, hang me, Captain, if I ain't a mind to spread myself for the widow, five children notwithstanding."

"Go it! I'll back you. If I wasn't a married man, I'd take a hand in the game myself. But you go it, you're young, good looking (Dodge fainted twice, came to, and the Captain put on the putty), sing, play the guitar, and drum the piano; the widow dotes on music, and has a plantation worth twenty thousand dollars, including a hundred and fifty niggers and—"

"Five babies!" chimes Dodge. "Where does she reside, Captain?"

"On the Mississippi. Been up to Cincinnati to buy some winter goods; got heaps of baggage and stuff on board."

"How long will she be on board?"

"Three or four days, sir. Oh, plenty of time for you to operate, only you square yourself, don't pretend to make *love*, at first; rather let on that you are fond of company and wish to be agreeable."

For the next three or four days and evenings as the floating palace "boomed" down the Ohio and glided into the Mississippi, Dodge did the amiable, clear up to the handle! He became *chaperone* for all the "unprotected females," and "the widow" he cottoned up to particularly strong. Acting upon the advice of the Captain, Dodge fought shy of particulars; assuming or pretending to assume that it was a holy regard he had for the combined female race that made him solicitous for the comfort, pleasure, and pastime of the ladies on the boat, and by way of parenthesis, hinted that as Mrs. Brown ("the widow") appeared in the weeds of woe, she needed diversion from the melancholy thoughts that naturally rise in the memory and daydreams of one deprived of a near and dear friend.

"Yes," said Mrs. Brown, "yes, I have lost a friend, a kind good friend," and she sighed deeply while she plied her elegantly wrought and highly perfumed *mouchoir* to her beautiful eyes.

"Yes, so I understand," says Dodge. "Doubtless you feel, deeply feel, the loss of one so near, one whom you have cherished in your heart so long and sacredly?"

"Well, no," says Mrs. Brown, adjusting her gloves upon her beautiful fingers. "I can't really say I was ever very greatly attached to him (Dodge opened his eyes); I surely liked him, *respected* him as a *guardian*; as a, as a—"

"Yes, yes!" said Dodge, a little excited, as to the *simile* a woman could draw between the love and affection of a late husband and anything or anybody else—"as a—as a—."

"As a near and dear *friend*," said Mrs. Brown.

"As a near and dear *friend*," says Dodge to himself. "Well, hand me, if that ain't cool! The father of her children, a man who has evidently nobly provided for her, loved her, and—died, and she, as cool as an icicle, calls him — *friend!*"

"What was the cause of your dear *friend's* decease, may I be allowed to ask, Madam?"

"Well, poor dear man, he died of old age, premature old age, I think."

"Premature old age?" inquiringly echoes Dodge.

"Yes, he toiled, and worked, and fretted to amass a fortune for me, poor dear man," and then Mrs. Brown really cast down her pretty eyes and agitated her divine breast with a sigh. "He was only sixty when he died."

"Only sixty!" says Dodge with some surprise. "Then," says he to himself, "there must have been room for fatherly regard more than the warm love of a young and tender, ardent and beautiful wife. 'Egad I like the widow more and more! I'll lean to her like a kitten to a hot brick!'"

Just then the bell tapped, the boat headed in shore, and Mrs. Brown in some glee, began to bid her *compagnons d'voyage* adieu. Dodge flew around to do the amiable, attend to the landing of the "fair widow," and they chatted as they walked ashore. "The widow" complimented Dodge for gallantry to the ladies and attentions to her in particular.

Dodge having gotten "the widow," a bandbox, and satchel ashore asked her what other baggage she had on the boat.

"Five barrels of pippin apples and three hogs," said the blooming Mrs. Brown. "Oh! dear, there he comes! there he comes!" she fairly shouted.

"Who is that coming, Madam?"

"My dear, dear husband, Mr. Brown."

"And the *friend* you have been mourning for?" anxiously inquired Dodge.

"My dear old Uncle, Josh Grubbs!" said the widow; and the next moment she was in the arms of her affectionate Brown, while Dodge with about five jumps mizzled on to the steamer. The Captain was the first man he met.

"What's the matter?" says the Captain to the sly old joker.

"Matter? You said Mrs. Brown was a widow."

"Well."

"Had lots of baggage and freight on the boat?"

"Well."

"And owned and lived on a charming plantation?"

"Well."

"*Well!*" says the trapped joker, "Mrs. Brown is a married woman; there's her husband. Her baggage and freight consists of bandboxes, pippin apples, and hogs!"

"Well, what of that, anything more?"

"Yes, *sir!* The Browns live here on what they call *Shirttail Bend!*"

The last fact was no new feature to the Captain or anybody acquainted with old Mississippi, but it knocked Dodge *flat!*

An Arkansas "Sell"

by "Plenoir"

§ This example of the backwoodsman getting even with the inquisitive outsider was printed in the *Spirit*, XXVI, No. 2 (June 28, 1856), 230.

PERHAPS you have never been in Arkansas. If you have not, although you may have made a most intimate acquaintance with the elephant in all his grandeur, you can form no conception of the physical properties of the great rhinoceros, armed in proof and ready to enter the lists against all and singular who venture into his dominions. I have been unfortunate enough to encounter the animal, having passed a year and a half within the limits of that border state above referred to—being a member of that profession which demands of its votaries that they forsake the world, live in tents, and wander about the wilderness until they come to resemble in more ways than one the Ishmaelites of the desert.

Having made an engagement to make a survey for a railroad through the state from the Mississippi to Red River, I found myself one bright morning in October on the banks of the Mississippi some two hundred and fifty miles below Memphis with my assistants, camp equipage, etc., on the search for my team and the laborers of the party whom I had been apprised by the president of the company would be found waiting for me at that place. After a little exploration I found within half a mile of the landing a lilliputian wagon with a diminutive bull and an ox which presented the appearance of one of those animals seen through a reversed telescope. Accompanying this extensive preparation for hauling about three thousand pounds of baggage, tents, etc., was my party consisting of six cadaverous-looking natives armed to the teeth with rifles and whiskey flasks charged with the celebrated "R.G." brand of whiskey.

On my accosting this formidable troup (which in respect of linen suggested an obvious comparison with Falstaff's scarecrows), I found another "corps d'arme" of six which with the force encamped made up the entire of the grand army; they looked upon the railroad as a myth (and I have since reason to respect their views), had broken from the camp, and separated like so many Whittingtons in search of their several fortunes. I could congratulate myself on an event which seemed at first sight to delay our proceedings for some indefinite time.

My first effort in this contingency was to try to levy on the neighboring planters for a Negro force, but it being the season for cotton picking, I was unsuccessful. Finding that I must rely upon my natives, I returned to the camp where I found two or three stragglers of the same breed as the first. My teamster informed me that if I wanted to increase my force, this *gentleman,* pointing to an "outre" looking scarecrow in dirty yellow garments, would join. Upon my stating emphatically that I wanted no *gentlemen* but *men,* I had the feeling that I might be fusilladed by the whole army of rampant republicans. However, the excitement soon subsided. I obtained three or four recruits, and after haranguing the army in humble imitation of the great Napoleon, I commenced the survey by setting up for the first time in the history of Arkansas a surveying instrument on the banks of the river. Then turning westward, the party struck out for unknown parts.

Not to weary you with the endless adventures which we encountered in the swamps, through impassable roads, the annoyances to which I was subjected through the eccentricities of my democrat troops, nor to do more than mention a hurricane which picked up our tents and whirled them over the prairie where they fluttered on like so many gigantic butterflies, I will relate an anecdote which is characteristic in a remarkable degree of the peculiarities of an Arkansas backwoodsman.

With all the laziness and degradation of the race, they are by no means deficient in shrewdness and cunning, and the stranger who thinks to get the advantage of them in any way will find to his chagrin that he is very much in the position of the trusting individual who went out for fleece and came home shorn. I myself on one occasion met with an adventure which sufficiently illustrated those peculiarities.

Passing through a swamp which from its bogholes and general impassability might have passed for a very happy material type of the slough of despond, I came suddenly upon a team of five yoke of oxen whose straining muscles were encouraged by the howling and shriekings of one white man and two Negroes who were endeavoring to force a wagon upon which were *three* bales of cotton through one of the least miry spots in the road. My horse, blown with the efforts he had made in plunging through this morass, came to a dead halt by the wagon; the driver of the team, a tall, lank wretch with piercing black eyes like a snake's, ceased his efforts and opened upon me in this style: "Stranger, have you got na'er a drap of whiskey about you? That *ar* black insect (pointing to one of the Negroes) *drapped* the jug a piece back, and the wheel run over it. Hain't had a morsel for two miles and almost froze for a drink." Having a flask of genuine Old Bourbon, part of a supply which I had brought from Kentucky, I uncorked the piece and presented it. With a nod to me, he took an immense pull and handed it back with a sigh. There was a terrible vacuum in the flask after this attack, but the sequel will show that this slight courtesy was most generously acknowledged. After some few remarks upon the road and inquiring the distance to the hills, I jocularly asked him if he had in his journey seen any hats floating upon the surface of the bog where their owners had sunk down over head and ears. His reply was that, if I wanted to see that, I must go on the other road.

"Where is that?" I asked in the tender innocence of my heart.

"Why," he said with a leer and a grin of intense meaning, as if he enjoyed in anticipation the effect of the "coup" before it had parted: *"It is just six feet under the old one.* Come up, Bright, Buck!" Need I add that, as fast as the nature of the ground permitted, I made my escape; my last glance at the party showed the black "insects" enjoying my confusion and defeat by a display of ivory from mouths which seemed as capacious as the mammoth cave.

About a mile farther on, this same countryman who had sold me so easily met my camp wagon stuck in a bog. He put his whole team to the load and hauled it through the worst of the swamp. He refused to be paid for it and remarked that he had just met the chief of the party who had *bought something of him* and that when he paid for the first it would be time enough to talk about the present service.

Moral. — Trust not to the rusticity of an Arkansian; before asking questions, be very sure that you want to *buy*, for you will soon be satisfied that they all have something to *sell*.

Why Phil Weston Didn't Rise in the Profession

by "The Little 'Un," of Louisiana

§ Coddington C. Jackson, planter and horse fancier, adopted a pseudonym that was a kind of private joke among a group of writers of sporting epistles. Jackson was "The Little 'Un," Francis A. Durivage of Boston was "The Old 'Un," George P. Burnham of Roxbury was "The Young 'Un," and two unidentified writers were "The Middle Aged 'Un," of Bayou Sara, Louisiana, and "The Very Young 'Un" of Alabama. Yates, who identified this group (*Porter and the Spirit*, p. 77), says that an obituary notice of Jackson appeared in the *Spirit*, XXV (1856), 534.

"The Little 'Un's" story of Phil Weston was printed in the *Spirit*, XX, No. 3 (March 9, 1850), 31.

P HIL Weston and Archy Walton were college chums, both entered and graduated at the same time. They were always seen together, and if any severe *saw* was started the two W.'s were bound to be accused of being in some way connected with it and often justly, too, for they were full of the Dev—"Ancient Henry," I mean. They left college and together commenced the study of the law in the same office.

Many were the mad pranks they cut up during their novitiate, one of which the substance I here give, though I render the credit of its originality to *Mac,* of the N. O. Press.

The two W.'s had retired to their rooms one evening, when Archy said, "Phil, what's the state of the finance?"

Phil replied by sundry taps on the various pockets from which emanated no musical jingle while Archy held out his empty purse and grinned a ghastly smile. This expressive pantomime was well understood by each. "By the bones of Pat Murphy's *kay* bugle!" exclaimed Phil, "but it's 'tight papers' with us." Meanwhile Archy paced the floor with hands thrust elbow-deep into his pockets. A quiet smile at length stole over his face, and he exclaimed, "I have it, Phil!—and if you'll lend a hand, we can ring right *silvery* sounds and pretty *notes* by it."

"Spit it out, Archy! I'm on hand for all things agreeable to our common weal," said Phil, and he did spit it out for the "wee sma hours ayont the twal" found them arranging their plans.

The next morning our two disciples of Cooke on Littleton took their seats in a stagecoach for a small country town some twenty miles distant, at which place they arrived about dark that evening (Friday). Enquiring their way to the residence of the principal minister of the place, they called on him and stated that they were young Divines from ————, traveling West, and having run short of funds would willingly relieve the old gent on the following Sunday by holding forth in his stead for the purpose of raising a small amount to enable them to continue their journey. The next day Archy caused it to be pretty generally known about the town that a celebrated preacher would hold forth in the pulpit of the Methodist parson. Now Phil was quite a good orator, though very nearsighted, which caused him to wear thick glasses thus giving him quite a clerical appearance. 'Twas agreed that Archy should write a sermon and Phil deliver it. Phil's nearsightedness was to be obviated by Archy's prompting him, for which purpose he privately established himself under the desk of the pulpit, inside. When quite a goodly assembly had arrived, Phil arose and stated the purpose of his appearance before them, and then after a prayer more noted for its brevity than aught else, a hymn was sung and a collection was taken up, and the plate, with thoughtful delicacy, placed on the seat in the pulpit. Phil's text (as selected by Archy) was "And Jereboam waxed fat and kicked." The singularity of the text surprised while it interested the audience. Phil proceeded quite smoothly along as far as he had committed to memory the sermon, which for the convenience of Archy, he held down in front of him, between the thumb and forefinger of each hand, occasionally letting go to make some necessary gesture but always putting his thumb over the writing and in Archy's way when he again took hold of it.

"And in conclusion, my Christian friends," said Phil, "I would remark—" here he came to a sudden pull up awaiting Archy's prompting. But Archy finding that Phil got along very well had commenced examining the contents of the plate which he held between his knees while squatting under the desk. Archy had just pocketed the last of it when a whisper from Phil reminded him of his duty to him. Phil meanwhile was getting very much excited, having paused for some time. Again he repeated, "In conclusion, my Christian friends, I would remark—" and here he gave no very gentle punch with his foot to Arch, who having converted the collection into a *sinking fund* was for cutting it short. The punch from Phil riled him and said thumb being again in his way he replied, "D––n you, move your thumb." Scarcely were the words out of his mouth, when Phil much excited exclaimed, "D––n you, move your thumb, my Christian friends!" accompanied with a severe "dig" at the cushion. The next instant he was conscious of his blunder, but 'twas too late to remedy it now.

"Bolt, Archy!" said Phil, and the next moment the two worthies were striking a beautiful quarter-horse lick down the middle aisle.

Phil rushed past a portly old deacon, who now stood ready to intercept Archy's retreat. The astonished audience, indignant at this sudden termination of their hitherto interesting discourse, now arose, and Archy seeing no time was to be lost, stepped back, and throwing himself into an attitude, exclaimed to the Deacon, "Deal me out a hand, old cock! Deal me out a hand." Then he went in and spread the old gent out, and bounding over him he shot down the street before the thing was fairly understood except by the deacon whose eyes were already in mourning.

Phil and Arch returned to ––––– that night, though not on the coach, nor on the direct road. Phil's sudden "break up," as Archy called it, was the reason, "Why Phil Weston didn't rise in the profession."

Getting a Railroad Subscription

by Anonymous of Mississippi

§ The following example of a nineteenth century con game was printed under the caption "Life in Mississippi" in the *Spirit*, XIX (August 2, 1851), 281.

HAVING seen nobody for thirty miles, I was overtaken by night at the center of Jones County. The road was visible only by the three "scores" on the trees and the grass growing on it, rank and tall like that in the adjacent woods. I was striking for the courthouse. I passed a small opening in which stood three rickety cabins, but they were untenanted. The road branched off into a dozen trails. Completely puzzled, I threw down the reins and left the matter to the instinct of my horse. He struck into one of the paths, and in fifteen minutes halted at a large farmhouse.

"Halloo!" cried I.

"It's halloo yourself," said the man in the gallery.

"How far to the courthouse?"

"Where are you from?" said the man.

"From Winchester."

"Then," said he, "the courthouse is behind you, and you have come right by it there," pointing to the deserted cabins.

"Why, I saw nobody there."

"I reckon you didn't," said he. "There's a doggery and a tavern twice a year, two days at a time, but they come with the court and go with the court."

"And the clerk and the sheriff," said I, "where do they live?"

"Oh, the sheriff is the clerk, and the clerk is squire, assessor, and tax collector in the bargain, and he lives away down on the Leaf [River]."

"But the lots, my friend—who owns the lots?"

"The same individual that owns the best part of Jones County—the only landlord who never sues for rent—Uncle Sam."

"Well, sir, I am tired and hungry; can I stop with you tonight?"

"Light, stranger, light. Michael Anderson never shuts his door on man or beast."

Having carefully housed and fed my horse, I soon sat down to a substantial supper of fried chickens and stewed venison, corn cake, peach cobbler, milk, butter, and honey served with a welcome and abundance peculiar to the pine woods. My host was a shrewd man, well to do in the world, preferring Jones County to any place this side of Paradise, having lived there twenty years without administering a dose of medicine and having never been crossed but once during all that time. I was curious to know what had disturbed the serenity of such a life as his.

"Why, sir," said he, "I don't make a practice of talking about it, but being as you're a stranger and I've taken a liking to you, I will narrate the circumstance. May be you've heard how the legislature chartered the Brandon bank to build a railway through the pine woods away down to the seashore. In these parts, we go against banks — but roads sort of shuck our prejudices. Before the bank could be set agoing the law required so much of the coin to be planked up. The managers all lived about Brandon, but the metal was mighty scarce and the folks about there didn't have it, or they wouldn't trust em.

"They strung what little they had around the babies' necks, to cut their teeth with. Well, it got wind that I had some of the genuine, and the managers kept sending to me for it, offering to take me in the board. But I always answered that my money was safer in the old woman's stocking than in the bank. I heard nothing more about it for three months when one night a big, likely looking man rode up and asked me for a shuck of fire."

"'Squire Anderson,' said he, 'my men have camped a quarter of a mile down there on the creek. We are surveying the railway to Mississippi City, but have come to a dead halt because our line runs chuck up against your clearing, and we shall have to make a bend to get around to the courthouse.' The big man said this with so serious an air and seemed so mystified at having to crook his line around my field that his words went right through me. I invited him in. We talked it over and emptied a bottle of liquor on the strength of it. Next morning we went down to the camp. He took his compass and run the line right spang up against my smokehouse, which I had just finished after six months' labor.

"'Well,' says he, 'this is unlucky. The road will come right through your new smokehouse; what's to be done?'

"'You shall see,' said I; so calling my boys I ordered them to tear it down. Stranger, there lay the logs, the prettiest timber within fifty miles, all hewed by my own hand. I have never had the heart to put them up again. Well, the big man never changed countenance. He ran on with his line, and the next day he came back on his return to Brandon. I was mightily lifted with the notion of the railroad and a stopping place right before my door. I entered six hundred and forty acres of land. My neighbors said we'd get the statehouse here. The big man smiled and nodded; he pointed out where the cars would stop and where the governor would like to have a summer seat—and when he went, he carried away three thousand dollars from me, all in two-bit pieces and picayunes."

"Well, Squire," said I, "I suppose you got the value of it?"

"Stranger," solemnly replied the squire; "I never saw the big man afterwards; I heard no more of the road. Here's my smoke house logs. My old woman's got the empty stocking. Here's what they sent me (a certificate on the Brandon bank stock) for the money, and if you've got a ten dollar mint drop in your purse, I'm ready for a swap!"

Masculine Amusements

The men of the Old Southwest as portrayed in popular humor were indeed a lusty, convivial lot who amused themselves by attending horse races on which they gambled recklessly while consuming great quantities of liquor. So boisterous and fun-loving were they that they refused to take even war seriously and consequently found humor in the nation's first foreign war, the War with Mexico. Popular humor, therefore, reflects the optimism of the youthful republic, epitomized in the "go-ahead" philosophy of Davy Crockett. In frontier humor, the masculine world of racing, gambling, drinking, and soldiering is noisy and rough.

A difference of opinion leads to a horse race, according to an old saying, and horse racing was as much the national pastime in the early nineteenth century as baseball is said to be today. The horse, as the chief means of transportation for most people of that day, served the same general purpose as the automobile now does. There were all kinds of horses then as there are all kinds of cars now: the blooded animals of wealthy horse fanciers, the less expensive but useful horses of many townspeople and landowners, and the nondescript nags of the poor people. Just as most young men today take pride in the knowledge and ownership of automobiles, so most young men of the last century knew and valued horseflesh. Whether a man owned a fine race horse or a "tickey-tail" nag, he was likely to believe that his horse could outrun his neighbor's—hence horse racing.

Men also liked to read about horses and horse racing. *The Spirit of the Times,* subtitle of which was "A Chronicle of the Turf, Agriculture, Field

Sports, Literature and the Stage," was founded with the intent of imitating the famous English sporting journal, *Bell's Life in London.* Porter, Yates says, "definitely catered to the well-to-do classes among the sporting fraternity."[1] He printed the results of races in England, annual statistics on race horses, and pictures of famous horses, along with the turf news in the United States. Race courses on the Atlantic seaboard and the upper South were covered, and as he gradually built up his list of correspondents in the South and Southwest the paper carried reports of races from Virginia to Louisiana, and eventually as far west as Austin, Texas, in the 1850s. National interest in racing reached a peak in 1842 with the widely publicized match between Fashion and Boston at the Union Course in New York City. Billed as a "North-versus-South" race, the match featured Fashion, owned by Henry K. Toler of New Jersey, and Boston, owned by William R. Johnson of North Carolina and later Virginia. Run for a purse of $20,000, the race attracted 70,000 people, among them forty U. S. Senators and Congressmen. Fashion, called "the greatest race mare America has produced," won and went on in her time to win fifty-two of the sixty-four races she ran and to set a four-mile record that stood for thirteen years.[2]

Despite the great interest in the Fashion-Boston match, big-time racing gradually declined and big races and big stakes became less common. Many planters of the upper South migrated to the newer states in the Southwest, and the center of racing shifted westward. Just as this migration to a new environment affected other popular customs, so it did horse racing;

1. *Porter and the Spirit*, p. 15.
2. John Hervey, *Racing in America, 1665-1865* (New York: The Jockey Club, 1944), II, 79, 85, 156, 158. (Privately printed)

the emphasis shifted from the traditional long race to the quarter race more suited to less expensive horses.

The quarter race became a staple of popular humor. Thomas Kirkman's "A Quarter Race in Kentucky," one of the earliest humorous accounts, served well as a model for sketches that followed. Racing as the gentleman's and dandy's pastime continued in New Orleans, as shown in "Josh Silsbee at the Races."

Horse racing and gambling are apparently a natural pair. Of course, man gambled long before he raced horses—folklore shows gambling as one of man's oldest amusements—but gambling in the Old Southwest is so intimately connected with horse racing that one is tempted to say there would not have been one without the other. On the other hand, there was plenty of gambling for its own sake. Out of the fondness of men of the period for games of chance has emerged one of the most durable figures in American folklore—the Mississippi riverboat gambler, a type perpetuated by movies and television.

More often, however, popular humor portrays ordinary men at such games of chance as poker, euchre, loo, and faro: backwoodsmen such as Chunkey and Jim in the "Turkey Runner" sketches, riverboatmen in the dives of Natchez-under-the-Hill as pictured by "Yazoo," New Orleans sportsmen ("Josh Silsbee at the Races"), and theater men such as Sol Smith, who, when he was mistaken for a preacher on a Mississippi steamer, broke up a faro bank by winning all the money, all in the cause of religion.[3]

References to the drinking of liquor are so

3. "Breaking a Bank," *Spirit.*

common in the humor of the Old Southwest that one is led to believe that it was a universal practice—and it was, according to Everett Dick, who in *The Dixie Frontier* says that a man "no more thought of acting the host to a visitor, be he preacher or statesman, without a dram or eggnog than he would of hunting without a gun."[4] At working bees, land sales, Fourth of July celebrations, political gatherings, wedding frolics, and dances the whiskey jug was in evidence. Consequently, the vocabulary that dealt with liquor and the consumption of it was extensive. Whiskey was called "baldface," "blue ruin," "red eye," "Monongaheely" (after the Monongahela River in Pennsylvania where it was made), "the stranger" (because it came to the western frontier from a distance), "red head" (after casks made in Cincinnati), "har" (the hair of the dog), and "the 'crater'" ("creature," in imitation of Irish dialect and the Irishman's love of liquor). Equally imaginative terms described drinking: "to wood up" (from the practice of loading cordwood on steamboats to fire boilers), "to tighten the hide" (from stretching hides of wild and domestic animals to dry), "to horn" (perhaps from the hunting horn), "to lumber" (from clearing land), "to take a smile of 'baldface,'" "to fight the tiger," "to fight the stranger," "to julepize," and "to touch transparencies" (touching glasses in a toast). Euphemisms for the effects of drinking included: "seeing red (or blue) monkeys," "seeing blue devils," "seeing the man with the poker," and "the bust head." A man who needed a drink badly was described as "being so dry he had the rattles."

4. Dick, *The Dixie Frontier,* p. 292.

Taverns where whiskey was sold were called "groceries" and "doggeries." Whiskey was available everywhere—from the backcountry store where the storekeeper merely knocked in the head of a barrel and handed his customers the common dipper, to the elaborate bar of the St. Charles Hotel in New Orleans, presided over by its suave bartender. Drinking was so common that it attracted little attention unless a man made a spectacle of himself as happened to the New Orleans toper who had seen an exhibit of rare insects and lizards in the lobby of the St. Charles Hotel, a collection brought back from the Mexican War by an army officer. When the toper developed delirium tremens, he imagined that he was being eaten alive by those insects. A doctor who knew him was called in and proceeded to belabor the drunk with a boot-jack, saying all the while that he was killing the insects that the patient claimed were crawling over him.[5]

The temperance movement that began in the 1840s had as its goal the abolition of drinking, but it met with great resistance from most men and especially from newspaper editors. The editor of the *Richmond Compiler*, Richmond, Louisiana, for instance, wrote in 1842 that the movement was spreading like wildfire and noted with some alarm that saloons were closing on Sunday; within a month he spoke calmly of a flatboat load of whiskey at the dock on Roundaway Bayou in Richmond awaiting the next session of the district court.[6]

Drinking was not entirely responsible for the popularity of fighting in the early nineteenth century, though it doubtless contributed greatly,

5. "Irregular Practice of a Regular Practitioner," See Section V.
6. *Richmond Compiler*, I, No. 2 (April 26, 1842), 2.

as is shown in Obe Oilstone's description of "That Big Dog Fight at Myers's." Mere animal spirits apparently accounted for such friendly fights as those of Chunkey and Jim in the "Turkey Runner" sketches. A certain chip-on-the-shoulder attitude seems to have existed among "the sovereigns" (as ordinary citizens are frequently called in popular humor), an outgrowth perhaps of the rise of the common man in the Jacksonian era and his newly found importance. Popular humor is usually silent on the method of fighting employed by gentlemen, the *code duello*, although an issue of a newspaper that humorously reported an eye-gouging, nose-biting fight between two backwoodsmen might print a serious account of a European duel at the same time.

The same attitude of levity toward fighting existed toward war generally, as shown by the many humorous sketches dealing with the experiences of soldiers in the War with Mexico. The great admiration for General Jackson and the remembrance of the triumph of the backwoods riflemen at the Battle of New Orleans were still vividly alive. The Mexican War was, in fact, popular in the Old Southwest from the start, particularly in Mississippi and Louisiana; young men from those states had previously helped the Texans fight the Mexicans. The soldier lore[7] of that first national war does not glorify the soldier, however. The tradition of satirizing the militia and the citizen-soldier begun by Oliver H. Prince in his "The Militia Company Drill" (1835)[8] prevailed; thus popular humor of the Mexican War concentrates on the laughable blunders and lack of military

7. See John Q. Anderson, "Soldier Lore of the War with Mexico," *Western Humanities Review*, XI (Autumn 1957), 321-330.
8. Printed in Longstreet's *Georgia Scenes*.

knowledge of backwoodsmen turned soldier, as seen in the sketches of Pardon Jones ("Soldiering in Mexico") and Ruff Sam ("Seeing the Elephant at Buena Vista"). The common soldier's attempt to eat and drink as well as his officers is shown in Solitaire's (John S. Robb) account of stealing whiskey ("The Barrel Movement"). Popular humor makes soldiering not unlike fighting with the neighborhood boys for the fun of it or laughs at the problems in camp of obtaining food, shelter, and clothing; it takes little heed of the tragedy of war.

Thus, masculine society of the Old Southwest as portrayed in newspaper humor is convivial, raucous, and brawling—a man's world, full of danger, chance, and broken bones, as befitted the American frontier.

A Quarter Race in Kentucky

By Anonymous of Alabama

§ Porter so admired the following story by Thomas Kirkman that he used it as the title piece for his second anthology of popular humor, *A Quarter Race in Kentucky and Other Sketches,* published by Carey & Hart of Philadelphia in 1846. While the book was in preparation, Porter wrote his publishers that the author of the title story "is none other than Thomas Kirkman, Esq. of Alabama, the owner of the famous Peytona and a gentleman of immense fortune. He would not have his name divulged, however, for any amount, and I mention it to you confidentially." (Yates, *Porter and the Spirit,* p. 80). When the book issued, Kirkman's story carried this introduction by Porter: "The following inimitable story, perhaps the most humorous of its kind in the language, was originally published in the N.Y. 'Spirit of the Times' in 1836; since that period the unceasing demand for copies of it has rendered its re-publication necessary several times. It was written by a country gentleman of North Alabama, the author of 'Jones's Fight.' It is a matter of infinite regret that he cannot be induced to write more frequently; his friends would be 'after him with a sharp stick' were we to disclose his name which is familiar to tens of thousands of his countrymen, if they only knew it."

The following version is reprinted from *A Quarter Race* as reissued in Peterson's Illustrated Uniform edition of *Humorous American Works* (Philadelphia, 1858), published by T. B. Peterson, who bought plates to this and other books on popular humor after Carey & Hart went out of business.

NOTHING would start against the Old Mare, and after more formal preparation in making weight and posting judges than is customary when there is a contest "the sateful old kritter" went off crippling as if she was not fit to run for sour cider and anything could take the shine out of her that had the audacity to try it. The muster at the stand was slim, it having been understood up town that as to sport today the races would prove a *water-haul.* I missed all that class of old and young gentlemen who annoy owners, trainers, and riders, particularly if they observe that they are much engaged with questions that should not be asked and either can't or should not be answered. The business folks and men of gumption were generally on the *grit*, and much of the chaff certainly had been blown off.

A walk or gallop over is a slow affair; and without being in any way able to account for it, it seemed to be an extremely dry affair; for while the four mile was *being* done (*as the prigs have it*) I noticed many a centaur of a fellow force his skeary nag up to the opening in the little clapboard shanty and shout out impatiently, "Colonel, let us have some of your *byled* corn — pour me out a buck load — there — never mind about the water, I drank a heap of it yesterday" — and then wheel off to the crowd as if intent on something.

The race, like all things, had an end, and I had some idea in imitation of Sardanapalus, "all in one day to see the race, then go home, eat, drink, and be merry, for all the rest was not worth a fillip," when I met Dan. He knows a little, finds out a little, and guesses the rest and, of course, is a prime authority. I inquired if the hunt was up. "Oh, no, just hold on a while, and there will be as bursting a quarter race as ever was read of, and I will give it em so you can make expenses." I always make a hand when about, and thinking I might get a wrinkle by prying into the mystery of quarter racing, I accordingly rode to the thickest of the crowd. A rough-hewn fellow, who either was or pretended to be drunk, was bantering to run his mare against any horse that had ploughed as much that season, his mare having, as he assured us, tended twenty-five acres in corn. Another chap sidled up to him and offered to plough against him for as much liquor as the company could drink or for who should have both nags — his horse had never run as he did not follow racing. Sorrel got mad and offered to beat him in the cart, wagon, or plough, or he could beat him running one hundred miles, his weight on each, for five hundred dollars. Bay still disclaimed racing but would run the quarter stretch to amuse the company for one hundred dollars. Sorrel took him up, provided Bay carried his present rider, and he would get somebody; Bay agreed, provided he would not get a lighter rider. It was closed at that, and two of Senator Benton's abominations — $100 United States Bank Bills — were planked up.[9] Bay inquired if

9. Thomas Hart Benton (1782-1858), Senator from Missouri, called the Second Bank of the U. S. "The Monster."

they could stand another $50; agreed to by Sorrel, who observing Bay shell out a $100 note said there was no use of making change as his note was the same amount and they might as well go the $100. This was promptly agreed to and another one hundred dollars offered and immediately covered, there now being three hundred dollars aside. Now came a proposal to increase it three hundred dollars more; Bay said, "You oversize my pile, but if I can borrow the money I'll accommodate you" and immediately slipped off to consult his banker. Dan now whispered, *"Spread yourself on the Bay."* Thinking I should run in while I was hot, I observed aloud that I should admire to bet some gentleman ten dollars on the bay. A Mr. Wash, or as he was familiarly called "Big Wash," snapped me up like a duck does a June-bug, by taking the bill out of my hand and observing that either of us could hold the stakes put it in his pocket. Finding this so easily done, I pushed off to consult my friend Crump, the most knowing man about short races I ever knew and one who can see as far into a millstone as the man that pecks it. I met him with the man that made the race on the bay; he was coming to get a peep at the sorrel. As soon as he laid eyes on her he exclaimed, "Why, Dave, you made a pretty pick up of it. I'm afraid *our cake is all dough*; that's Old Grapevine, and I told you point blank to walk round her, but you're like a member of the Kentucky legislature who admitted that if he had a failing it was being a *leetle* too brave."

"How could I know Grapevine," replied Dave doggedly; "and you told me you could beat her anyhow."

"Yes," said Crump, "I think I can, but I didn't come a hundred and fifty miles to run them kind of races. Old Tompkins has brought her here, and I like him for a *sucker!*"

"Well," says Dave, "maybe I can get off with the race if you think you'll be licked."

"No," said Crump, "when I go a catting, I go a catting. It's mighty mixed up, and there's no telling who's constable until the election is over; it will be like the old bitch and the rabbit, nip and tack [tuck?] every jump and sometimes the bitch a *leetle* ahead."

Old Tompkins, who had not appeared during the making of the race, now came round and seeing the bay said, "Popcorn, by G--d."

He now came forward and addressed the other party. "Boys," said he, "it's no use to run the thing into the ground. If a man goes in for betting, I say let him go his load, but we have no ambition against you; so draw the bet to one hundred dollars. That is enough for a little tacky race like this, just made for amusement." His recommendation carried by acclamation.

Now the judges were selected: a *good* judge does not mean exactly the same thing here as on the bench, though some of the same kind may be found there; it means one who is obstinate in going for his own friends. It did not seem to be considered courteous to object to the selections on either side, perhaps from a mutual consciousness of invulnerability. But one of the nominees for the ermine was a hickory over anybody's persimmon in the way of ugliness. He was said to be the undisputed possessor of the celebrated jack-knife; his likeness had been moulded on dog-irons to frighten the children from going too near the fire, and his face ached perpetually; but his eyes! his eyes!! He was said to have caught a turkey buzzard by the neck, the bird being deceived and thinking he was looking another way, and several of the crowd said he was so cross-eyed he could *look at his own head!* It was objected to him that he could not keep his eyes on the score as he did not see *straight,* and it was leaving the race to the accident of which of his optics obtained the true bearing when the horses were coming out. The objections were finally overruled, the crooked party contending that nature had designed him for a quarter judge as he could station one eye to watch when the foremost horse's toe struck the score and could note the track of the horse that followed at the same moment with the other eye.[10]

10. A persistent folk tradition is that of the Ugly Man, a title playfully given to a man in the community who was expected to take the joke gracefully. An Ugly Club is mentioned in England in 1745. In the United States this masculine prank is mentioned as early as 1813 when Longstreet was presented with a large knife when he entered law school, a "reward" for being the ugliest man there. (Wade, *Augustus Baldwin Longstreet,* p. 40). Davy Crockett popularized the idea that a candidate for public office must be an Ugly Man, a term sometimes applied to Andrew Jackson. J. J. Hooper burlesqued the custom in his sketch "A Night at the Ugly Man's" by having a great number of horn-handled knives given to the main character. According

The riders now attracted my attention. It is customary, I believe, to call such "a feather," but they seemed to me about the size of a big Christmas turkey gobbler without feathers; and I was highly delighted with the precocity of the youths. They could swear with as much energy as men of six feet, and they used fourth-proof oaths with a volubility that would bother a congressional reporter.

There now arose a dispute as to whether they should run to or from the stand, it being a part of the mile track and there being some supposed advantage to one of the horses or the other, according as this might be arranged. It was determined by a toss-up at last to run to the stand. After another toss for choice of tracks and another for the word, the horses walked off towards the head of the stretch. Now it was, "Hurrah, my Popcorn — I believe in you — come it strong, lumber — to it with a looseness — root little pig, or die." And "Oh! my Grapevine! tear the hindsights off him! — you'll lay him out cold as a wagon tire — roll your bones — go it, you cripples!" Etc., etc., etc.

Beginning to doubt from all I heard whether my friend Dave had been regularly appointed almanac maker for this year, I hedged a five and staked it with a young man that was next to me riding a remarkable wall-eyed horse. Some time after I staked another five dollars with a person I had noticed assisting about the bar and would be able to recognize again. I now flattered myself on my situation; I had all the pleasurable excitement of wagering and nothing at risk.

Each side of the track was lined with eager faces, necks elongated and chins projected, a posture very conducive to health in a bilious climate as it facilitates the operation of emetics. I was deafened with loud cries of "Clear the track!" "Stand back!" "Get off the fence!" "The riders are mounted!" "They are coming!" "Now they are off!" But still they came not. Without intending it, I found myself and indeed most of the crowd moving up towards the start, and after every failure or false alarm I would move a few yards. I overheard a fellow telling with great glee, "Well, I guess I warmed the wax in the ears of that fellow with the narrow-brimmed white hat; he had

to tradition Abraham Lincoln was given such a knife by a stranger on a Washington horse-car. See John Q. Anderson, "For the Ugliest Man: An Example of Folk Humor," *Southern Folklore Quarterly*, XXVIII, No. 3 (September, 1964), 199-209.

an elegant watch that he offered to bet against a good riding horse. You know my seventeen year old horse that I always call the bay colt; I proposed to stake him against the watch, and the fellow agreed to it without ever looking in his mouth. If he had, he would have seen teeth as long as tenpenny nails. It is easy fooling any of them New York collectors; they ain't cute. The watch is a bang-up lever, and he says if he was going to travel he would not be without it for any consideration. He made me promise if I won it to let him have it back at one hundred dollars in case he went into Georgia this fall. It is staked in the hands of the Squire there — Squire, show it to this here entire stranger." The Squire produced a splendid specimen of the tin manufacture; I pronounced it valuable but thought it most prudent not to mention for what purpose.

Alarms that the horses were coming continued, and I gradually reached the starting place. I then found that Crump, who was to turn Popcorn, had won the word — that is, he was to ask, "Are you ready?" and if answered "Yes!" it was to be a race. Popcorn jumped about like a pea on a griddle and fretted greatly; he was all over in a lather of sweat. He was managed very judiciously and every attempt was made to sooth him and keep him cool, though he evidently was somewhat exhausted. All this time Grapevine was led about as cool as a cucumber, an awkward-looking *striker* of Old Tompkins' holding her by the cheek of the bridle with instructions, I presume, *not to let loose in any case*, as he managed adroitly to be turning round whenever Popcorn put the question.

Old Tompkins had been sitting doubled up sideways on his sleepy-looking old horse, it now being near dark. He rode slowly off a short distance and hitched his horse. He deliberately took off his coat, folded it carefully, and laid it on a stump; his neckcloth was with equal care deposited on it and then his weather-beaten hat; he stroked down the few remaining hairs on his caput and came and took the mare from his striker. Crump was anxious for a start as his horse was worsted by delay, and as soon as he saw Grapevine in motion to please her turner Old Tompkins swung her off ahead, shouting triumphantly "Go! d——n you!" and away she went with an *ungovernable*. Crump wheeled his horse round before reaching the poles and opened on Old Tompkins, "That's now say; if you mean to run, let us run and quit fooling; you should say 'Yes!' if you mean it to be a race, and then I would have turned loose, had my nag been tail forward. It was no use for me to let go as it would have been no race anyhow until you give the word."

Old Tompkins looked as if the boat had left him or like the fellow that was fighting and discovered that he had been biting his own thumb. He paused a moment and without trying to raise a squabble (an unusual thing) he broke down the track to his mare, slacked her girths, and led her back, soothing and trying to quiet her. She was somewhat blown by the run as the little imp on her was not strong enough to take her up soon. There were now so good and so good, and he proposed they should lead up and take a fair start. "Oh!" said Crump, "I thought that would bring you to your milk, so lead up." By this time you could see a horse twenty yards off, but you could not be positive as to his color. It was proposed to call in candles. The horses were led up and got off the first trial. "Ready?" "Yes!" A fairer start was never made. Away they went in a hurry, "Glimmering through the gloam."

All hands made for the winning post. Here I heard, "Mare's race!" —"No! she crossed over the horse's path!"—"The boy with the shirt rode foul!"—"The horse was ahead when he passed me!" After much squabbling, it was admitted by both parties that the nag that come out on the lefthand side of the track was ahead, but they were about equally divided as to whether the horse or the mare came through on the lefthand side. The judges of the start agreed to give it in as even. When they came down, it appeared that one of the outcome judges got angry and had gone home an hour ago. My friend that looked so many ways for Sunday, after a very ominous silence and waiting until frequently appealed to, gave the race to the horse by ten inches. This brought a yell from the crowd, winners and losers, that beat anything yet. A dozen of men were produced who were ready to swear that gimlet-eye was a hundred yards off, that he was drinking a cocktail at the booth, and that he was at the far side of it when the horses came out and consequently must have judged the result through two pine planks an inch thick. Others swore he did not know when the race was won and was not at the post for five minutes after. Babel was a quiet retired place compared with the little assemblage at this time. Some bets were given up, occasional symptoms of a fight appeared, a general examination was going on to be assured that the knife was in the pocket, and those hard to open were opened and slipped up the sleeve. The crowd clustered together like a bee swarm. This continued until about nine o'clock, when Crump finding he could not get the stakes compromised the matter and announced that by agreement it was a drawn race. This was received with a yell louder if possible than any former one. Everyone seemed glad of it, and there was a unanimous adjournment to the bar.

Though tired and weary, I confess that I (for no earthly reason that I can give but the force of example) was inclined to join them, when I was accosted by a person with whom I had bet and had staked in the hands of the young man riding the wall-eyed horse. "Well," said he, "shell out my five dollars that I put up with that friend of yours—I can't find *him*." I protested that I did not know the young man at all and stated that he had my stake also. He replied that I need not try to feed him on *soft corn* that way and called on several persons to prove that I selected the stakeholder and we were seen together and we must be acquainted as we were both *furreigners* from the cut of our coats. He began to talk hostile and was, as they brag in the timber districts, twenty foot in the clear, without limb, knot, windshake, or woodpecker hole. To appease him, I agreed if the stakeholder could not be found to be responsible for his stake. He very industriously made proclamation for the young man with the wall-eyed horse. Being informed that he had *done gone* three hours ago, he claimed of me and I had to shell out.

Feeling somewhat worsted by this transaction, I concluded I would look up my other bets. Mr. Wash I did not see and concluded he had retired. I found the stakeholder that assisted about the bar and claimed my five dollars on the draw race. To my surprise I learned that he had given up the stakes. Having been previously irritated, I made some severe remarks to all of which he replied in perfect good temper and assured me he was the most punctilious person in the world about such matters. It was his invariable rule, he said, never to give up stakes except by the direction of some of the judges; he called up proof of his having declined delivering the stakes until he and the claimant went to old screw-eye, and he decided I had lost. This seemed to put the matter out of dispute so far as he was concerned, but thinking I would make an appeal to my opponent I inquired if he knew him. He satisfied me by assuring me that he did not *know him from a side of sole leather.*

I left the course, and on returning next morning I looked out for Mr. Wash. I discovered him drinking and offering large bets. He saw me plainly but affected a perfect forgetfulness and did not recognize me. After waiting some time and finding he would not address me, I approached him and requested an opportunity of speaking to him apart. Mr. Wash instantly accompanied me and began telling me that he had got in a scrape and had never in his life been in such a fix. Perceiving what he was at, I concluded to take the whip-hand of him and observed, "Mr. Wash, if you design to intimate by your preliminary remarks that you cannot return to me my own money, staked in your hands, I must say I consider such conduct extremely ungentlemanly." Upon this he whipped out a spring-back dirk-knife nine inches in the blade and whetted to cut a hair, stepped off, picked up a piece of cedar, and commenced whittling. "Now, stranger," says he, "I would not advise any man to try to run over me, for I ask no man any odds further than civility. I consider myself as honest a man as any in Harris County, Kentucky, but I tell you, stranger, exactly how it happened. You see, when you offered to bet on the sorrel, I was out of soap, but it was too good a chance to let slip as I was dead sure Popcorn would win, and if he had won, you know, of course it made no difference to you whether I had a stake or not. Well, it was none of my business to hunt you up, so I went to town last night to the confectionary [a whiskey shop in a log pen fourteen feet square], and I thought I'd make rise on chuck-a-luck, but you *prehaps* never saw such a run of luck. Everywhere I touched was *pizen,* and I came out of the *leetle end* of the horn. But I'll tell you what, I'm a man that always stands up to my fodder, rack or no rack; so, as you don't want the money, I'll negotiate to suit you exactly. I'll give you my *dubisary:* I don't know that I can pay it this year unless the *crap* of hemp turns out well, but if I can't this year I will next year probably. And I'll tell you exactly my principle — if a man waits with me like a gentleman, I'm sure to pay him when I'm ready, but if a man tries to bear down on me and make me pay whether or no you see it is his own look out, and he'll see sights before he gets his money."

My respect for Mr. Wash's dirk-knife together with my perceiving there was nothing else to be had induced me to express my entire satisfaction with Mr. Wash's *dubisary,* hoping at the same time that at least *enough* of hemp would grow that year. He proposed that I should let him have five dollars more for a stake, but on my declining he said, "Well, there is no harm in mentioning it." He went to the bar, borrowed pen and ink, and presently returned with a splendid specimen of caligraphy to the following effect:

State of Kentucky

Jessamine County.
   Due Dempsey, the just and lawful sum of ten dollars, for value received, payable on the 26th day of December, 1836 or 1837, or any time after that I am able to discharge the same. As witness my hand and seal, this 30th day of May, 1836.
                GEORGE WASHINGTON BRIGGS. (Seal)

I wish you would try Wall Street with this paper, as I wish to cash it, but I'll run the mile before I wait for a quarter race again.

Josh Silsbee at the Races

by "Thomas the Rhymer"

§ Thomas Dunn English (1819-1902), physician and lawyer, wrote novels, plays, and poems but is mainly remembered as the author of the song "Ben Bolt." He contributed many sketches to the *Spirit* under the pen name "Thomas the Rhymer."

Josh Silsbee, subject of the following story, was a popular actor who was known for his characterizations of the stage Yankee. During the 1846-1847 theatrical season in New Orleans, he appeared as "Solon Shingle," the simplehearted old New Englander; Kendall, *The Golden Age of the New Orleans Theater,* p. 240. The story was printed in the *Spirit,* XXI (July 19, 1851), 253.

RATHER dull work there was at the Metairie races in 1847 in our opinion, whatever some men may say to the contrary, but one little incident deserves to be rescued from oblivion. I intend to tell the story as it was told to me by an eyewitness; and I appeal to Col. Oliver, Jim Valentine, Dan Hickok, and Yankee Silsbee for its truth. If I have been "sawed," I'll own up, and you call on me for the penalty the first time I set foot in "the lower office."

Everybody who has ever been to New Orleans — at least everybody who is anybody — knows the parties I have named. The Colonel is as good a fellow as ever craned his neck from the stand to watch the "coming" or took a telescopic view through the bottom of a tumbler and about as fair a specimen of a Southerner as one would desire to meet. As for Jim Valentine, he can sing a good song, and is — or was, at the time I write of — a jolly, good looking boy, full of fun, spirit, and whimsicality. Dan Hickok, who now keeps a crack horse on the Shell Road at the Lake End, was then engaged in steam-boating and could laugh longer, yell louder, and gain plumpness quicker — but I'll spare Dan's blushes. A dull day at a spring meeting to three such was an abomination; and when I tell you that Josh Silsbee, who was playing an engagement at the American Theater,[11] was also in the

11. The American Theater, the second of that name, was an arena as well as a theater in which both plays and equestrian troupes appeared. S. P. Stickney was at the time the manager of the American; Lucian Place was also a theatrical manager; Kendall, *The Golden Age of the New Orleans Theater,* p. 240.

crowd, aided and abetted by Jim Jones, the treasurer of the theater, with his managers, Place and Stickney, you may imagine the general horror as the sport was not likely to be diminished. A proposition was made as a desperate resort to get up a *scrub* race, but even that failed. A feeling of *ennui* began to steal over the party, and in the midst of an anxious debate it was discovered that Silsbee had eloped and that no traces could be found of the runaway.

Jim Valentine determined to have some fun, cost what it might, and bantered a French planter from up near the Old Red Church to run his blood mare — a fine animal she was — against something or somebody. But Monsieur Hypolite D'Anzac declared that he had come to see races not to make them and therefore declined. As they were debating the matter, a queer-looking yellow wagon, drawn by a rough-coated, but clean-limbed horse, drove up. The occupant was at once recognized by his dress, not less than his general appearance, to be a live Yankee, one of the greenest of his kind; Valentine tackled him without delay, criticized his wagon, made fun of his horse, and in the space of five minutes, managed to "rifle" his customer to his heart's content.

"Leuk a here, yeou!" said the Yankee, "that 'ere hoss of mine is clear grit — a hull race-cose, and no backin eout. I never race hosses, myself; it's awful risky business; but I'd bet the ole wagon, hoss an all, that he could lick that sleek lookin mare there in a mile spirt around this medder in less time than you could say beeswax when your mouth was puckered. That critter yonder's mighty nice to look at, but she can't run, no how." So saying, he pointed at the French-man's mare with every mark of contempt.

"Aha!" cried the Frenchman, not a little nettled, "you zink ze mare cannot run, eh? *Ma foi!* your dam ole horse nevair overtake her, nevair!"

"That's if he don't try, mister," cooly replied the Yankee.

"No, sare," said the Frenchman, "eet ees not trying. I will not run my mare 'gainst your dam ole pedlar horse — for I should win him an' all your money, by dam!"

"Oh, waell," replied the Yankee, calmly, "I didn't mean no offence. If you're afeard to make a match, there ain't no harm done, I spose."

"Sare," exclaimed the excited Frenchman, "I am not afeard, but I do not shoose to make ze race, zat is all."

"I'd advise you not to run your mare, myself," said Oliver, "for that Yankee horse has got bottom."

"Bottome!" exclaimed D'Anzac, contemptuously. "Ah, oui! ze bottome of his bellee — nossing more."

"Monsieur D'Anzac's horse would walk clear away from him," said Valentine.

"I'll go you a hundred on that, Jim!" said the Colonel.

"Done!" was the reply, "and if Monsieur D'Anzac goes half with me, I'll treble it."

"Yes, sare; I will go you two, tree hundred," exclaimed the Frenchman, now fully roused.

"Hello!" said the Yankee, "sposen yeou let me mix in this hasty puddin myself, I've got a leetle pewter for you tu size on this question. I'll take a hundred on Ole Jehosaphat, by Jehu."

The match was made, the horses were led out to get ready, and the spectators began to make their bets. As the Yankee declared he never would ride a horse — it was against his principles — a Negro boy of Oliver's was appointed to the responsible station of jockey. The Frenchman insisted on backing his own mare. Just as they were about to start, Oliver said to Valentine, "See here, Jim, I don't want to take your money. The Frenchman's horse will be beat."

"If you want to draw, I don't object," replied Valentine, "provided you own up; but otherwise I'm on hand."

"As you please," replied Oliver.

Old Jesse Smith had been looking on in the meanwhile and broke the silence with, "I'll go any gentleman fifty or one hundred on the mare!"

"Done!" said the Yankee.

"Me too, if you please," said Oliver.

Dan Hickok, after looking at the Yankee's horse, burst into a tremendous explosion of laughter. "Christopher Columbus never discovered *that* beast," cried Dan. "How could he? He wasn't born! I'll double that hundred, Jesse, if you have the pewter to spare."

Jesse had hardly time to say "yes," when at the word "go!" off went both horses with a whirr like arrows. The mare took the lead and maintained it during the first quarter. On the second the horse lapped her and kept there during the third. Up to within a hundred yards of the winning post you could have covered both animals with a sheet. Suddenly the Yankee's horse shot forward and came in a good four lengths ahead. The Frenchman was nowhere and sat on his splendid animal the picture of despair while three hearty hurrahs for the winner broke from the throats of the crowd.

"What will you take for that horse?" eagerly asked Valentine, as he forked over the dough.

"Can't sell him! He ain't mine! only borried him," replied the Yankee.

At that moment a groom came forward to sponge the horse's mouth and neck. A single wipe of the sponge brought the brown paint away in a stream from the Col.'s filly and the scales fell from Jim Valentine's eyes.

"Oliver's colt," cried he, "and who the devil are you, sir?"

"I *was* the green Yankee," said the party addressed, at the same time pulling off his yellow wig, "but I *am* Josh Silsbee. Colonel," continued he, before their surprise abated, "I bet you a cool hundred, you know, that our friends would never discover me, and if you'll just fork it over, we'll have the tallest kind of a blowout at the St. Charles tomorrow. Monsieur D'Anzac, I take my benefit at the American tonight, and if you'll have a private box, it's heartily at your service."

That Big Dog Fight at Myers's

by "Obe Oilstone," Fayette, Mississippi

§ The most widely known of all Phillip B. January's tales about "Uncle Johnny," the story following appeared in the *Spirit*, XIV, No. 33 (October 12, 1844), 391, and was reprinted the next year in Porter's first anthology, *The Big Bear of Arkansas and Other Sketches*.

"WELL, them was great times, and *men* lived about here them days, too!—not saying they're all dead, but the settlement is got too thick for em to splurge, and they are old—beside, they're waitin for thar *boys* to do somethin when they gets *men!* I tell you what, if they lived till kingdom come *they* wouldn't be men. I'd like to see one single one of em that ever rid his horse up two pair of stars, jumpt him thru—"

"Stop, stop, Uncle Johnny! Do tell us about *that big dog fight at Myers's.*"

"Ha, ha, boy! You thar? Had your bitters yet? Well, well—we'll take em together; licker is better now than it use to was, but people don't drink so much, and that's strange! ain't it? Well, I was talkin to these men about old Greensville and about them same men, for they was all at that same dog fite; Fe-atte, the Devil! never be a patchin to what old Greensville was about the time *Old Colonel* was sheriff! I'll just bet all the licker I ever *expect* to drink that thar ain't no second story in Featte that's got hoss tracks on the floor and up agin the ceil—"

"I must stop you again, Uncle Johnny; Fayette is yet in its youth, and promises—"

"Youth, H---! yes, like the youth of some of my old friends' sons —upwards of thirty, an they're expectin to make *men* out'n em yet! I tell you what, young men in my time'd just git in a spree, sorter open thar shirt collars, and shuck tharselves with a growl, and come out reddy-made men; and most on em has *staid* reddy for fifty-one years! I ain't failed now, yet, and—"

"Uncle Johnny, for God's sake stick to the dog story; we'll hear all this after."

"Ah, you boy, you never will let me tell a story my way, but here goes; let me see—yes, yes. Well, it was a grate day in Greensville, anyhow Charly Cox had run old Saltrum agin a hoss from the Red-licks and beat him shameful—run rite plum up the street in Greensville so as evrybody mite see. Well, a power of licker was wasted—nily evry house in town rid thru—women and children skeared out—and evry drink we took was a *gineral* invite, and about night thar was *one* gineral in *town*—Gineral Intoxication. Well, 'bout sundown the old Gineral—God bless him!— called up his troops; some of the same ones who was at Orleans; let's see—thar was the High Sheriff, Dick, Bat, Jim, old Iron Tooth, an—"

"Iron Tooth! who's he?" suggested I.

"Why, *he's* the man what fite the dog! Ain't you never seen a man here in Featte when he gits *high* up just pulls out his knife and goes to chewin it as if he'd made a bet he could bite it in two?"

"Yes, yes, go on."

"Well, the ginral made em all mount, formed line, and rid rite into the grocery—formed line agin, had a big stir-up drink handed to em all, and when the Ginral raised *his* hat and said 'the Hero of Orleans,' the yell that went up put a head on that man's licker that staid nily a month, I hearn. We come a-farin out'n the grocery, charged up and down two or three times, cleared the streets of all *weak* things, then started out home, all in a brest; evry one of us had a Polk stalk—"

"Hel-lo—Polk stalks that early?"

"Well, well, Hickry sticks—same thing—out of town we went, chargin evrything we see—fences, cattle, or teams—and at last we got to old Myers's farly squeelin to rar over somethin! Old Myers's dog was awful bad—the worst in anybody's nolledge—why people sent fifty miles to git pups from him! Well, he come a-chargin, too, and met us at the gate lookin like a young hyena. Iron Tooth just turned himself round to us and says he, 'Men, I'll take this fite off'n your hands'; so down he got, ondressed to his shirt, *stock,* and boots—got down on his all fours in the road, walkin backards and forards, pitchin up the dust and hollerin like a bull! When the dog see him at that sort of work, he did sorter stop barkin, but soon as he see *our* animal strut up to the gate and begin to smell, then, like another dog, he got fairly crazy to git thru at him—rarin, cavortin, and *tarin* off pickets! Our animal was takin all this quite easy—smellin thru at him, whinin *me-you, me-you, me-you*—struttin backards and forards, histin up one leg agin the gate (and you know what dogs do, then!). Well, after a while the dog begin to git sorter tired, and then our animal begin to git mad! Snap for snap he gin the dog, and the spit and slobber flew, and soon the dog was worse than he *had* been. Thar we was settin on our horses, rollin with laughin and licker, and thought the thing was rich, as it was; but just then, our animal riz on his hinders, onlatched the gate, and the dog *lunged* for him. Ain't you never noticed when one dog bounces at another, he sorter whirls around sideways to keep him from hittin him a fair lick? Well, just so our animal; he whirled round sideways to let the dog have a glancin lick, and true to the caracter he was goin to allow the dog a dog's chance, and he stuck to his all fours. The dog didn't make but one lunge, and he stopt—as still as the picter of the wolf in the spellin book—for you see our animal was right starn end facin him, his shirt smartly up over his back, and standin mity high up on his hind legs at that! We all raised the old Indian yell, for you never did see sich a *site*, and thar stood the dog with the awfullest countenance you ever seen a *dog* ware! Our man, sorter thinkin he'd bluffed the dog, now give two or three short goat-pitches backards at him! Ha! ha! ha!"

"What did he do? What did he do?"

"Do? why, *run!* wouldn't a d----d hyena run! The dog had a big block and chain to him, and soon our animal was after him, givin some of the awfullest leaps and yelps—'twarnt but a little squar picket yard round the house, and the dog couldn't git out, so round and round he went—at last, turnin a corner the chain rapt round a stump, and thar the dog was *fast and he had to fite!* But he did give powerful licks to get loose! When he see his inemy right on him agin, and when Iron Tooth seen the dog *was* fast, round and round he'd strut, and sich struttin! Ain't you never seen one of these big, long-legged, short-tailed baboons struttin round on the top of the lion's cage? Well, so he'd go—sorter smellin at the dog (and his tongue out right smart, for he was tired)—*me-you! me-you!* Snap! snap! the dog would go, and he begin to show fite d--n plain agin, for our varmint was a-facin him, and he seen *'twas a man* after all! But our animal knowed how to come the giraffe over him—so round he turnd and gives him the starn view agin! *That* farly broke the dog's hart, and he just rared back a-pullin and got loose! One or two goat-pitches backards and the dog was flat on his back, playin his fore-paws mity fast, and perhaps some of the awfullest barks you ever hearn a dog gin! Old Iron Tooth he seen he had the dog at about the rite pint; and he give one mortal lunge backards, held with both hands on the dog's throat, turned quick as lightnin, div down his head and fastened his teeth on the dog's ears! Such a shakin and howlin! The dog was too skeared to fite, and our animal had it all his own way. We hollered to 'give him *some* in the short ribs,' but he only held on and growled at us, playin the dog clean out, I tell you. Well, thar they was, rollin and tumblin in the dirt—first one on top and tother—our animal holdin on like pitch to a waggin wheel, the dog never thinkin 'bout fitein once but making rale onest licks to git loose. At last our varmint's hold broke—the dog ris—made one *tiger* lunge—the chain snapt, and Lord J----! He tucked *his* tail, and— and—but you all know what skeared dogs *will* do!

"Nobody ain't never got no pups from Myers since—the blood run rite out!"

Up Fool River

by "Obe Oilstone," Cole's Creek,
Jefferson Co., Mississippi

§ Another of January's stories, the following tale appeared in the *Spirit*,
XVIII, No. 4 (March 18, 1848), 43, as "Another Story, 'Uncle Johnny.'"

I WAS busily engaged the other night over at Buntin's in
Natchez, when the hours, like the late commercial affairs in England,
had seen their lowest and were slowly improving, watching a game
of billiards between A. L. B., Jr., and another of the b'hoys, when
simultaneously with a tap on the shoulder, I was greeted with,
"Howdy, Obe." It was Uncle Johnny, who said, "Less take sumthin,
boy, you look sleepy?" I was glad to see him and of course touched
transparencies with him.

"Ah!" said he, putting down his glass, "this is whar towns beats
the woods—better licker, and eny sort of d--- thing to put in it, at
that, but as regards licker, I'm like *Chunkey*—thar is good and better
licker. I don't 'stand the comparison, good or bad. I ain't never seen
no *bad* yit; but drinkin licker with the fixins jest makes a man
thirsty; 'taint like takin it out of a junk bottle away in the woods;
thar he'll take three or four good mouthfuls afore he takes her down,
and that'll git all over him in a minit."

"Well," said I, "that'll do about liquor, now. Where have you
been all this while?"

"Been? Why all over the 'swamp,' mostly, tho', at Gabe's thar at
the mouth of Fool River on Tensas.[12] Bless your soul, boy, I don't
bleeve I've seen you sence that new Captain tuck his boat up Fool
River. No? In course, then, not sence we run that other new boat
out in the trade?"

"I'm behind the times, certainly; but you know, Uncle Johnny,
I live in *White* settlement."

"Yes—mity fur back in it, though. Well, you see, ginerally the
Tensas ain't more'n about two hundred yards wide, at common

12. The Tensas (pronounced Tin'-saw) River heads in northeast Louisiana, runs
parallel to the Mississippi, and eventually empties into it.

water, but jest whar Gabe lives it widens out to about half a mile or so, spang up to the mouth of the Maçon. They call this wide place Tensas Lake; well just whar it begins to widen, Fool River comes into it right squar from the West."

"What river is *that?*" inquired I.

"Ruther a strange name, ain't it? Lissen about the Cap'm and you'll see 'taint nuthin else. It's got one of the prettiest mouths *for* a river you ever seen; smooth, slopin banks, kivered with sand, mussle shells, and beautiful trees down to the very water's edge; water's as clear as a sunshiney day, and it's so deep that the water at the bottom's as cold as Buntin's ice — we git it a purpose to mix it, sometimes. Well, this Cap'm came along late one evenin; 'twas his first trip in them branches (me and Gabe was off huntin) and when he got thar and see sich awful spreadin out of the waters, I recon he, too, thot he'd tuck the wrong shute sumwhar and got out in the ocean. After knockin about awhile, he see the other river off to his left, so up that he puts. Gabe's niggers was workin up Fool River, and when they heard a steamboat up thar, *they* knowed sumthin was wrong, so they drops hoes and plows and puts off to head it. They all got thar on the bank in a lump and began to holler, 'Hello, master! — hello de boat! You's wrong! — dat ain't de road.' 'Yah, yah! des lissen at de fool Henson callin de river de road! — git away nigger! Hello! you's wrong; dat ain't de *river* you's in! dat's Fool River! *It* don't run no whars, it stops — ' 'Golly, now, des hear Uncle Daniel! It do run out in Sandy Bio!' Such like was gwine on mong the niggers, and the Cap'm seein the commotion, stopt steam and told em he was only gwine up a piece to put out frate. 'Da ain't nuffin up dar to git it, den, but bars and allergates!' Well, he kept on; they all come home and sot on the bank watin for the boat to come back.

"Well, me and Gabe got back bout dark; the niggers told us of the boat and had their laff over agin. I'd killed a fat, barren doe, and knowin the boat would be back by supper, we had a nice lot ready for the fellers. 'Bout nine o'clock here she comes. *We* was busy at buckshot poker. Gabe had jest went three; I seen it and was gwine five better, when the Cap'm opened. 'Good landin here?' 'Yes, massa, fus rate! Whar you put dat frate? — we gwine take de siff [skiff] and git it, fore de wolf!'

"We jest turned our hands over on the table and left the bottle, nily half full, standin between em, and got out jest in time to keep the feller from wollapin sum of the darkies. He was very polite and asked if he could *lay* at the landin all night? Gabe told him, 'No, him and the balance of the fellers had better come up and *sleep* in the house; plenty er room, plenty licker, and a big supper a-gettin, and so they must all come up.' 'No,' says he, 'they'll stay aboard; I'd like to git sum infermation bout these rivers, fore I move.'

"After he got in the house, he looks all round, and seein the cards and the bottle, he turns round to Gabe, and says he, 'Stranger, whar do you *live?*' 'Right here,' says Gabe. 'Oh, I know,' says he, 'but whar *is* it?' 'Catahoula—mouth of Fool River.' 'Yes, I'm d---d ef it ain't Fool River, and I'm one of em, too!' says the Cap'm. 'One uther piece of infermation, ef you please. How fur is it to the head of that river?' 'Jest three miles,' says Gabe, 'and navigable plum up to its head!' 'I'm lost—turned round; when I was comin out of it, it seemed to me we was gwine to the upper end, and I stopped two or three times to find out; at last I hearn them infernal niggers; but *they* seemed to be at the wrong end.' 'Well,' says Gabe, 'we'll straten you by mornin; less take sumthin for supper.' That Cap'm was a fair drinkin man, and between that poker and that licker we sot up twill about this time.

"Obe, talkin so much makes me mity dry!"

"Certainly, let's take a sweetner and go to bed."

"Oh no, we'll git that over at McDonnel's; less set a while—I see Lewis is beatin that feller."

"Well, what became of the Captain?"

"After tightenin his hide with licker and supper, he bid us good evenin and put for his boat; but he was lost yit, and diden't know the way, so we tuck him down; he roused up the whole crew, and had somethin for us to take. Just then Gabe says, 'Cap'm, will you be so good as to tell me where it is that a steamboat Cap'm ain't a man?' 'Raly, sir,' says he, 'I'm so bad lost I don't know nothin; ef you'll be so good as to give the information.' 'Oh, certny,' says Gabe, 'it's when he's *a board!*' In course we had to drink again. We left the Cap'm 'bout sun rise, and then he tuck the back track down Tensas and ain't never bin hearn of sence."

Liquoring on the Mississippi

by Anonymous

§ Porter, like the sporting crowd to which his publication appealed, liked his drinks. He printed the following description in the *Spirit*, XVII, No. 4 (March 7, 1847), 44, with a note implying that the writer was a "Son of Temperance": "We do not know the writer of the following, but we admire the coolness with which, after exhibiting so intimate a knowledge of the subject upon which he writes, he affects to be innocent of any practical experience touching it."

OUR readers have heard of wooding on the Mississippi and gambling on the Mississippi. A late trip on that famous highway introduced us to what is not less than any of these a peculiarity, liquoring on the Mississippi.

Did you ever, reader, salt cattle on a lick-log, or give vermifuge to a score of little niggers on a plantation? Unless you have done both, you cannot conceive of a morning liquoring scene on a Mississippi steamboat. It takes the first to give an idea of the relish and the second of coming up to it one by one. We rose early and by accident drew a chair on the guards where a full and inside view of the bar presented itself.

The barkeeper knows the habits of his customers singularly well. At certain times he strolls about, at others constantly in attendance. Like a surgeon who before going into operation has all his bandages, liniments, and knives arranged in reach, so the barkeeper did. We saw him do it. Here the sugar and the ice, and there the pick to break off more small pieces from the lump when needed. The slop tub, just under the counter for passing tumblers through, is replenished; the corks are drawn and fitted in easy; the faucets are in order. If, peradventure, a weak stomach craves it, a lemon is cut and laid by the squeeze. All ready, he wipes off the board again and again.

Here comes a man in shirt sleeves, dry as a fish; he takes a pull at the big bottle — goes back to bed. Next one fills up the glass to taper point, works his lips together as his hand touches it, turns it round on the bottom, and stops it in an appreciable part of a second. Just before the final tilt into a dry and thirsty abyss that doubtless had swallowed a cotton plantation in detail, he held it sunward to contemplate the prismatic beauties; down went the liquid, slow and easy; he took his chair nearby and looked thoughtfully out on the shore. (We wondered how his inwards felt.)

A man below the ordinary stature but thickset, wearing calico pants and a loose linen coat, leads the way with two others, one looking seedy, the other careless. After consultation they agree as to the dram; they don't seem hard to suit, and it works like a charm. They draw two chairs close and the third sits on the railing in front of them; they talk and laugh boisterously till breakfast.

Next comes an elderly gentleman who looks rather shy; he is quick in his movement; he has the change ready—drinks, wipes his mouth, and is gone.

A young man, neatly dressed with a hat on, saunters up and says, "Cocktail" (or something with a tail to it). Did you ever see a cocktail mixed up? It requires two glasses and mixing requires genius. From one to the other glass, right, left, right up, left down, the sparkling fluid falls in a lengthening curve. It actually seems to rope—the liquor does. At last it rests in one glass. The gentleman who ordered that extra article toyed with it until he feared the foam that had been got up with such effort would subside before he got it down.

They come thick and fast, and the barkeeper is fortunate in foresight to have everything where he can lay hand on it. Young men come, very young men, and men old enough to know better. We saw no father take up his son; they do these things apart. In some cases, we painfully suspected that a member of the Christian Church, feeling away from witnesses and restraint was indulging an old appetite.

Ever and awhile a deckhand—these were mostly Irishmen—would come to a side door near and pulling out a bag with money get a dram without ice, sugar, or water—the undiluted stuff.

The variety of all this dreadful unity is not the least interesting fact. One comes for the liquor and nothing else—gets it and goes. Another likes the place—lounges about it—and is in no hurry and orders the dram with an air of indifference. The concoction is not strong enough for this man, and he says something to the barkeeper who sprinkles something in it. The man throws down the drink at a gulp and throws a glass of water after it as though he had swallowed fire. One takes it for his stomach's sake and doesn't want to get the taste of it on its way there. Another seems to wish his throat was as long as a fence rail so that he might taste it all the way down. The ardent and pure stuff is good enough for some; others coax and combine the elements in every variety:

> *A little ginger to make it hot,*
> *A little ice to make it cool;*
> *A little water to make it weak,*
> *A little brandy to make it strong;*
> *A little sugar to make it sweet,*
> *A little lemon to make it sour;*
> *A little effort to make it go down.*

Verily, temperance has this stronghold of her enemy yet to take—a Mississippi steamboat.

Soldiering in Mexico

by "Pardon Jones" of Louisiana

§ The Mexican War was generally popular in the South and Southwest, though it was strongly opposed by many in the North, especially in New England. Southern journalists and writers of newspaper humor favored the war and pictured the lighter side of soldiering, in contrast to the ridicule inherent in the letters of Birdofredom Sawin of James Russell Lowell's *The Biglow Papers*.

C. M. Haile, serving as a war correspondent for the *Picayune*, took his "Pardon Jones" to the front with amusing results. The following report appeared in the *Picayune* under the dateline "Up the Rio Grande, not far from Camargo" and was reprinted in the *Spirit*, XVI, No. 31 (September 26, 1846), 362.

IF you was to see my regiment now, camp in ra'al military stile, you'd be proud of our 'quaintance, I know. Bein all officers, my regiment all sleeps under one big tent, and we've sowed our muskeeter bars all intu one and sleep in one bed. The mules is tied clos't to the tent and tu sentinals sets up every night tu keep the Mexicans from stealing the *cabballos*. Leftenant Zeke Tucker went tu sleep on post t'other night, and some rascal stole his own *caballo*. The next day Zeke went out tu try and find him. Bout ten o'clock, I and Capting Potter was ridin out tu give our mules some fresh grass, and we see Zeke, creepin up, sly, to'ads a little mustang stallion. Zeke could jest see the critter's head round a bunch of bushes. He crawled up, bridle in hand, got holt of the hosses head, and put on the bridle, lookin back all the time tu see if nobody want lookin at him, and then jumped sudden ontu him, and stuck both of his rockerchaws intu his sides, plum up tu the hubs. The hoss jumped like lightnin, 'bout four jumps, and fell heels over head, stretched out as flat as a pancake. Zeke couldn't a-fell less than fourteen foot, and rolled over half a duzzan times, and jumped ontu his feet, skeert half tu deth, but not the least hurt in the world. I'n the Capting rid up and azed him what the matter was, but when we looked at the hoss we see right off. He was tied fast tu a long hair lasso! Zeke didn't see the lasso, but he felt it, plain 'nuff. The fact is, Zeke was so mad cause he couldn't

279

find his mule that he determined to steal a hoss. I am glad he got
sarved so.

Ginral Taylor had a big trainin t'other day. It beat all the gineral
trainins ever I see in the Bay State. I come putty near not seein much
on it, for when fellers begin to shute off their cannons to salute the
Ginral—they call them cannons *light* artillery, but I hope to never
breathe again if it don't take four or five horses to draw them—my
mule started off full strip threw the chapperels, and I had to fall off
to go back in time to see the trainin out. I never see men march
and shoulder arms as they did; they all know'd 'zactly what to du
without being told the perticklers. I don't wonder that sech men is
honored with garlands, for every mother's child on em desarves
miles of lorrels sowed together by a Taylor that knows his trade. But
that artillery took my eye. I'll be darned if they won't gallop the
hosses with them cannons and turn round as quick as a man can on
hossback. Some of them guns was in Fort Brown, and no wonder if
the cuntry duz Bragg a little over em, for tho' they didn't speak quite
so Lowd as the bigge guns, I guess history will lend a Page at least
in honor to em, for everything they was expected tu du was dun
up Brown. And out on the praries and in them infernal thornbushes
tu, didn't Ridgley take one of his pieces every now and then and
Shover right into the Mexicans faces, whilst t'other gun was talkin
French tu em, right alongside? May will long be remembered, for
'twas on the 9th that the Americans Twigg'd Arista's proud camp,
and didn't they walk purty straight into it and Sackett? of course
they did!—but where *onder* the sun am I goin tu? I was talkin 'bout
the Gineral, trainin. Wall, we all went hum, and I didn't see nobody
drunk nor fitin out on the fields. It would put a temperance society
into a style of Bliss to a-seen how reg'lar and sober everybody was.[13]

Next day Leftenant Zeke Tucker got himself into another scrape.
He was standin sentinel when Ginral Taylor come ridin 'long with
his orderly riding ten or twelve rods behind. Zeke hadn't never seen
the Ginral. I told him that he was comin and that he must salute him.
Well, Zeke see a 'spectable lookin old gentleman ride 'long and didn't
take no notice on him, but when the gay lookin draggoon rid by, he

13. Foregoing sentences make puns on officers' names: Taylor, Brown, Bragg, etc.

slapped his gun on the britch and presented arms at him.[14] The soger
spurred up and rid on, but I was mad as furry and had Zeke 'rested,
right off. We shall drumhead him tomorrow or next day, if it don't rain.

We've made considerable improvement in my regiment, sense I
writ afore. Most all of the reg'lar rigiments has got bands of music,
and Capting Potter kept botherin on me so much 'bout it that at last
I 'greed to have a band, tu. To save money and not to have to hire a
band, we all volunteered to larn to play and make a band ourselves.
Capting Potter advised this. The next question was the choice of
instruments. Finally we concluded to go it every man for himself,
'cordin to his taste and ear, and the next day everyone on us was to
go and get his instrument, leaf of absence bein gin to the hull
rigiment, 'cept Zeke Tucker, who was under 'rest for salutin the
Ginral's orderly, and he hed to stand sentinel. We borrid the instruments from Volunteer musicianers that hadn't no use for em, on
account as they could not play, 'cause they hadn't no bands in their
rigiments. Wall, when we got together, nineteen on us had bought a
clarynet—Zeke had sent for one—and Capting Potter had borrered
a ho-boy.

There wont many on us could get the plaguy things to blow, fust
start, but we practiced four hours a day for a few days and have got
so now that we can play "Greenland's Icy Mountains" putty fair,
and have started a little tu playin "Yankee Doodle," kinder slow.
The clarynets will squeak a little when we get up ontu the high
teches, but we don't get stuck often. Capting Potter won't stop for
nobody, right or rong, when he gets to goin. He stomps and blows
so hard that it makes his eyes kinder pop out, and he alyers has a
headache arter it. We sent an invite to some officers of the reglars and
volunteers yesterday to come and hear us give a consart, but everyone on em refused. I can't understand that, but mebby it's cause
they think we ought tu go and surreynade em. We'll wait till the
moon gets big nuff, and then we'll tetch em up.

14. Taylor, no stickler for spit-and-polish, seldom wore a complete uniform or
insignia of rank; in his old brown coat he was often mistaken for a civilian. His
officers once estimated that his disreputable uniform was worth $7.50; Holman
Hamilton, *Zachary Taylor, Soldier in the White House* (Indianapolis: Bobbs-Merrill,
1951), p. 22; see also Florence J. Scott, *Old Rough and Ready on the Rio Grande* (San
Antonio: The Naylor Co. 1935), *passim*.

Seeing the Elephant at the Battle of Buena Vista

by "Ruff Sam" of Mississippi

§ "Ruff Sam," who also joined the citizen-soldier Volunteers in our first foreign war, sent back the following report to the New Orleans *Delta.* It was reprinted in the *Spirit,* XVII, No. 37 (November 6, 1847).

As I have just got here and ain't never told the folks 'bout what I've seen out in the Mexikin country, I'll begin at onst, afore they charge me with keepin back somethin from the public. I'm a Mississippi backwoodsman and was a soger 'long in Kernal Davis' Regiment, and I helpt to fite at Monteray an Bony Vista. Thar's whar I seed the elephant what I'm going to tell about—not the live elephant stuffed with straw, but the rale Mexikin elephant, horns an all.

You see, we were all at Bony Vista, 'long with a hole heap of yether sodgers. Thar war Gineral Taylor a-ridin roun talkin to the officers, an a-lookin sort o'serious like. God bless the old Gineral's countenance—I know'd somethin was comin, for he kept on goin 'bout from one regiment to the yether, lookin kinder anxious. Presently I seed him makin a beeline for our Kernal. Says he, "Kernal Davis, how is your men! Is they all fit for service! kin you depind on em shortly?"

"Why," says our Kernal, "what's left on em I *kin;* my men will fite; that's what they kum here for. Look at em; they're all ready for it rite now."

"Well," says the Gineral, "I think the Mississippi boys *kin* be depinded on," says he, a-turnin round to us—we was all out and in arms—and I declar to you I was o' bilin all over; and to see the Gineral a-lookin rite at us so incouragin'ly—it made me feel jist like my dog Boss does when he's arter a bar an me a-hissin him on an he a-smellin an a-yelpin as if the solid yearth couldn't hold him.

Arter the Gineral went away, Kernal Davis says, says he, "My men, I want you to do somethin for Mississippi today, and I spects it out of you. Obey my orders and follow me, and no repudiation."

We all hurrah'd an said we'd do it or bust. Hardly had we done hollerin afore we hearn em a-firin.

"Forward march!" said our Kernal, and off we went 'twill we come into line with the yethers. Thar was the Mexikins a-firin at us and a-flying fust one way an another an then the yether way an makin more noise an smoke and beatin more drums with a few more colors than you ever hearn tell of. I began to think, then, that I had seen the elephant, and so I had, but I hadn't seen him *clost*. We kep firin an counter-marchin an swarin for some time 'twill all of a sudden Kernal Davis sung out, "Heads of columns, to the rite! quick march!" — an off we started on a rale dogtrot 'twill we come to a smuthe place 'bout a quarter of a mile off, and thar we halted an let drive at a parcel on em mounted on mustangs, and a powerful sight they was — must ha-been a thousan' or more. We sorter know'd somthin was comin onusual 'cause they manuvered 'bout so. Thar sot our Kernal as if nothin on yearth ailed him while the bullits and cannonballs was flyin round him so thick that you couldn't tell which way to dodge. Suddenly says he, "Now's the time for you all to show yourselves *men*," an he hollered out a hole heap of orders; an the first thing I know'd we was all a-standin like a par of kompusses stretched wide open. I hearn somethin comin like thunder an looked up, and thar kum the Mexikins like a parcel of wild Injuns, rite strate at us. The Kernal, says he, "Stand firm, boys — not a word — mind what I say!" The Mexikins sorter stopped a little when they seed our kompuss, for they naturally know'd we'd kompuss em — down they cum tho'; in a twinkle they was *into* us, just as our Kernal sung out, "Fire, boys, and use your knives on em!" You ain't never seen a bar fite, is you? Well, bar fitin ain't begun to tetch it. I jist let one on em have the inside of my gun which throw'd him for good, and I picked out a fat feller close by, an if I didn't cut the stuffin clean out of him, I wouldn't tell you so. Sich cussin an ponitataroin you never hearn. Well, it didn't last long, or we'd ha' rid the yearth of the whole on em. No, no they was off — them that could ride — an the yethers cum the *amigos* over us, altho' I'll tell you that I did sorter *feel* one of em with my bowie knife when he said *amigos* to me; for you see, I ain't wantin sich friends, an I thot maybe he mout fool me. In course, we had some more fitin, but what I've jist told 'bout was the genwine elephant jist as sure as my name is Ruff Sam.

The Barrel Movement

by "Solitaire" of St. Louis, Missouri

§ As "Solitaire," John S. Robb published many humorous sketches in the St. Louis *Reveille,* most of which were reprinted in the *Spirit.* Born in Philadelphia, Robb became a journeyman printer and worked in Detroit and New Orleans before coming to St. Louis, where for a time in 1842 he edited the *Ledger.* After the *Reveille* was established in 1844, he became foreman of the composition department in 1845 and assistant editor in 1846. As a special correspondent, he went to California in the gold rush of 1849, remained there, published a paper in Stockton, and died in San Francisco in 1856. (John F. McDermott, introduction to a facsimile reproduction of Robb's *Streaks of Squatter Life and Far-West Scenes* [Gainesville, Fla.: Scholars' Facsimiles & Reprints, 1962], pp. vi-vii.)

Robb's most popular piece was "Swallowing an Oyster Alive," a typical practical joke in which a city wag convinces an Illinois backwoodsman that the oysters he has just swallowed will eat his insides out. Porter reprinted the sketch in *The Big Bear of Arkansas* and was perhaps influential in getting Carey & Hart of Philadelphia to publish a collection of Robb's tales as *Streaks of Squatter Life and Far-West Scenes* in 1847 (not 1843 according to the spurious copyright date of some editions).

"Solitare's" account of soldier ingenuity which follows was first printed in the St. Louis *Reveille* and reprinted in the *Spirit,* XVI, No. 31 (September 26, 1846), 362.

WHEN the St. Louis Legion was encamped on the island at the mouth of the Brazos Santiago,[15] the boys began for the first time to feel the inconvenience of Uncle Sam's fodder arrangements—not that they expected to find "chicken fixins" every morning, but they at least felt confident the *beans* would be nourishing. About eleven o'clock, a.m., everyday, the little round vegetables were put in the camp kettles, and in an hour, or probably an hour and a half, were served out. To those skilled in the matter of dried beans, we need not explain how little effect an hour's boiling would have upon them. The different messes cracked away, however, chewed the hard pebbles up and left off their meals in a very unsatisfied manner. A

15. The mouth of the Brazos River, near present Brownsville, Texas.

few days had scarcely elapsed when a general grumble was set in circulation against the commissary department, Uncle Sam and his *beans*, in particular. One tall volunteer swore in the mess that he would cross to the main land and provision himself if he had to eat a live *Ranchero*, before he would starve on such fare; his comrades chimed in with his rebellious resolve, and all of them asked leave of the Captain to take a short excursion for a few hours in search of game. Leave was granted, and off the party started.

In the course of a few hours, one came strolling into camp with a bundle under his arm, and as he passed the sentry on the way to their tent, he was accosted with, "Jo, what luck had you?"

"Oh," says Jo, "I only killed a 'gutter snipe!'"

"Well," says the sentry, "that is the largest snipe, judging from the bundle, I have ever seen. Let me look at his *bill*."

Jo uncovered it, and there was the snout of as fine a young *pig* as ever poked his nose into a swill tub. Both winked at each other, exchanged quiet grins, and then the *snipe* was carefully covered and carried to quarters.

In a few moments along came another of the mess, who reported that he had only secured a haunch of "slow deer," i.e., a young *calf;* and, to wind up the captured game of the party, three more appeared, carrying a quarter of a "short-horned elk," which some envious members of other messes declared looked as if it might have been the *"slow deer's"* mammy!

The spoils were put together and covered over, after which the mess went into council of war upon how to get something to wash down the *game* and make the whole affair a comfortable one.

"Do you think we can execute a *'barrel movement,'* boys?" said an orderly belonging to the mess.

"What is it like?" was the general inquiry.

"Simply this," says the sergeant; "the Commissary General is landing stores down at the beach, among which is some first rate *brandy* for the officers, and if we could only make one of his half-barrels keep step in a hollow square, we might easily execute the new march of a 'barrel movement.'"

All the mess expressed themselves ready for duty instantor, and having added a few more rank and file to the enterprise, off they started on a commendably earnest march to practice the new drill. The hollow square was admirably formed and re-formed half a dozen times before they reached the beach, and advancing in line towards the commissary's stores, with a rapid evolution they formed around a liquor cask and commenced their march across the island. The drill was now full of interest—it was new—and one of the lieutenants, attracted by the strange maneuvering, approached them just as they were performing a hollow square *countermarch.* He observed one of the men carrying two muskets and thought it queer, but a glance at the center of the squad explained the secret. A strong volunteer was keeping the barrel rolling in the inside—they were representing a square retreating with store, and it was really beautiful, the skill with which they did it! Now the barrel roller would get tired, and the squad would countermarch while another took his place; again a discovery would threaten, and they would close up to receive charge of cavalry, and thus, moving with caution and steadiness, they reached a small sandhill in the rear of the camp. Now commenced some brilliant slow movements, all in one spot, which were followed by the squad forming line again and moving into camp.

At the spot where the square broke, a fresh hillock of sand *might* have been discovered but only by those who knew the former levelness of the spot.

The Lieutenant, who had critically watched the maneuvering of the men, congratulated the orderly on the perfection of their drill. The subordinates looked him in the eye and knew by the slight curl in the muscles of his face that he "smoked" the new tactics; so, touching his cap politely, he asked the officer if when they cooked their *game* he would accept a slice.

"If the cook in your mess seasons it carefully and it's not *overdone,* I wouldn't mind tasting it," says the Lieutenant.

The orderly winked and they separated. It was refreshing to an old campaigner just to see how "gutter snipe," "short-horned elk," and "slow deer" were disposed of that evening in the mess which executed the above described strange drill; and ever after that night it became a byword, when a volunteer was seen moving in a zigzag fashion, that he was practicing the Legion's new march called *"the barrel movement!"*

A Breach of Promise Case

by "Azul" of Mississippi

§ "Azul" contributed stories from both Alabama and Mississippi. The following tale, by-lined "By an Old Alabama Correspondent," appeared in the *Spirit*, XVII, No. 18 (June 26, 1847), 202-203.

Having just returned from Mexico, after an absence of twelve months, and being on my way home through this state (Alabama), I stopped one evening at the only inn of a small country village. On stepping into the barroom I observed an acquaintance of mine, rather an odd genius (to whom I shall give the appellation of Wm. Purdy) who was so very busy talking with some of his cronies that he did not observe me as I came in; I sat down to wait until he should get through talking.

They were speaking of some circumstances that had occurred in Mexico, for Bill was with the troops that were discharged in the summer of 1846.

Says one, "Now, Bill, you know that it war the same day wot Thomas got his arm broke, which I am sartain sure war on the 6th of July."

"You don't know nuthin a bout it," replied Bill, "kase it war on the 10th day of July, which cum on a Friday, an ef you'll go to home with me, I'll show ye whar I sot it down in black an wite. Kase I kept a *diarrhea* of all the princepal events what transpired whilst we war out thar in camp."

As he finished he observed me, and jumping up, gave me a real Alabama welcome and began the usual inquiries that a soldier is bound to answer the moment he arrives in the United States. After replying to all his inquiries, I asked him what he had been doing for himself since his return.

"Why almost the fust thing I done war to git spliced to the pootiest gal what ever did live in these diggins."

"Your *old honey* stuck to you like pitch, I suppose? She only loved you the better after your return?"

"No! Dodfetch me if she did. Kase when I got back and went over to see her, she talked mity independent and almost as good as told me she had no more use for me. So I got mad an tuck an made her marry me out on spite."

"How did that happen, Bill?"

"Why it war jest so. Last corn-plantin time when I tuck my departure, me and her war very nigh as good as engaged to wun nuther, and I thot it war all rite an didn't bother myself bout it untwell I cum back. Whilst I war gone thar war a passel of fellers flyin round her smartly, and that's what put her out with me. When she talked in that kind a way to me, I never sed nuthin but jest axed her fur to give me back all my notes and letters and billy duxes what I writ to her whilst I wur a-coortin on her. I war tarnation mad when she giv em all up to me, an I started rite off for to burn em all up an, *at the same time and place*, to destroy them what she had writ to me during the same time. I war determined, too, to have revenge, so I watched round and walloped every feller what went to her house durin the space of better nor six weeks. At last I cum to the resolve to level on her for a *brich o' promis*, and I did, too. I tuck all the whole bundle of letters and billy duxes what she had writ to me and what I had writ to her and carried em all down to Squire Ellis; I told him how as I had a brich o' promis case for him and never said nuthin more bout it but jest left the papers. I then went rite down to her pap's and told him what I'd done, and he 'lowed it war all rite, kase the old codger wanted his gal for to marry me. I never thot nuthin more bout the matter twell court time. The squire not knowin me thot from the bundle of papers that I war the gal's pap and at court time brot in a case agin Wm. Purdy for brich o' promis to Miss Louisa Edson an tuck an red all my letters an billy duxes to her, rite out in the Court House, an then made a big speech agin me. Why it war the beatinest thing what I ever hearn tell of! A man to employ a Squire for him, and then for him to git up an make a speech agin him; so afore I got thar the jury cided 'gainst me an gin a verdict fur her fur $1,000. So I war compelled to ither marry her or pay the $1,000 which I wouldn't a-done untwell yet, so I jest went and married her immediately. Her pap, in the meantime, told her how the Judge had cided that she should have me, an she didn't know no better, an went and did accordinly, an I blieve she didn't mind it a bit; and in that kind o' manner I got won of the best little wives what a man ever laid up to his face."

*Politicians, Actors, Yokels
in the City*

Less frequent as figures in the humor of the Old Southwest are the politicians, the theatrical people, and the backwoods yokel in the city. The reluctance of newspaper editors to get involved in political squabbles accounts for the scarcity of sketches about politicians, and since actors and theatrical managers were seen mostly in the larger towns and the cities, they were less common than hunters, doctors, lawyers, and preachers. The antics of the countryman in the city were most evident to the residents of New Orleans, the only city of any size in the Old Southwest.

Although whiskey was responsible for a great amount of intoxication in the Old Southwest, the idea that most men could vote and elect public officials was a more permanent kind of intoxication. The movement to abolish property-holding and taxpaying as qualifications for voting initiated before the War of 1812 gradually gained momentum so that by the beginning of the Jackson administration in 1829 the mingling of Western frontiersmen with Washington society became a symbol of the common people's arrival at political power. The success of such "coonskin" politicians as Davy Crockett horrified the conservatives and delighted the so-called common people, "the sovereigns" as they were facetiously called. The fact that men of little education and even less experience could be elected to public office was indeed a heady idea, and the practice worked best on the frontier, of course. Thus, in the Old Southwest a "nobody" from the older states could easily become a "somebody," especially if he were clever enough to size up his constituents

correctly. Davy Crockett told the tale on himself
of appearing at a political rally in Tennessee
without enough money to buy drinks for the
crowd. Since coonskins were legal tender, he
laid one on the counter and treated the
bystanders; then while the bartender was busy
he sneaked the coonskin from under the
counter and offered it again in payment for
another round. The tale, true or not, illustrates
the practical politician's ability to evaluate a
situation quickly and make the most of it.

When a generous candidate did not provide
the drinks, "It was quite customary," Everett
Dick says, "for someone to carry a bucket about,
asking people to 'throw in' for a general treat."
After the solicitor got enough money, he went
to a tavern for whiskey and "returned with a
bucket filled with liquor and bearing
a goard dipper."[1]

Not only was the candidate for office expected
to treat, but he was also expected to deliver long
speeches in the style of the spread-eagle oratory
of the day. Popular humor burlesqued the
inflated rhetoric of such speeches in the
mouths of uneducated politicians. Apparently in
some instances when the candidate was shrewd
enough to know that he could not handle big
words, he simply made up high-sounding
language, as may be seen in "Stump Speaking
in Arkansas."[2] Politicians appeared and made
speeches when they could at all sorts of public
gatherings—court days, fish fries, picnics, and
holiday celebrations. A politician, new at the
business as "Pardon Jones" was, soon learned
that "the sovereigns" could be fickle; Jones
found that he must dress neither too well lest

1. Dick, *The Dixie Frontier,*
p. 242.
2. "Stump Speaking in
Arkansas," *Spirit,* XIV, No. 7
(April 13, 1844), 81. "Feller
Citizens—this are a day for the
people of Wolf's Mouth, and I
mought say, if I warn't modest,
that our carnal entranchasemen
(that's a hard word but I got
through with it) depends on
our heterognous exertions. . . .
I'm going to sand my speech
with quotations from Sezem the
celebrated Latin cricket. . . ."

he be thought "aristocratic" nor too poorly lest he be considered illiterate. Even the most experienced candidates sometimes got in trouble when electioneering, as did silver-tongued S. S. Prentiss, who had to compete with a circus—a disadvantage which he cleverly turned to an advantage.

As with other topics in the humor of the Old Southwest, the picture of politics and politicians is doubtless exaggerated. Fewer sketches deal with politics because Porter did not favor the subject. Although he had said as early as 1832, "We have abjured politics," he found it necessary to repeat in 1843, "No Smoking (Nor Politics) Allowed Here!"[3] In those sketches that he did print, politicians seem to have changed little between then and now, even though the language and the causes are different.

The make-believe world of the theater was not as out of place in the frontier conditions of the Old Southwest as it might seem to a twentieth-century reader. Whereas today legitimate theater is available largely to residents of cities and university communities, all cities and many small towns in the nineteenth century were regularly visited by theatrical companies, some of which included the great actors of the English and American stage. The large theater-going public saw nothing strange about the most famous tragic actors appearing in a theater in New Orleans, for example, in a week following the bill of equestrian performers or so-called "Ethiopian" singers and dancers. For that matter, opera and plays in French were not uncommon in the early decades of the century before the Americanization of the city became more evident.[4]

3. As cited in Yates, *Porter and the Spirit*, p. 22
4. John S. Kendall's *The Golden Age of the New Orleans Theater* is an exhaustive treatment of the subject.

Live theater was also a vital force in towns outside of New Orleans in the Old Southwest—Natchez, Vicksburg, Nashville, Mobile to name but the better known ones. Some of the resident companies of New Orleans visited other cities, especially when the periodic yellow fever or cholera epidemics caused people to flee from the Crescent City. Actors and entertainers temporarily out of work often played in the upriver towns until they got money for passage to New Orleans.[5]

Since theater was part of the community experience of so many people in the Old Southwest—all the way from amateur theatricals in villages to professional companies—stage people were probably of even greater interest to the general public than such celebrities are today. The very thought that Junius Brutus Booth or William Macready might also be a passenger on a Mississippi steamer, or that Josh Silsbee, widely known for his impersonations of the typical Yankee, might be aboard was exciting. Furthermore, subscribers to the *Spirit of the Times* read weekly columns of theatrical activities in England, France, New York, and other northern cities. Other newspapers devoted space to theatrical news, especially the New Orleans newspapers, some of which had discerning drama critics. The result was that many people were familiar with actors of all kinds—old and young, good and bad—and anecdotes about them were part of the oral and printed lore of the period. Of course, some people were led to brag of their intimate knowledge of actors and hence indulged in a practice that has come to be called name-dropping today, as is shown in Sol Smith's

5. Sol. Smith, the most widely known theatrical manager and producer in the Old Southwest, describes vividly the vicissitudes of traveling theater in his books *Theatrical Apprenticeship* (Philadelphia, 1854), *Theatrical Journeywork* (Philadelphia, 1854), and *Theatrical Management* (New York, 1868). See also N. M. Ludlow, *Dramatic Life as I Found It, A Record of Personal Experience: With an Account of the Rise and Progress of the Drama in the West and South* (St. Louis, 1880).

sketch, "An Intimate Friend"; but in a period of practical joking, others were at no loss for a means of putting the braggart in his place.

Aside from the humorous anecdotes about actors and entertainers some of the humor of the Old Southwest deals with the audiences of provincial theaters. The story was told many times over of the backwoodsman who found himself in a theater in a village or town and who became so entranced with the action of the play that he bounded onto the stage to defend the helpless heroine from the advances of a braggart villain. Other tales deal with the reactions of backwoodsmen in New Orleans who see for the first time circuses, fights between animals, ballet, and other theatrical performances.

Behind the exaggerations of popular humor are glimpses of ordinary people of the Old Southwest who were as lusty in their enjoyment of live theater and live entertainers as they were in their other activities, and fortunate they were in having the drama and the world of make-believe to effect the purgation of emotions men have for centuries found rewarding.

The New Orleans of the Old Southwest was not the glamorous city of moonlight, magnolias, and Mardi Gras that it became to many people in the late nineteenth century, an image perpetuated in the travel folders still. It was rather a bustling, booming American town superimposed on an Old World setting. A. Oakey Hall of New York, probably a journalist, visited the city in 1850, spent some time there, and published his impressions in a book in 1851.[6] Visually the city was dominated, he says,

6. A. Oakey Hall, *The Manhattaner in New Orleans, or Phases of "Crescent City" Life* (New York, 1851), p. 27.

by the St. Charles Hotel, the dome of which
soared high above narrow streets filled with
oyster bars, fruit shops, billiard parlors, and
boarding houses—a polyglot mass that Hall
called "hog-pens." The Crescent City, as New
Orleans was often called then, was truly a
rivertown that drew its life from the Mississippi.
Hall, who viewed the river from the top of the
St. Charles, says the levee was a wilderness
of steamboats.[7]

Thousands of hogs heads, bales and bags and
packages crowd and jostle each other in. Adown the
riverward streets flow rapid streams of human heads
and legs . . . sailors, stevedores, steamboat hands,
clerks, planters, wealthy merchants, too, running to
and fro with divers projects in their heads. . . . A
million dollars could not buy the articles of traffic
taken in at one glance, articles of traffic that before
twenty-four hours have gone by will all have
disappeared—their place supplied by different lots
and newer samples.

"Work, work, work, is the unceasing cry,"
Hall says; everyone, except for the Creole
man-of-leisure is trying to make money. Men
from all parts of the nation sought their fortunes
in New Orleans. More prosperous visitors stayed
at one of the three better hotels, the St. Charles,
the St. Louis, or the Verandah; others filled the
numerous boarding houses and frequented
cheap restaurants, bars, and places of
amusement clustered in the vicinity
of the St. Charles Hotel.

The land that had enticed farmers and planters
from the older states into the Old Southwest
had by the 1850s produced the cotton, cane, and
livestock that came down the river and made

7. *Ibid.,* p. 24.

New Orleans the booming city that it was. Similarly, business opportunities in that city enticed traders, merchants, and businessmen from all sections of the country. Some came to make their fortunes and depart; others came to stay. Aggressive as they were, they had little patience with what they thought were the languid ways of the Creoles of the city. In popular humor there are glimpses of a new commercially oriented society made up of young men who had come to seek their fortunes in the Crescent City; they frequented the elaborate bar of the St. Charles Hotel, the Bingaman Race Track, the American and St. Charles theaters, and the French opera; they dressed as extravagantly as they could afford; they drove fine horses hitched to gigs over the Shell Road out to Dan Hickok's bar and restaurant on Lake Pontchartrain; and they entertained actors and out-of-town celebrities at dinners in the St. Charles Hotel. The rush for business and pleasure that lasted through the fall, winter, and spring came to a halt in the summer, especially in years when the yellow fever threatened the city, as it often did.

New Orleans of the 1850's was a city to delight the curious. Amid the hustle and bustle of the crowded streets the visitor could see people from many parts of the nation, and Europe and the Carribean as well. In this hurdy-gurdy atmosphere, a sight that natives and out-of-towners apparently enjoyed was the backwoodsman gawking about the streets. Whether he was a small farmer from upriver, an Arkansas bear hunter, a Kentuckian, or a miner returned from California, the yokel in the

Crescent City was among the main topics of popular humor.

Thus the politician (in the hustings, in the state capitol, in Washington), the actor (before an experienced audience in New Orleans or Natchez, or before backwoodsmen in a makeshift theater in the backcountry), and the countryman bemused by the sights of the city— these three types round out the varied cast of characters that amused readers of popular humor of the Old Southwest.

"Seeing the Elephant"

by Anonymous, New Orleans, Louisiana

§ In 1835 Longstreet used the phrase "seeing the elephant" in *Georgia Scenes* (p. 6) to describe a country yokel's reaction to city sights. A few years later George W. Kendall, *Santa Fe Expedition*, I, 110, defined the popular phrase as follows: "When a man is disappointed in anything he undertakes, when he has seen enough, when he gets sick and tired of any job he may have set himself about, he has 'seen the elephant.'" The following anecdote about the famous orator S. S. Prentiss uses the phrase both literally and figuratively. The tale appeared in the *Spirit*, XIX, No. 51 (February 9, 1850), 605.

AT the New England Supper, as "the wee hours" approached, the following toast was proposed:

"The State of Mississippi—She has sent her best *apprentice.*"

Judge Ballard moved as an amendment the addition of—

"And we have made him a master workman."

It is needless to say that the toast was drunk with the honors. Mr. Prentiss[8] replied in his happiest style. He spoke with deep feeling of his attachment to Mississippi and of the honor and chivalry of its many gentlemen of all parties. In the course of his speech he told two of his electioneering reminiscences which "set the table in a roar."

He said that six, or eight, or twelve years ago—he did not like to be particular about dates—he went to Washington thinking he was a member of Congress, but he found out his mistake and came home as fast as possible to get right. He made speeches in fifty-four out of the fifty-six counties in the state. He sent printed bills containing his appointments twenty-six days ahead of him. Now there was a caravan [circus] just at this time perambulating the state, and the proprietor availed himself of the gatherings collected by Mr. P.'s notices. This, by the way, said Mr. P., was quite in the ordinary course of things, as an observer of political excitements must have remarked that a caravan of some kind or other usually follows in their wake.

8. For information on S. S. Prentiss, see Section V, "The Professions," preceding.

298

The first time Mr. P. "saw the elephant" was in ———— County in the northern part of the state near the Alabama line. It is one of the most beautiful counties in Mississippi; its population was chiefly from South Carolina, and though they had voted against him on the previous election, he hoped their State Rights notions would bring them into his support at this contest when he did not run so much the candidate of a party as the representative of the state whose dignity and sovereignty had been outraged in his person. At the appointed hour he found over three hundred ladies and gentlemen assembled to hear him. He was in "high feather" and began to speak with more than usual energy. The audience listened with marked attention, and he felt sure of bagging game. When he had spoken about an hour, he began to observe some of the outsiders looking over their shoulders, and this movement was gradually followed by more and more of his audience. He began to think he was growing dull and endeavored to rouse himself up to more animation; but it was no go. He at length looked in the popular direction, and there to his horror, just coming over the hill, was the *elephant*, dressed in his scarlet trappings and Oriental splendor with a houdah occupied by the musicians on his back, and in the rear came a long line of wagons and cages. A foolish feeling of vanity not to be outdone by the elephant came over him, and he continued to talk appealing to the people in the name of the state, their patriotism, etc., etc., but all in vain. A few well-mannered persons remained, but evidently they were retained only by their politeness.

He found it was no use. So he said, "Well, ladies and gentlemen, I am beaten, but I have the consolation of knowing that it is not by the competitor. I will not knock under to any two-legged beast, but I yield to the elephant." To be sure, he was at first provoked by the preference shown to the beast over himself, but on reflection he was inclined to think the people were right. A Bengal tiger or an India elephant was an animal to be seen once in a lifetime, but politicians they could see everyday.

He said, however, he had his revenge a few days after. He found that he must come to some understanding with the caravan. So he agreed with the proprietor that at Holly Springs he would address the people under the great awning for one hour, and then he would give way to the monkey and clown. He hoped this would not be charged on him as "bargain with corruption." At any rate it was honestly carried out by both parties. Between himself and the caravan, a large assemblage was gathered under the immense awning.

One of the cages was converted into a rostrum. He heard a low sound which resembled a growl and learned that the hyena was the nearest listener. There were large augur holes in the top of the box for the admission of air. He commenced speaking, and when he reached the blood-and-thunder portion of his speech, he ran his cane into the cage and called forth a most horrid yell from the enraged animal, at the same time gesticulating violently with the other hand. The effect was electric; he called down the house in a perfect tempest of enthusiasm. From this time he had it all his own way. He hurled his anathemas at his foes and enforced them by the yells of his neighbor. The hyena was good for a hundred votes, and he thus converted a mischief into a profit.

Electioneering

by "Pardon Jones" of Louisiana

§ C. M. Haile's account of "Pardon Jones's" experience in politics was printed in the New Orleans *Picayune*, VI, No. 129 (June 23, 1842), 1.

I'VE broke out in a new place—or rather, I'm returnin to first principles, and it keeps me bizzy 'nuff, I can tell you. When I fust come out in the *Picayune* for Congress, I put up for the "fust vacant deestrick." Well, Mister Dawson and Mister Butler, they begged so hard for me to haul off and give em a chance for this beat that I took pity on em and give the place up for them to fight for. But now ther's a-goin to be *tu* vacant deestricks in the state afore long, and Christopher Quilp and I is going to run to fill em. Mr. Quilp come up 'spressly to see me 'bout it t'other day, and we fixed the hull matter. He wanted me to 'gree to go'n 'lectioneer in his deestrick for him, and let him come and du the same for me; but that I wouldn't du for I've hed my speeches and everything fixed for that same bizzness this year or tu.

Soon's Quilp went off I went'n fixed up for a 'lectioneerin tower 'mong my futur constityents. A good many on em has got the notion sence I begin to write letters to you that I was gittin proud, and no sooner did I git the Curnel up to the Bay State then they set me down for a ra'al airistocrat, and my ennemies has bin very bizzy spreadin the story all over the country.

"Wall," says I to Jerushy, "now then let's put the lie to this slander to once. I'm a-goin to show myself to the people, and I'll show em that Curnel Pardon Jones ain't nothin but a man arter all. Bring me my old tow and linen breeches, pepper and salt jacket, chip hat, and cowhide boots and checkered neck-handkerchiff. Now for a bandanner handkerchiff, and tie it up full of sugar plums and other nicknacks for the babies."

Wall, I kissed Jerushy, and off I started, hossback, 'lectioneerin. I didn't call on nobody till I got down putty near the old disputed territory where I wan't much known. I left my hoss to a grogshop and thought I'd walk out and see an old cock that lives there, a kind of a "leadin carrackter" 'mong the *soverins*. Wall, I went into his yard and walked up to the door and axed if the "gentleman of the house was to hum."

"*Wee*," says madam, says she, lookin at me hard; "*wee, ker vooly voo der luee?*"

"O," says I, smilin, "I thought I'd jest call round and eat dinner with you—that's all."

"*Noos avoon deenay. Passay par la porte darneair a lar domesteek voos on donnerrar.*"

Just then the old gentleman come to the door scratchin his back and holdin a paper in his hand. "What for you come here?" says he.

"Why," says I, bowin, "my name is Curnel Jones, and I'm canvassin the people, and I thought I'd jest call in and take a bite with you and talk matters over in a free and easy sort of way."

"Ha, ha! *wee*, you *dam* 'free and easy' to come here and tell me your name Coronel Jones and get a dinner out of me! No, *bate!* you no Coronel Jones—he is one *gentleman*—*you* is one dam *peggar*—*allay*—go fast out of my yard."

By grashus!—if I warn't mad! Wall, I went back to the grogshop and ordered suthin to eat, but the feller wouldn't bring nothin on the table till I showed him some money to pay for it! A little while arterwards I met our old frend and told him all about it. He laffed at me a good while and told me that I 'was tu d————d shabby for sich a bizziness. "You'd ought to dress," says he, "sost to not 'tract no 'tentions—sost to be genteel and rich and shabby at the same time."

"I take," says I, and started for hum. The next day I rigged out in a different fashion altogether. I borrered a gold watch and chain and put on fine boots, yaller for want of blackin; an old Panama hat, black with mildew; an old black coat not very old; and breeches made out of cottonade. I stuck the gold watch keerless-like into my underjacket pocket and let the chain hang round most enny way. I kerried the sugar plums along in my saddlebags and started off. The fust day's ride was putty fine. Most everyboddy agreed to vote for me when the deestrick was laid off, if they didn't see noboddy up that they liked better, and I was in putty high sperrits when it cum night.

Well, I put up with a fust rate, good-natered old feller that I met at a billiard room, and when we got to his house 'twas jest a dusk. We went in and I was introduced to his wife, a fine, fat woman, that looked as if she got fat on laffin, her face was so full of fun. Arter a while, arter we'd talked 'bout my little gal and 'bout the garden, and so on, in come three or four children, laffin and skippin along as merry as crickets. There warn't no candle lit, but I could see't they was fine lookin little fellers, and I started for the saddlebags the fust thing. "Come here," says I, "you little rogues — come along here and tell me what your name is." The oldest come up to me, and says he, "*My* name's Peter Smith, sir."

"And what's *your* name?" says I to the next.

"Bob Smith, sir."

The next said his name was "Bill Smith," and the furth said *his* name was "Tommy Smith." Wall, I got em up on my knees and kissed em over and over agin, and gin em a lot of sugar candy, and old Miss Smith was so tickled that she laffed all the time. Mister Smith looked on, but didn't say much. "Why," says I, "Miss Smith, I wouldn't take a good deal for them four boys if I had em — they're so beautiful and sprightly."

"No," says she, laffin, "I set a good deal by em, but we *spile* em tu much."

"O no," says I, "they're ra'al well behaved children; and, by grashus!" says I, pretendin to be started by a sudden idea, "what a *strikin* resemblance 'tween them boys and their father!" and I looked at Mister Smith. "I never *did* see nothin equal tu it," says I — "your eyes, mouth, forrard — a *perfect picter* on you sir," says I, tappin the oldest boy on the pate. I thought Miss Smith would a-died laffin at that; her arms fell down to her side, and her head fell°back, and she shook the hull house, laffin.

"*Du* you think so, Curnel Jones?" says she, and she looked towards Mister Smith, and I thought she'd a-gone off in a fit.

"Yes," says I, "I du, ra'ally now."

"Ha, ha, haw — w — w!" says Mister Smith, kinder haff laffin, "you're tu hard on me, Curnel, with your jokes."

"I ain't a-jokin at all," says I, "they're hansum children, and they *du* look wonderfully like you."

Jest then a gal brought in a light, and I'll be darn'd if the little brats didn't turn out to be *mulattoes* every one on em, and their heads was as curly as the blackest niggers! Mister Smith and Miss Smith never had no children, and they sort o' petted them little niggers for playthings! I never felt so streaked in my life as I did when I see how things stood. If I hadn't a *kissed* the little nasty things, I could a-got over it, but I kissed em and showed that I was in airnest (though I was soft soapin on em, as I thought, all the time). How to get out of the scrape I didn't know. Miss Smith laffed so hard when she see how confused I looked that she most suffercated. A little while arterwards there was a hull fammerly of relations arriv from the city and turned the matter off, but the next mornin I could see't Mister Smith didn't like the remembrances on't at all, and I don't bleeve he'll vote for me when the 'lection comes on. I 'spect Miss Smith will keep the old feller under with that joke a good while.

Fun at the Capitol of Mississippi

by D. V. M. of Mississippi

§ No more than the initials is known of the author of the following sketch which appeared in the New Orleans *Tropic* and was reprinted in the *Spirit*, XIV, No. 3 (March 16, 1844), 27.

W E have had quite an exciting day in Jackson, the metropolis of Mississippi, and as the events are worth chronicling, I snatch an hour from the night to give you my memoranda in their original freshness. About 11 o'clock, a.m., the fire bell of the city sounded with portentous earnestness. The Capitol, the just pride of every Mississippian, was pronounced to be on fire! The House of Representatives hurried through the form of adjournment, but the Senate dissolved without form or order in the most individual manner. "Mr. President, the Capitol is on fire," said a Senator. "The hell it is!" said the President, and without his hat he instantly ran out of the place followed by the whole of the august body in a *sauve qui peut* dismay. The fire never made itself visible, but a little smoke from a flue served as an excuse for the fire company to pump and play against the chimneys and over the roof, after dragging an interminable quantity of leaky hose through every department of the Capitol.

There never has been a positive fire in the city of Jackson. Judge, then, of the excitement of our firemen, when, in the early part of the evening the bell again sounded, and a body of flame was seen ascending from the roof of the Eagle, the principal hotel in the city. Another disappointment—a drunken gambler had thrown his whiskey bottle into the fire, and the blaze passed through the chimney without even igniting the roof.

At the evening session every member of the House was in his place, and a crowd of ladies graced the gallery. Some rare fun was expected as it was known that Lindsay, the Representative from Itawamba County, was to speak. This person, a repudiating locofoco, is, or was, a Methodist preacher, uncouth in his manners, ungainly in his person, and illiterate in his discourse. Some idea of this man's fitness for his position may be gathered from the following verbatim report of his speech on the motion to reduce the salaries of the judiciary, a locofoco measure introduced a few days since and opposed by the respectable of both parties. "Where I was raised in Old Alarbarm, we never gin a judge of any sort more nor fifteen hundred in a year; and if I may be allowed to conjecture, I do reckon that we had just as good judges in Alarbarm as you can raise in Messeysap. My consti-chew-ents sent me here to practice 'conomy — tharfore, I goes for 'conomy; and sorry am I to observe that many which I thought knowed better are a-strainin and a-reachin arter the high puss (purse)."

This learned legislator on this evening, Thursday, introduced a bill, which the Clerk of the House several times attempted to read, but was prevented by his own fits of laughter and the tumultuous cachinations of the members.

"A Bill to relieve the Free Citizens of Mississippi and Travellers. Be it hereby enacted, that it is lawful for any white citizen of Mississippi to sell alcoholous, vinous, and other fermenting liquors in any quantity over a quart, provided he keeps order in the house when the same is drunk."

Amid the heartiest laughter, the speaker left the chair, and the House resolved itself into a committee of the whole to consider the bill which was again and again read over by the Clerk. Dr. L. was desired to explain who was to keep order and who was to be drunk! He arose and uttered the following speech:

"Well, I railly ain't no objection myself to 'splain the bill, becas I think the bill 'splains itself. We all on us like a little drap o' suthin ardent — some genelemen carries a bottle — some genelemen don't — I allus carries a bottle myself, and I knows many genelemen now standin and sittin around me who takes a drop whenever they kin — and those genelemen, as well as myself, is now by law obleeged to buy a gallon when we oney wants half a pint, which is contrary to the Constitution, contrary to human natur, and contrary to the rights of all free white citizens of the State of Masseysap, and travellers in giniral.

"I knowed a gentleman—a right genteel gentleman too he was, I do assure you, gentlemen—who was travellin in this state with his wife and hull crowd o' leetle ones in a waggin, and his lady was tuck with the shakes, and his bottle was run out. There was a fix to be in, gentlemen! He didn't want to buy a gallon of ardent becas it warn't convenient; so he asked the landlord to fill his bottle at a fair price; and the landlord, who was a clever feller and knowed what it was to have the shakes and be out o' licker, why he filled the gentleman's bottle at a fair price, when another gentleman who was standing by, says, 'You're a-goin contrary to the laws of Misseysap,' and then this gentleman goes out and informs agin the landlord for selling licker to the gentleman whose wife had the shakes by less than a gallon; and if they hadn't knowed him well all round them parts he'd been fined and imprisoned for doin as any gentleman would like to be done when his bottle is run out, which is contrary to the rights of any white man, traveller or not.

"I knowed another gentleman whose horse was tuck right sick, and he was told that a little brandy and a half pint o' campfire would cure the beast. Now he was temperate and never drinked, but for all that he was obleeged to buy a gallon when he oney wanted a drap to mix with the campfire. Is this law for any white man to live by!

"Why, I myself, gentlemen, were once travellin down there by the Yellerbusher,[9] with a friend beside myself, when I felt like takin a small horn, havin been movin right smartly through the swamps the hull day, which my friend said was correct and unanimously agreed with me in the same. Well, I myself was obleeged to pay for a gallon when I oney wanted to fill a three half pint bottle—which is my size as it fits well into the side pocket of my topcoat, though some gentlemen's bottles is larger, but I never knowed a gentleman carry a bottle big enough to hold a gallon."

This speech was loudly cheered throughout, and Mr. L.'s solemn earnestness of manner contributed materially to heighten the effect. The best of the joke is that his bugbear, "the gallon law," as it

9. The Yalobusha River, a tributary of the Yazoo River in northern Mississippi.

is called, has been repealed for some considerable length of time.

A member moved to strike out "alcoholous and vinous," and insert "table beer."

An amendment was moved and seconded and put on paper; the Clerk read it aloud, and it proved to be a parody on Russell's song, "A Life on the Ocean Wave," beginning "A day in a muddy swamp."

Another "amendment" introduced the epigram now going the rounds of the papers about the marriage of a Mr. Bee to a Miss Flower, ending with

And soon there will, if heaven pleases,
Be a swarm of little Beeses.

Here the fun grew fast and furious—the ladies left the gallery—the chairman rapped in vain, and Mr. Balfour rose in great heat and said:

"Mr. Speaker, look at that chandelier!—look at this splendid pile of building—look at everybody about us—is this a place to play the fool? I look—I look upon the bill proposed as a disgrace to the nation—a disgrace to the state—a disgrace to the house of God!"

The committee reported progress; the bill was ordered to lay upon the table, and the house adjourned about ten o'clock at night.

A Texian Hero

by Anonymous

§ Porter credited the following story to the Cincinnati *Mercury* when he reprinted it in the *Spirit*, XIII, No. 50 (February 10, 1844), 580.

JIM Wills was a queer compound of human nature—a man who could with ease make others laugh, but seldom ever laughed himself—a melancholy man through life, which caused him to "shuffle off this mortal coil" ere "half his race was run."

About the time Texas excitement ran so high in the United States,[10] Jim wills was in Pittsburgh in that situation so common to play actors, viz., flat broke. Standing on the wharf with his serious visage expanded, planning how he should get down the river without money, he heard a drum and fife. On looking round, he saw a company of reckless-looking, half-uniformed soldiers bearing a Texian banner and embarking for New Orleans. A thought struck him. Next day, he sent his trunk on board the first boat to start, and just as the captain was tapping the bell for the last time, Wills stepped on board and dragged his trunks into an unoccupied stateroom. He took from his theatrical wardrobe a soldier coat with a buff breast and three rows of buttons, a chapeau with an immense plume, a red sash, a pair of military trowsers, a grizzly black wig, and a pair of false whiskers. By the time the boat had got fairly under way, Jim was full equipped with his stage sword gracefully hanging by his side. Drawing on his white gloves, he hesitated for a moment, but relying on his peculair powers he opened the door, gave the usual military stoop, and walked into the cabin which was filled with passengers. In a moment all eyes were directed towards him, but he walked up to the bar and drank a glass of brandy and water. In the meantime all was bustle and confusion to find out who the officer was. A general rush was made for the register, but he had not yet put down his

10. After the Fall of the Alamo and the Battle of San Jacinto in the spring of 1836, resolutions calling for the recognition of Texas were adopted by the U. S. Senate (July 1) and the House (July 4).

name. The Captain was consulted, but he know nothing. At length, however, feeling a little curiosity, the Captain, walking up to Jim and bowing politely to him, said, "Sir."

"Sir to you," said Wills, touching his chapeau *a la militaire.*

"Will you do me the favor to register your name, so that I can provide a stateroom for you?"

"Oh, with pleasure," said Jim; walking up to the register, he flourished in round text,

"C. P. Edwards, Major, Texas Army."

The crowd pressed around the table—they read the name—universal enthusiasm prevailed, and three tremendous cheers were given for Texas and liberty!

It is almost needless to say that from this moment the *soi disant* Major was a lion. Everyone sought to make his acquaintance; the ladies opened the cabin door to get a peep at him; he was placed at the head of the table; and at night he was made as drunk as Bacchus on champagne.

Next day he was promenading the hurricane deck, linked arm-in-arm with the Captain and a warm-hearted Southerner, who resided in Vicksburg.

"Major," said the Southerner, "I know very well that you have been on a mission to collect arms, ammunition, and recruits; but on that subject you must, of course, be mum, in consequence of the treaty between Mexico and the United States. For my part, I could see every copper-colored radical hung like dogs on trees!"

"Whatever my business may have been," said Jim, "I find that I have exhausted all my means in the cause; in fact, I fear I shall not be able to pay my passage until I get to New Orleans."

"Don't mention it," said the Captain; "I could not think of taking anything of you."

"I have it," said the Southerner. "Come with me."

The trio adjourned to the clerk's office where a stirring appeal for aid to Texas was written. The Southern gentleman carried it among the passengers and collected $150 which was handed over to Wills. At night a grand supper was given at which speeches were made and toasts were drunk. The cabin was decorated with the Star-

Spangled Banner, entwined with the flag of the Lone Star, manufactured by the ladies for the occasion.

About 12 o'clock the company commenced singing songs, and at length the Major was called upon to favor the company with a song. He complied by "favoring the company" with his favorite song of "Billy Barlow."

"Bravo!" said one.

"Excellent!" said another.

"Capital!" said a third.

"I could do it a d----d sight better," said Jim, who was fast verging into the fourth stage of intoxication, "if I had the proper togs on."

After giving three faint huzzas for Texas, the party broke up.

Next morning the clerk went into the stateroom to call him to breakfast. Imagine his surprise when he discovered that the Major had actually turned in all standing—with boots, chapeau, and sword on, the feet snugly laid on the pillow. He was a Texas Major, and of course no fault was found.

Thus things ran on, and Wills reached New Orleans in triumph. There he doffed his unifrom and returned to Vicksburg, where he got an engagement in the theater. He became a great favorite; and when he was at the zenith of his glory, the old gentleman whom he had met on the boat went to the theater. Between the pieces Wills sang "Billy Barlow." The old fellow was bewildered. The afterpiece came on and Wills appeared in the identical suit in which he had enacted the Texas Major.

After the theater let out the old fellow sought an interview with Jim. "You rascal, I ought to shoot you, but the trick was so clever that I forgive you; so let us say no more about it."

Jim looked at him a moment with a serious expression, then replied, "Man in his time plays many parts."

An Intimate Friend

by Sol Smith

§ Under the title "From the Unpublished Anecdotical Recollections of Sol. Smith," Porter reprinted the following story from the New Orleans *Crescent* in the *Spirit*, XX, No. 47 (January 11, 1851), 561.

THERE is a class of individuals who claim to *know everybody*. Actors particularly, and particularly *great* actors, are their most familiar companions. Macready,[11] Forrest, and Booth are their most valued professional friends—they have known them *so* long and *so* intimately—interchanged *so* many civilities with them—been in their society under *so* many peculiar circumstances—indeed, they have known them from childhood—*they consider them as brothers!*

In 1844 one of this class happened to be passenger on the *White* on her trip from New Orleans to St. Louis during the month of March. He was a jolly fellow, full of anecdote and always ready with his joke, conundrum, repartee or pun. Snatches of the fashionable Negro songs—called for fashion's sake *Ethiopian melodies*—quaint sayings, and quotations from Shakespeare were at his tongue's end; he was the life of the social hall. Not knowing his real name, we shall call him *Spriggins.*

The great tragedian, Macready, had been performing an engagement at the St. Charles Theater, and he was, of course, *the* subject of conversation in the cabin of all steamboats leaving New Orleans. Spriggins had, according to his own statement, attended the theater every night Macready had acted.

"His Macbeth was great," said Spriggins, joining in a conversation by the stove in the Social Hall where the passengers were picking their teeth and smoking cigars after breakfast—"his Hamlet superb, and his Werner magnificent! I have frequently said to him at supper after he has been personating the latter character—"

11. William Charles Macready (1793-1873), English tragedian, widely known for his Shakespearean roles.

312

"You know him, then?" interrupted a passenger, who was at the moment lighting a cigar by Spriggins's.

"*Know* him? Know Bill Macready? Well, I should rather think I *do!*—intimately—intimately—spent most of my leisure time with him while he was in New Orleans. It was by *my* advice he came out to the South."

"Indeed!"

"Yes, indeed—it was a lucky thing for the managers that I happened to be in New York on his arrival from England; he never would have visited the South had it not been for me."

"What sort of man is he in private life?" inquired a gentleman.

"Oh!" replied Spriggins, "he is devilish haughty and austere to *strangers,* but in his intercourse with friends, he is a very companionable sort of fellow, I assure you."

"Are you acquainted with Mr. Forrest?" asked a passenger.

"Acquainted with *him?—Ned Forrest?* Have known him since he was a boy. We were schoolmates in Philadelphia—saw him make his first appearance as Young Norval at the Chestnut Street [Theater]. It was by my advice he adopted the stage as a profession. Great man, Ned is, but after seeing Macready, one doesn't relish Ned's acting as formerly. He is all very well as Metamora and Jack Cade, but when he attempts Shakespearian character—," Spriggins concluded this criticism by shaking his head and slightly shuddering as a man does when he has just taken a dose of salts.

"Did you see him act during his late engagement at the St. Charles?" asked one.

"No, I didn't," replied Spriggins, "though I like Ned, I couldn't persuade myself to undergo his stentorian inflections. He called to see me once or twice, and I dined with him three times, I believe, and that's the extent of our intercourse this season."

Spriggins went on chattering about actors and actresses till near dinner time, giving amusing accounts of their adventures during his long and intimate acquaintances with them. He knew them all "*like a book.*" The Southern managers were under great obligations to him for *advice*—indeed, they very seldom made any engagement of consequence without consulting *him.* He knew all the stars and principal stock actors and actresses. He had been the prime agent in getting up most of the complimentary benefits; he had written nearly all of the criticisms and puffs that had appeared in the New Orleans papers during the past theatrical season; in short, if his veracity might be relied on, he was the connecting link between the public and the theater; and to a casual observer, it would be a matter of wonder how theatrical affairs could proceed for a single week without him.

Who was he?

He knew everybody connected with the stage or who *had* been connected with it during the last twenty years. He dined with Mr. Caldwell twice a week; it was by his advice that gentleman had built the old St. Charles. We have already seen that he was on terms of intimacy with the two great tragedians of the age. Before the ringing of the dinner bell, the congregational passengers in the Social Hall had become aware that the more humble followers of Thespis were also honored with Mr. Spriggins's acquaintance and limited regard. In reply to questions judiciously propounded by the cigar smokers, it became known that the season at New Orleans had closed and that the company were about leaving for St. Louis and that *he* was bound for the same city, but declined the invitation of Bill Macready, Jim Ryder, Joe Field,[12] Jack Weston,[13] and Sol Smith, to go with them in the *Alexander Scott* in consequence of being obliged to stop on the way at several towns on the river.

"Besides," he observed, "it is a relief to be by one's self during a journey of this kind for I knew how it would be if I went with them — long sitting over the winebottle after dinner, late suppers, tedious stories, and professional reminiscences — I am *such* a favorite with them all that I should be bored to death with their attentions."

The bell rang out the summons to dinner. After the cloth had been removed, it was observed that five gentlemen remained, enjoying their wine at the middle of the table. Spriggins cast a wistful look

12. Joseph M. Field, actor, playright, and journalist; his newspaper and periodical sketches were published as *The Drama in Pokerville* (1847).

13. J. M. Weston, stage manager of a stock company in New Orleans in 1844-1845; Kendall, *The New Orleans Theater*, p. 258.

towards the party but did not venture to move his chair up to the place occupied by the *bon vivants*. One of the five, a *reverend-looking* individual, observed that a gentleman lingered at the lower end of the table; after a short whispering consultation with his companions, he sent the steward with the compliments of the party and a request that Spriggins would honor them with his company and partake of a glass of wine with them. He accepted the invitation with alacrity and was soon the merriest of the group.

During the "sittin," Spriggins imparted the information that he was *connected with the press* and that he was on a tour through the river towns for the purpose of increasing the circulation of one of the New Orleans papers. He *might* proceed as far as St. Louis — Bill *Macready* was going to that place and didn't know how he could get along in a city so far west without some friend to take care of him; but he didn't see — *he* didn't — how people could expect people to leave their business to attend to other people's business; Jim *Ryder* had insisted on his going — Joe *Field* had expressed a great desire that he would go and assist him to establish his projected new paper — Jack *Weston* had said he *must* go, and *Old Sol* wouldn't take no for an answer.

"So," said Capt. Converse, who had just joined the party, "you are very well acquainted with these actor-folk, Mr. Spriggins?"

"*Acquainted* with actors? Oh, no — I don't know any of them — ha! ha! ha!" answered and laughed Spriggins, winking at the wine-drinkers all round. "Never met any of them in all my life."

At this moment Mr. Bebee, the clerk of the boat, happened to be passing by that section of the table where the party were enjoying themselves.

"What's that you say, Mr. Spriggins? — not know any of the actors!" said he. "Allow me to introduce you to a few: Mr. Macready, Mr. Spriggins — Mr. Ryder, Mr. Field, Mr. Weston, Mr. Sol Smith — Mr. Spriggins! Spriggins — Macready — Weston — Spriggins — Field — Ryder — Spriggins!"

The party rose to do honor to the introduction — all but Spriggins, who sat in his chair, holding a wine glass midway between the table and his mouth, the very picture of astonishment.

"Steward!" faltered Spriggins, when he found the use of his tongue, "bring forward my trunk—I get out Natchez!"

He *did* get out at Natchez, and I have been told that he now stoutly denies ever having been acquainted with any member of the theatrical profession.

If there is any point or joke in this sketch, it consists in the fact that the wine-drinkers were actors *only for that occasion*—the personages whose names they assumed for the purpose of exposing a pretending coxcomb and boaster were a hundred miles ahead in the famous *Alexander Scott.*

Uncle Billy Brown — "Glorious!"

by "Rambler" of New Orleans

§ When Porter included the following story in *A Quarter Race in Kentucky*, he introduced it with this note: "By 'Rambler' of the N.O. 'Picayune'. Whether 'Rambler' is the veritable 'Ex Santa Fe Prisoner' himself [Kendall], or the senior editor of the editorial brotherhood who stands sponsors for the New Orleans 'Picayune'—a sort of 'child of thirty-six father' [Francis A. Lumsden]—we cannot undertake to decide; but the story of 'Uncle Billy Brown' is 'glorious' and worthy of either of them. Both Lumsden and Kendall have left their editorial sanctum for 'the Halls of the Montezumas' where each, we are glad to learn, has greatly distinguished himself."

The version following is from Peterson's Illustrated Uniform edition of *A Quarter Race*, 1848.

TAKE a large stick, a fence rail for instance, and rake it violently down a Venetian window blind or the side of a weatherboarded house, and you are very apt to make *some* noise, especially of a still evening.

A correspondent of ours, "Rambler," as he signs himself, says that he had just risen from the supper table of the tavern in the little village of G----- in the interior of Mississippi one hot evening last summer and was passing out to the front gallery to rest himself after a long day's ride, when suddenly he heard a tremendous racket as someone raking a fence rail down the side of a weatherboarded house, each rake followed by a shout of "Glorious! Glorious!" from a pair of lungs of ten trombone power. Something extra was "going on," that was certain, and tired as he was our friend at once hobbled off towards the point whence the unwonted sounds proceeded.

He soon arrived at a door over which a light hung and round which a score of little and big Negroes were assembled. "What's the fun here?" was a question answered by an individual standing in the door who said it was "a theater." While paying for his ticket, he heard another rake from the interior and another "Glorious!" accompanied this time by a loud shout as of a large political multitude assembled. He was soon inside the room, a large and long one,

317

two-thirds of which was occupied by the audience and the remainder by the stage, leaving a small space between. It was crowded too—the benches and chairs all full—while upon the floor was seated, his arms locked around his knees and his chin nestled closely on his wrists, Uncle Billy Brown, two-thirds inebriated and the other third fast asleep.

On one side of the room, near the row of candles which served for footlights, sat "the band," consisting of a large black fellow and no more in a very high chair, a violin in his hands and a brass drum between his legs. After repeated calls for "music," he finally struck up "Hey, Jim Along," playing his fiddle in the ordinary way with the true cornfield *abandon* and at the same time beating a rumbling accompaniment with his knees upon the drum. This over, the bell, borrowed from the tavern after it rang the boarders in to supper, now gave signal for the curtain to rise. "Pizarro, or the Death of Rolla,"[14] got up by a Thespian corps of the town, was to be the first performance. The Peruvian appeared and applause was so violent that the young amateur who personated the character bowed. The applause continued and he bowed lower. Another round, and he bowed so low that his tights gave way. A perfect earthquake of applause followed close upon the heel of this disaster, accompanied by a rake from the man with the fence rail—it was a man with a sure-enough fence rail—and Rolla backed out and hauled off to repair damages while the curtain was falling.

The affair so tickled the individual with the fence rail that nothing could stop him. He raked the sides of the house and then shouted "Glorious!" and kept it up till his friends gathered round and begged him to desist. But his steam was up, and the only way he could keep from bursting was to rail and shout with all his might. A compromise was finally made with him; he agreed that, if they would allow him to "make a short exhort" at the door and "sing a hymn," he would not use his rail again unless something extra turned up.

14. A drama supposedly by Richard Brinsly Sheridan (1799); based on a previous drama, *Spaniards in Peru* by August Kotzebue (1761-1819), German writer and dramatist.

Silence having been restored, the play was progressing towards a termination, when another interruption occurred. In one of the most affecting scenes and while the audience sat motionless, speechless, and apparently breathless, a very large gentleman from the country rose in his seat, leaned himself forward, and fixed his gaze intently on one of the performers. Suddenly he threw out his arms and exclaimed, "Good God! ain't that McDonald?" Away the audience went in perfect convulsions of laughter, down came the fence rail against the blinds with a rake that made all rattle again, and high above the din arose the shout of "Glorious!" The fat man from the country heeded not the noise and commotion around him but kept his eye fixed on the half-stupified performer. "Down in front!" came from those on the back seats, but the fat man heard not the summons. He raised his open hand over his eyes to obtain a closer sight and bent himself still farther forward. "Why, no it ain't," ejaculated he, half in doubt—"Why, yes it is"—and then straightening himself and slapping his right hand violently in his open left he finished with "D———n me, if it *isn't* McDonald sure enough." If there had been a din before, there was a perfect earthquake of noise now. The old fence rail came down on the weatherboarding with a rake that started the nails, the shout of "Glorious!" appeared louder from its very hoarseness, every pair of feet was stamping, every pair of hands was clapping, every throat was open and yelling, while outside the theater the horses tied to the fences broke their bridles and were stampeding and cavorting about amid shouts of "Stop him!" "Whoa!" "Hold my critter, there!" and similar ejaculations. Never had there been such an uproar in the little village of G—————.

Order was finally restored but only until sheer exhaustion left the audience unable to make further noisy demonstrations. Now the part enacted by the fat gentleman from the country was explained; it seemed that the Thespian's name who had attracted his attention was really McDonald. Some four months previous he had been reported dead to the fat gentleman; the report had never been contradicted, and he was bewildered at seeing his quondam acquaintance, for he had finally made him out through all his paint, feathers, and stage trappings and was led to depart a shade from the ordinary etiquette established among theatrical audiences. He sat down and once more the play commenced. All was hushed, a perfect quiet reigned, when suddenly it struck the fat man that he had made himself supremely ridiculous by the part he had played a few moments before. No sooner had this fancy fairly taken foothold in his mind than, in the very midst of a silence which would have become a graveyard at midnight, he laid himself back in his seat, raised both his hands above his head, and broke out with a "Ha! ha! ha!" that might have been heard a mile. Again the audience was thrown into convulsions, again the fence rail came rattling down the sides of the house, again the shout of "Glorious!" rose above the din, and as if this was not enough the actors forgot Sheridan's poetry and fairly screamed in chorus; the moody and relentless Pizarro took a part and laughed until the perspiration wore furrows through the red and black ferocity which rouge and burnt cork had given his countenance. It was not until exhaustion had once more got the mastery that order was restored, and the performance now went on with little interruption until "Pizarro" ended with the "Death of Rolla."

All this while, notwithstanding the din, Uncle Billy Brown had continued to snooze upon the floor; nor did the bustle attendant upon the fall of the curtain serve to raise him. The afterpiece of the "Mock Doctor" commenced, and yet Uncle Billy was perfectly unconscious of what was going on around him. He was well known as the captain of a "land packet"—in plain terms, the driver of an ox team which plied between G————— and the river towns—other than his occasionally muttered "Gee," "Whoa," and the like, as in his dreams he imagined himself alone with his team, no sounds escaped him. As the farce advanced, he gave a species of groan, a forerunner of returning consciousness, yet still he did not raise his head. The sham doctor was now proceeding to administer one of his nostrums to a patient, but the latter being backward he endeavored to persuade him. Uncle Billy groaned again and partially raised his head. The doctor continued his endeavors to force his drugs down his patient's throat; Uncle Billy gave still another groan and opened his eyes.

He had half recognized the voice of the doctor who was an old enemy of his and entirely forgetting where he was and imagining the Thespian endeavoring to force the vile mixture down *his* throat, he broke out with, "No — you — don't! To _____ with your pills; take em yourself, d–––n you, I don't like you, no how!"

Here was fresh and most abundant cause of uproar, and a new episode in the performance was introduced. The manager came forward and ordered that Uncle Billy be turned out. Uncle Billy drew a bowie and intimated a desire to see the chap willing to undertake the job. An assistant about the theater grappled him, and they were soon upon the floor engaged in a regular rough-and-tumble fight. Two-thirds of the footlights were at once kicked over, while shouts of "Fair play," "Turn em out," "Give him goss," "No gouging," were heard on all sides. The ladies scrambled and scampered out, the actors mingled with the audience, the fat gentleman laughed louder than ever, Uncle Billy tusseled and swore, but high above the laughing, cursing, and swearing arose the efforts of the rail-man. He had started off the boards on one side of the room, but having found a fresh spot he was raking away with all his might to the accompaniment of "Glorious! Glorious!"

Thus ended a theatrical performance in Mississippi. Our correspondent says that he dug his way out of the house and made the best speed he could to the tavern and to bed. The scenes of the evening haunted him in his dreams, and several times he awoke with his hands clasped to his ears to shut out the dreadful raking of the "glorious" fellow with the fence rail.

A "Crack" Hotel

by H. P. L.

§ Henry P. Leland wrote sketches for the *Spirit* and published a collection of popular humor entitled *The Grey Bay Mare* (Philadelphia, 1856, 1870). He was the brother of author Charles Godfrey Leland, whose "Frogs Shot Without Powder," *Spirit*, XXV (1855), 170, has been considered an early analogue of Mark Twain's "Celebrated Jumping Frog."

Printed as "How Old Zeb Went to a 'Crack' Hotel," the following story appeared in the *Spirit*, XXVI, No. 8 (April 5, 1856), 87.

ZEB Beeswing was as hard lookin an old nut as you'd find on a twelve hours' travel. The first time I saw him he was sitting on a mule, meek as Moses, dressed in an old, dark-brown, soap-colored blanket coat, originally white, an old battered, broad-brim, low-crown, black felt hat, old cottonade breeches of an invisible blue color, and a very square pair of old russet shoes. Zeb had probably seen sixty summers and remembered them. His face—well! I don't believe I can do it justice. However, if you'll take a hickory nut, one that age has stained a dark-brown shade, leave the sharp end for a nose, drill two holes each side of it and put in black glass beads for eyes, cut a long slit from the right under the nose to the corner of the left eye for a mouth—perhaps you can approach it. The cords of his neck were loose, for which, possibly, his head hung down. When you spoke to him, he'd slowly turn his head round sideways and shut his right eye—if you were on that side of him—till he could see you with his left eye and then he'd open on you.

Wishing to reach the landing at St. Joseph's in time to take the morning boat which left there on her way down the Mississippi, I had pushed my horse pretty well until I came within sight of the river. When the mist rose as the sun came up, I saw that the boat was not yet in sight and so held in and walked my horse. Turning a corner of the road, I met Zeb, looking as I have described and riding the same old mule. As I came up to him, he slowly twisted his head round until he could see who it was and then he drawled out:

"Mornin Squar. How d'ye do, this mornin?"

"Right well, Zeb. What brings you out so early before the fog's off?"

"Cottin, cottin, ollaways cottin, in course! Sent a load down t'other day to the landin; heerd last nite it haddent been shipt. Am gwine there now to give somebody hell." And he gave himself at this moment some tobacco, first thrusting one hand down, down, down in the pocket of that old blanket coat till his whole arm disappeared; when he drew it up again, he brought up a "chunk of honeydew as big as a hymnbook!" to use his own expression.

"On-ly twist me into a b'y again, an I reckun" — here was a pause occasioned by the honeydew — "I'd ractify thengs. Squar em up. You're young, you can ractify for me."

"Certainly! What can I do for you?"

"Yew kno Dew-barry — Frenchman in P'ydras Street? Keeps licker — all kinds. I'm sore f'r about ten gallins of his best con-yag bran'ny. Got kinder racked down on whiskey an want a change of feed. Tell him ter drive it up by nex boat; ef he disappints me, he and me will have the severest kind of a battil nex occashun we meet." I promised to call and give his order and then asked him why he didn't visit the city occasionally; I mentioned to him that I heard that he had never been down the river but once in his life.

"True as trooth! Never was thar but one occasion, never go agin. Crack hotels! Hell!"

"What's the matter with crack hotels?"

"Cracks ar the matter with em. Cracks more'n siventy foot deep. Oh yes, I've been tho em from top to bottom!"

"How?"

"Yew lissen!" Here the honeydew caused a cessation of words for a second. "Some yares agone I travelled to the city fur the fust time, and mabbe I hadn't a few thangs to larn. I 'rived thar of a mornin, went strate to my marchant, drew on him, and then streaked for a first-class hotel — mind ye a crack hotel. The ho-tel was filled. Spring races and all that sort of thing on, an they lo-cated me up in the top loft. I proposed to work on their feelins sayin I was an ole man, week and fee-bull in the jints like an couldn't mount them air stairs. 'Twouldn't jerk. Had to stan it. In the arternoon jined forces with a onsightly fast crowd of ole b'ys, an the way they made thengs cirkoolate wos 'stoundin. Tore up everything as wos to be seen by the roots. We did! Drunk more licker nor one could bottel in a yare and then—wal, I've a faintish i-dea 'bout bein toted t'ord mornin up very high over one story and then 'nother, feelin orful mizzable 'bout the boddy ginerally, incloodin my hed. Rek'lect con-cloodin to git a leetle more licker to cure me, gittin out of my room, loosing my way in a entry, end of all, gittin to wot I s'posed to be my room, an layin rite down in bed an goin to sleep.

"All of a suddin I started out of a soun sleep, the room was as dark as black nite, an thar was the mos tearin and poundin soun a-ringin in my ears, like ef they wur tryin to bile down a thousan thunder-claps inter one. All at once I feels the floor a-sinkin an givin way under me. Way I went, fallin, fallin, the n'ise [noise] a-bein added all the time, sech a screamin, shriekin, yellin, thunderin, roarin row! Knew I was on the road to fire an brimstone when I started; sech kin uv low-com-motion ain't pious—goin down hill is always cussed bad biznis. Went on fallin, faster an faster, till I was brought up with a roun jerk an pitched right inter the black hole. Jes as I 'spected! Thar wos all the fires a-burnin an nigger devils busy, brilin, roastin, stewin; jes' as I 'spected! Smelt kind uv nateral down thar, though somethin like fried eggs an bacon, an may I never chaw honeydew more ef I didn't scent coffey. P'raps, sez I, I'm doomed to go into eggs and bacon—who knows? Jes' then up rushes a big devil, dressed in white, and pre-pares ter haul away at the clothes I was wrapped up in. Sez I, 'Hallo!'

"Sez he, 'The Devil! Air you here?'

"'Come at last!' sez I. 'Don't be hard on a poor ole man. Draw it easy. I always lived pie-ously on airth.'

"'Woter yer doin here?' sez he.

"'I'm sure I dun know,' sez I.

"'Clare out then!' sez he, 'thar's the door!' 'Twan't quite clare in my mind whether 'twas the quarters for bad sperrits or no, but I ash-shore you I didn't need no second invite to make myself scarce 'bout thar! I made a rush for the door like one of old Sanglier's bloodhounds war affer me an would you believe it! the nex minnit

I wos in the barroom of the i-dentical ho-tel I put up to when I come to the city. It was 'bout nine o'clock in the mornin, an fortoonitely thar wan't but preshus few roun thar; so I goes up ter the bar—I hadden't nothin on but a shirt an felt cool in the naberhood ov my legs—an gits a bruisin strong cocktail, tells um to send two more up to my room, then I got showed up myself. 'Tain't every feller gets inter the 'fernal regions and out again 'fore nine o'clock in the mornin!

"They wanted to make out a history 'bout my gettin inter a dum waiter, where clothes were histed up to the top o' the house to dry, an how as I had gone down it an stopped inter the kitchen. But that cock won't fight. Dum waiter! Whar did all tha n'ise [noise] come from then! No, sir, I'll stick to it; I went to a *crack* hotel, an I fell through the *crack*. Whar I went to is nobody's biznis, I conceit."

That Big Fiddle

by Anonymous of New Orleans, Louisiana

§ The following tale appeared in the *Spirit*, XXI, No. 12 (May 10, 1851), 137.

T HE following incident really took place not long since in one of the principal music stores in Camp Street. A bushy headed youth—an acquaintance of ours, a great wag in the bargain, and second guardian of the store aforesaid—was lazily engaged in humming an air from Strakosch's new opera and dusting a "Piccolo," when a bold, rough voice within a foot of his ear alarmed his sensibilities with the question:

"Stranger, d'you sell fiddles?"

"Fiddles?" said "Piccolo."

"Ya-as, fiddles."

"Stringed instruments?" queried the youth gravely.

"Ya-as, stringed," said the owner of the voice, somewhat puzzled.

"Such instruments as ancient Uncle Edward requested should be suspended to the wall?"

"No, I don't want them; I axed fur a fiddle!"

"What kind of a fiddle will you have, sir; a Stradevarius, an Amati, or a violin?" inquired bushyhead, looking businesslike.

"I don't want none of them fixins, stranger; I jist ax you fur a real, rake-down fiddle—regular old Virginny!"

"Oh! I understand; you want a *fiddle!*"

"Ya-as! thar you had me! You see, stranger," said the Hoosier (for he was one of that much abused race) "you see, stranger, my old woman tuk on mighty strong agin my comin down to Nee-u Orleans—I come down on Uncle Abrum's flatboat, I did—and, d'you see, I want to gin her some good music when I arriv back. My old woman likes music, stranger, and so do I. I'm a regular breakdown on the 'Arkansas Traveler'—I tell *yeou* I am!"

And the tall Hoosier, dawdling over the counter, laughed confidentially to bushyhead. The latter looked sympathizingly on the pattern husband and proceeded to show him a variety of "stringed instruments." Hoosier tried them all with "Arkansas Traveler" and said "them would do." He fixed on one that pleased him more than the rest, put his hand in his pocket, half drew out an old, greasy buckskin wallet, and asked the price of "that ere one."

"One hundred dollars!" coolly replied the sales-*youth*.

"What!"

"One hundred dollars."

The wallet disappeared, and the Hoosier looked as if some one were choking him.

"Here is one cheaper—only eighty dollars."

The Hoosier continued being choked.

"Ah! this one, sir, is a splendid fellow—just listen to the tone—I'll let you have it—being as it's you—for only two hundred dollars!"

The Hoosier's eyes rolled wildly as he heard the price. His hands disappeared entirely in the immense pockets of his yellow-dyed trowserloons. There was a look of blank despair in his countenance as he exclaimed:

"Old woman, good-bye to your fiddle!"

"Why, sir, what price did you think I was going to ask for this instrument?"

"Jist what our John gin for his, stranger—only a five."

"Is that the kind you want?" said bushyhead, looking surprised; "why didn't you say so before. We have plenty of them. Come this way and I'll show you one."

The wag gravely proceeded to uncase an immense double bass. It stood about a foot higher than he did. The Hoosier *was* astonished. He fell back a foot or two and gazed in silence on the formidable instrument. The *seller* busily proceeded to tune it and offered it to the Hoosier, requesting him to strike up the "Farewell."

The Hoosier was a study for a painter as he *reared back* and *roared* out, "*Whar's* the man that plays that big fiddle?—*whar* is he? I want to see him!"

"He plays tonight at Wymen's concert at the Lyceum Hall."

"He does! Give me a ticket, stranger; I want to see *that* man!"

We departed as the Hoosier was paying for his ticket and loudly calculating the height of the man that played "that big fiddle!"

A Returned Californian in New Orleans

by "Lambda"

§ For a number of years, "Lambda" contributed to the *Spirit* a column of town and theatrical gossip from New Orleans. The following story, one of the few complete tales he published under this pen name, was printed in the *Spirit*, XXII (December 18, 1852), 518.

T ALK of the Crescent City declining! Why 'tis preposterous. The season has opened with a brilliance unknown till now. Every steamboat from the Great West swarms with living cargoes of men, women, children, cattle, horses, sheep, turkeys, chickens.

Returned Californians, although they don't return now in such numbers as formerly, may be seen winding their anxious way to the gold-dust dealers "to get weighed." One of these the other day, with the crevices of his garments loaded with granite or with his pockets full of auriferous rocks, had bought everything in the fancy way offered for sale in this immense mart of elegant trifles. His tall, bony, stalwart frame was bedizened with trinkets and ruffles. He wore two watches of "pure gold" with precious chain cables around his neck that looked as if they could be relied on to hold a frigate at her anchorage on a lee shore in a gale of wind. He had white kid gloves dangling from his button hole and had purchased them for no other reason than that they cost money; two circumstances prevented their being of the slightest use to him: one, that no gloves of that texture were ever made large enough to cover his immense hand; the other, that if he *could* have forced them over his Gulliver-looking fingers *that* would have concealed what he was most anxious to display—the glittering jewelry that adorned each digit. He had eaten and he had drunken to sickening surfeit.

As Alexander sighed to think there were no more worlds to conquer, so our hero declared that

> *This world is all a fleeting show*
> *For man's illusion given*

because he could find no more ways and means of spending money.

He strolled up St. Charles Street; and when nearly opposite the magnificent structure which is rising on the ruins of the late celebrated hotel a brilliant display of steel springs and patent leather caught his eye. This is a store establishment for the sale of trusses of every description. Here are body braces, shoulder braces, knee braces, arm braces, and spine braces. Wooden legs—no not wooden—but steel legs, steel arms, ankles, hips, toes, fingers, and even noses, all of steel and cord and whalebone, displayed in all the attraction of orange-silk stitching, velvet padding, and red morrocco. But trusses predominate, and these are adapted to every part of the human frame and to every period of its existence.

Our Californian gazed in at the window at this amazing display in mute wonder. Being blessed with a powerful frame, he had never heard there were such things as surgical bandages—but he entered the *magazin.*

"What's them crooked things fur?" said he to the French *marchand,* pointing to the low window.

"Dem sare, is de truss."

"But what are they fur?"

"Da go round de body—dis is de inguinal—dis de umbilical."

"Which is the 'bilical?"

"Dis one, sare—you have him?"

"Yes, I'll take the 'bilical. What's them others thar in the winder?"

"Da are different construction to suit de variety of paresons who have use for dis mos necessary article. Me sell great nomebare to de first family every day."

"They wear em all round the body, you say?"

"Oui monsieur—all made in Paree. See, sare, vat supayrb vorman-sheep—dis little one for de shild—de infong—garcon—small baby."

"This just fits my arm. I reckon I might wear this little one on my wrist. Well, but do the people wear these things inside their clothes?"

"Yes sare—da fit so snug—no pareson know you wear heem."

"Then what the h–ll's the use of having them, if nobody can see em? But howsomever if they're the fashion, put me up a lot of em."

"How many of dese trusses vill you have, sare?"

"Give me a dozen of em—sorted sized."

"Yes, sare—any ting else, sare?"

"No. Put em up and send em to Col. Mudge at the St. Louis with the bill—good day."

"Adieu, monsieur."

Mudge says when he last saw his lodger he was *trussed* with different sized bandages, commencing at his neck and terminating at his ankles.

Index

Index

Alabama, 3, 206, 212, 255, 287*n*
Ambler, Charles H., 15*n*
American Theater (New Orleans),
  265, 268, 296
"Amite," 8, 171, 191
Amite River, Mississippi, 171*n*
Anderson, John Q., 6*n*, 21*n*, 42*n*, 62*n*,
  81*n*, 101*n*, 183*n*, 253*n*, 259*n*
"Arcola," 25*n*
Arkansas, 3, 8, 60*n*, 160, 176, 176*n*,
  177, 238, 296
Arkansas River, 49, 56
Atachafalaya River, Louisiana, 116
Athens, Georgia, 133*n*
"Attackapas," 29*n*
Augusta, Georgia, 138
Austin, Texas, 249
"Azul," 5, 8, 287, 287*n*

Baldwin, Leland D., 14*n*
Baltimore, Maryland, 53*n*
Bates County, Missouri, 147
Batesville, Arkansas, 60*n*
Baton Rouge, Louisiana, 29*n*
Bayou Chicot, Louisiana, 85
Bayou Lafourche, Louisiana, 117
Bayou Sara, Louisiana, 241*n*
Bell's Life in London, 3, 249
Benton, Thomas Hart, 256, 256*n*
"The Big Bear of Arkansas" (Thomas
  Bangs Thorpe), 16, 17, 82
*The Big Bear of Arkansas and Other
  Sketches* (William T. Porter, ed.),
  4*n*, 104*n*, 269*n*, 284*n*
"Bill Easel." *See* Brannan, William Penn
Bingaman Race Track
  (New Orleans), 296
Blair, Walter, 3*n*, 5*n*, 6*n*, 14*n*, 15, 79,
  79*n*, 133*n*, 154*n*, 168*n*
Boatright, Mody C., 19, 82*n*
Bogue Chitto, 65
Boone, Daniel, 78
Booth, Junius Brutus, 293, 312
Boston, Massachusetts, 53*n*
Brandon, Mississippi, 202*n*, 245
Brannan, William Penn ("Bill Easel"),
  202, 209, 209*n*
Brazos River, Texas, 284*n*
Brazos Santiago, Texas, 284

Brownsville, Texas, 284*n*
Buena Vista, battle of, 95, 95*n*, 250, 282
Buncombe County, North Carolina, 70,
  70*n*, 72, 174
Burke, Thomas H., 212*n*
Burnham, George P. ("The Young 'Un"),
  241*n*
Burton William E., 202*n*
Byron, George Gordon, Lord,
  65, 65*n*, 69

Cairo, Illinois, 33
Caldwell, John, 314
Calcasieu River, Louisiana, 85
California, 284*n*, 296
Californians, 328, 329
Carey & Hart, publishers, 4, 255*n*, 284*n*
Carter, Hodding, 15*n*
Catahoula Lake, Louisiana, 275
Chestnut Street Theater
  (Philadelphia), 313
"Chips," 8, 117
Chitty, Thomas, 65, 65*n*, 69
Choctaw Indians, 57, 66
Chujoy, Anatole, 90*n*
Cincinnati, Ohio, 17, 118, 202*n*, 235, 251
Cincinnati Commerical, 203*n*
Civil, Military and Naval Gazette, vii, 37*n*
Civil War, 4, 5, 116
Clark, Thomas D., vi, 46
Claiborne County, Mississippi, 195
Clay, Henry, 142
Cleveland, Ohio, 234*n*
Cohen, Hennig, 6*n*
"Col. J. J. Jenks," 62, 62*n*
Cole, Edward D., 202*n*
Colville, Derek, 82
"Concordia." *See* Patterson, Robert
Concordia Intelligencer (Vidalia,
  Louisiana), vii, 10, 21*n*, 47*n*, 49*n*,
  98*n*, 183*n*
Connecticut, 161
Cooper, James Fenimore, 78
Copeland, Fayette, 30*n*, 55*n*, 113*n*, 230*n*
Courier-Journal (Louisville, Kentucky),
  202*n*, 203*n*
Covici, Pascal, 5*n*
"Crawfish," 37
Crescent (New Orleans), vii, 18, 230*n*, 312*n*

Crockett, Davy, 10, 78, 80, 80*n*, 81, 248, 258*n*, 290, 291

Daily Courier (Louisville, Kentucky), vii, 209*n*
Daily Crescent (New Orleans), 202*n*
Daily Democrat (Louisville, Kentucky), 203*n*
Darley, F. O. C., 4*n*
Davis, Jefferson, 10, 282
Davis, William B., 82*n*
Delta (New Orleans), vii, 4, 8, 62*n*, 81, 85*n*, 150*n*, 157*n*, 230*n*, 282*n*
Detroit, Michigan, 284*n*
De Voto, Bernard, 5*n*
Dick, Everett, 128*n*, 251*n*, 291*n*
Dillingham, William B., 6*n*
Dobie, J. Frank, 18, 82
Dogs, hunting: Boss, 81, 96, 97; Brutus, 81; Constitutional, 81, 107; Gum, 122-125; Holdfast, 81; Juno, 81; Lead, 81; Loud, 81; Pete, 81; Polk, 81; Singer, 81, 107; Trail, 81; Rambler, 105.
Donaldsonville, Louisiana, 30
Dorsey, Dr. Washington, 62*n*
Dorson, Richard M., 3*n*
Dow, Lorenzo, 216
Durivage, Francis A. ("The Old 'Un"), 241*n*
D. V. M., 305

Elssler, Fanny, 90*n*
England, 258*n*, 293
English, Thomas Dunn ("Thomas the Rhymer"), 265*n*
Europe, 296
Everett, Frank E., Jr., 88*n*, 167*n*

"Falconbridge." *See* Kelley, Jonathan F.
Faulkner, William, 79
Fayette, Mississippi, 9, 269
Fiddle tunes: "Arkansas Traveler," 326, 327; "Billy in the Low Ground," 130; "Buckskin Britches," 130; "Buffalo Girls," 130; "Cluck Old Hen," 130; "Devil's Dream," 130; "Eighth of January," 130; "Forked Deer," 130; "Happy Hollow," 130; "Hell among the Yearlings," 130; "Jim Crack Corn," 130; "Hogs Are in the Cornfield," 148; "Leather Britches," 130; "Monkey

Mush," 130; "Natchez-under-the-hill, 130; "Old Dan Tucker," 130; "Old Van Buring," 130; "Old Zip Coon," 130; "Possum up a Gum Stump," 130; Ralley in the Canebrake," 130; "Roaring River," 130; "Sally Goodin," 130; "Sandy River," 130; "Scolding Wife," 130; "Sich a Gittin Up Stairs," 130; "Soldier's Joy," 130; "Sourwood Mountain," 130; "Turkey in the Straw," 130; "Waggoner," 130
Field, Joseph M., 314*n*, 315
Foote, Henry S., 167, 183*n*
Forest Garland, The, 176*n*
France, 293
Frantz, A. J., 202*n*
Fink, Mike, 14, 14*n*
Forrest, Edwin, 312, 313

Georgia, 3, 131, 133, 136, 139
"Green 'Un," 5
Greenville, Mississippi, 9, 269, 270

Haile, C. M. ("Pardon Jones"), 5, 8, 9, 10, 113, 113*n*, 122, 254, 279, 279*n*, 301, 301*n*
Hall, A. Oakey, 294*n*
Hall, William C., 62*n*, 81*n*
Hamilton, Holman, 281*n*
Harris, George Washington ("Roderick"), 7, 70, 70*n*
Hayes, Alexander H., 230*n*
Havana, Cuba, 90*n*
Hervey, John, 249*n*
Hoole, W. Stanley, 5*n*, 212*n*
Hooper, Johnson J. (Simon Suggs), 4, 5, 7, 9, 88*n*, 212*n*, 258*n*
Hooter, Michael (Mik), 9, 62*n*, 78, 81, 81*n*
Hot Springs, Arkansas, 145
Hubbel, Jay B., 202*n*
Hudson, Arthur P., 5*n*, 168
Hunter, Louis C., 15*n*, 18*n*

Illinois, 37*n*
Iowa, 145
Itawamba County, Mississippi, 305

Jackson, Andrew (Old Hickory), 10, 142, 253, 258*n*, 290
Jackson, Coddington C. ("The Little 'Un"), 241, 241*n*

Jackson, Mississippi, 305
January, Phillip B. ("Obe Oilstone"),
 7*n*, 8, 9, 194, 194*n*, 195*n*, 253, 269,
 269*n*, 273, 273*n*
Jefferson City, Missouri, 73
Jefferson County, Mississippi, 8, 273
"Jersey," 223
J. N. M. Harding, 147
"Joel Darlin," 150
"John of Oxford," 100
"John Smith," 8
Johnson, William R., 249
Jones County, Mississippi, 244
Journal (St. Louis, Missouri), 4

Kaintuck, 6, 14, 15
Kelley, Jonathan F. ("Falconbridge"),
 15, 25, 25*n*, 176, 176*n*, 234, 234*n*
Kendall, George W., 8, 298*n*, 317*n*
Kendall, John S., 32*n*, 255*n*, 292*n*
Kentuckian, 40, 50, 296
Kentucky, 14, 62*n*, 130, 264
Kidd, H. A., 18
Kirkman, Thomas, 250, 255*n*
Kotzebue, August, 318*n*
Kummer, George, 202*n*

Lafayette, Louisiana, 6*n*
La Grange, Tennessee, 100
"Lambda," 8, 328, 328*n*
Ledger, (St. Louis, Missouri), 284*n*
Leland, Charles Godfrey, 322
Leland, Henry P. (H. P. L.), 322, 322*n*
Lewis, Henry Clay ("Louisiana Swamp
 Doctor"), 7, 9, 10, 16, 18*n*, 21*n*, 62*n*, 81,
 168
Lewis, the Reverend Henry T., 202*n*,
 203*n*
Lincoln, Abraham, 259*n*
London, England, 234*n*
Louisiana, 3, 7, 8, 9, 10, 42, 49, 81, 98, 101*n*,
 113, 113*n*, 120, 122, 122*n*, 150, 157, 181,
 183, 215, 249, 253, 279, 301
Louisiana Chronicle, vii, 181*n*, 215*n*
Longstreet, Augustus Baldwin, 3, 5*n*, 6,
 131, 133*n*, 253*n*, 298*n*
Louisville, Kentucky, 15, 17, 53*n*, 202*n*
Lowell, James Russell, 279*n*
Ludlow, N. M., 293*n*
Lumsden, Francis A., 8, 317*n*
Lynn, Kenneth, 5*n*

McClure, J. E. "Sam," 230*n*
McDermott, John F., 284*n*
McNutt, Alexander G. ("The Turkey
 Runner"), 5, 8, 9, 80, 88, 88*n*, 104, 104*n*,
 118, 167*n*, 250, 253
Macready, William, 293, 312, 315, 312*n*
Madison County, Mississippi, 131
Madison Parish, Louisiana, 166*n*
Maj. Kelly, 181
"Man in the Swamp," 70*n*
Marble, Dan, 25
Massachusetts, 65
"Megatherium," 8, 157
Meine, Franklin J., 3*n*, 5*n*, 14*n*, 15
Memphis, Tennessee, 238
Mercury (Cincinnati, Ohio), vii, 309*n*
Mexican War, 95*n*, 113*n*, 248, 252, 253,
 279*n*
Mexicans, 283
Mexico, 8, 10, 113*n*, 198, 287, 310
Mississippi, 3, 7, 8, 10, 42, 65, 81, 88*n*, 95,
 100, 120, 167, 171*n*, 183*n*, 194, 194*n*, 202*n*,
 209, 227, 244, 253, 282, 287, 287*n*, 298,
 299, 305, 306, 307, 317, 321
Mississippi City, Mississippi, 245
Mississippi River, 7, 11, 14, 15, 18, 19, 25,
 33*n*, 37, 38, 40, 42, 81, 85, 89, 90, 111, 204,
 234, 235, 237, 238, 250, 273, 276, 293, 322
Missouri, 3, 8, 73, 147, 256*n*
Mobile, Alabama, 293
"Mock Doctor," a play, 320
Monongahela River, 100*n*, 251
Monterrey, Mexico, 282
Morris, Joshua S., 203*n*

Napoleon Bonaparte, 29
Nashville, Tennessee, 293
Natchez, Mississippi, 21, 223, 273, 293,
 297, 316
Natchez Trace, 14, 46
Natchez-under-the-Hill, 14, 21, 23, 250
"Neosho," 65
New England, 279*n*, 298
New Jersey, 223*n*, 249
New Orleans, vii, 4, 7, 8, 11, 14, 15, 16, 18,
 25, 29*n*, 30*n*, 32*n*, 33, 53*n*, 90*n*, 95*n*, 115,
 188, 189, 193, 230, 241, 250, 252, 265,
 284*n*, 290, 292-298, 309-312, 314, 314*n*,
 315, 326, 328; battle of, 128, 253
New York, vii, 3, 53*n*, 70*n*, 113*n*, 194*n*, 249,
 293, 294

"N. of Arkansas." *See* Noland,
  Charles F. M.
Noland, Charles Fenton Mercer ("N. of
  Arkansas," "Pete Whetseone"), 60*n*,
  104*n*
Nonpareil (Cincinnati, Ohio), vii, 214*n*
North, 128, 279*n*
North Carolina, 249
"Number Eight," 206

"Obe Oilstone." *See* January, Phillip B.
Ohio, 25*n*, 53, 235
Ohio River, 33*n*, 56, 64
Ohio State Journal, 202*n*
Old Southwest, 3, 5, 5*n*, 7, 11, 14, 18, 19,
  46, 47, 78, 80-82, 129, 131, 166, 168, 170,
  220, 248, 250, 251, 253, 254, 290, 292-295,
  297

"Pardon Jones." *See* Haile, C. M.
Pass Christian, Mississippi, 21*n*
Patterson, Robert ("Concordia"), 8, 10, 11,
  21*n*, 47*n*, 49, 49*n*, 98*n*, 183, 183*n*
Pearl River, Mississippi, 89
Pennsylvania, 251
"Pete Whetstone." *See* Noland,
  Charles F. M.
Peterson, T. B., 255*n*
"Phil," 8, 73
Philadelphia, Pennsylvania, 4, 255*n*, 284*n*,
  313
Picayune (New Orleans), vii, 4, 8, 95*n*,
  113*n*, 120*n*, 122*n*, 170*n*, 198*n*, 230*n*, 279*n*,
  301*n*
Pittsburg, Pennsylvania, 25*n*, 309
"Pizarro, or the Death of Rolla," a play,
  318, 320
Place, Lucian, 265*n*, 266
Planter's Gazette (Plaquemine,
  Louisiana), 113*n*
Plaquemine, Louisiana, 113*n*, 114
"Plenoir," 238
Polk, James K., 142, 270
*Polly Peablossom's Wedding & Other
  Tales*, ed. T. A. Burke, 212*n*
Port Gibson, Mississippi, 203*n*, 209
Port Gibson Reveille (Port Gibson,
  Mississippi), 203*n*
Porter, William T., vii, 3, 4, 4*n*, 7, 9, 10, 17,
  18*n*, 104*n*, 113*n*, 131, 132, 157*n*, 169, 181*n*,
  183*n*, 188*n*, 194*n*, 223*n*, 249, 255*n*, 276*n*,
  284*n*, 292, 309*n*, 312*n*, 317*n*

Powell, Thomas 202*n*
Prentiss, Sergeant S., 167, 167*n*, 292, 298*n*
Prince, Oliver H., 253

*Quarter Race in Kentucky and Other
  Sketches, A*, 4*n*, 181*n*, 255*n*, 317*n*
Quick, Edward and Herbert, 15*n*, 37*n*

Race horses, Boston and Fashion, 249
"Rambler," 317, 317*n*
Red River, 238
Republican (Brandon, Mississippi), 202*n*
Reveille (St. Louis, Missouri), vii, 4*n*,
  147*n*, 284*n*
Rhode Island, 113*n*
"Rial Owens," 8, 160, 160*n*
Richmond Compiler (Richmond,
  Louisiana), vii, 42*n*, 166*n*, 167*n*, 170*n*,
  215*n*, 252*n*
Richmond, Louisiana, 42*n*, 167*n*, 215*n*, 252
Rickels, Milton, 6*n*, 98*n*, 188*n*
Robb, John S. ("Solitaire"), 254, 284, 284*n*
Roberts, Mrs. Anne, 202*n*
Robinson, Rowland E. ("Uncle Solon"),
  133, 133*n*
"Roderick." *See* Harris, George W.
Roundaway Bayou, Louisiana, 252
Rourke, Constance, 3*n*, 5*n*
Roxbury, Massachusetts, 241*n*
"Ruff Sam," 5, 8, 10, 95, 95*n*, 227, 227*n*,
  254, 282, 282*n*

"S.," 29
St. Charles Hotel (New Orleans), 53, 198,
  252, 268, 295, 296
St. Charles Theater (New Orleans), 55*n*,
  296, 312, 314
St. Louis, Missouri, 4, 33, 214, 284, 312,
  314, 315
St. Paul, Minnesota, 234*n*
San Francisco, California, 284*n*
Satartia, Mississippi, 62*n*, 63
Scott, Florence J., 281*n*
Sevier, John, 128
Shakespeare, William, 167, 312
Sheridan, Richard Brinsly, 318*n*, 320
Silsbee, Josh, 250, 265, 268, 293
Simon Suggs, 9
"Skyscraper," 145, 145*n*
Sol Smith, 32, 32*n*, 250, 293*n*, 312, 312*n*, 314
"Solitaire." *See* Robb, John S.

Songs: "A Life on a Ocean Wave," 308; "Billy Barlow," 311; "Greenland's Icy Mountains," 281; "Haste to the Wedding," 69; "Yankee Doodle," 281.
South, 4, 128, 249, 279*n*
South Carolina, 299
Southwest, 3, 4, 6, 7, 65, 69, 191, 249, 279*n*
Southern Literary Messenger, 3*n*
Southern Watch-Tower, vii, 60*n*
Spirit of the Times (New York), vi, 3*n*, 7, 17, 21*n*, 25*n*, 29*n*, 32*n*, 37*n*, 40*n*, 49*n*, 62*n*, 65*n*, 70*n*, 73*n*, 79, 85*n*, 88*n*, 95*n*, 98*n*, 100*n*, 113*n*, 117*n*, 120*n*, 122*n*, 133*n*, 140*n*, 145*n*, 147*n*, 150*n*, 154*n*, 157*n*, 169, 170, 171*n*, 176*n*, 181*n*, 188*n*, 191*n*, 198*n*, 202*n*, 206*n*, 212*n*, 214*n*, 220, 223*n*, 227*n*, 230*n*; 234*n*, 238*n*, 241*n*, 244*n*, 248, 255*n*, 265*n*, 269*n*, 273*n*, 276*n*, 279*n*, 284*n*, 287*n*, 293, 298*n*, 305*n*, 309*n*, 312*n*, 322*n*, 326*n*, 328*n*
"Stahl." *See* Wharton, George M.
Steamboats: 7; *Alexander Scott*, 314-316; *Anglo-Norman*, 18; *Ben Sherrod*, 234; *Clipper*, 113*n*; *Dr. Franklin*, 32-33; *Magnol*, 29*n*
Stockton, California, 284*n*
Stickney, S. P. 265, 265*n*, 266
"Stoke Stout," 10, 49*n*
"Subscriber," 214
"Sulphur Fork," 85
Sunflower River, Mississippi, 89

Tallulah, Louisiana, 42*n*
Tandy, Jennette, 3*n*, 5*n*
Taylor, Zachary, 280, 280*n*, 281*n*
Tennessee, 3, 100, 118, 128, 142, 154
Tensas River, Louisiana, 273, 275
Texas, 3*n*, 101*n*, 163, 214, 253, 309, 309*n*, 310, 311
"The Middle Aged 'Un," 241*n*
"The Very Young 'Un," 241*n*
"The Young 'Un." *See* Burnham, George P.
Thompson, William Tappan, 133*n*
Thorpe, Thomas Bangs, 4, 5, 7, 10, 11, 17, 18*n*, 98*n*, 183*n*, 188*n*
Times (New Madrid, Missouri), vii
Toler, Henry K., 249
Transylvania College, 62*n*
Tribune (Chambers, Alabama), vii, 212*n*
Tropic (New Orleans), vii, 188*n*, 305*n*
"The Turkey Runner." *See* McNutt, Alexander G.

Turner, Arlin, 5*n*
Turner, Frederick Jackson, 5
Twain, Mark (Samuel Clemens), 5

"Uncle Solon." *See* Robinson, Rowland E.
United States, 3, 15, 258*n*, 287, 309, 310

Vera Cruz, Mexico, 113*n*
Verandah Hotel (New Orleans), 295
Vermont, 133*n*
"Viator," 8, 15
Vicksburg, Mississippi, 8, 15, 40, 88*n*, 140, 166*n*, 171, 191, 293
Vicksburg Evening Post, 88*n*, 167*n*
Vidalia, Louisiana, 21*n*, 47*n*, 98*n*, 183*n*
Virginia, 60*n*, 88*n*, 100, 104, 160*n*, 249

Wade, John Donald, 3*n*, 258*n*
War of 1812, 290
Warren County, Mississippi, 104
Washington, D.C., 259, 290, 297, 298
Waterproof, Louisiana, 202*n*
Watterson, Henry, 5*n*, 202*n*, 203*n*
Weber, Brom, 5*n*
West Point Military Academy, 60*n*, 113*n*
Weston, Jack, 314, 314*n*
Wetumpka, Alabama, 212
Wharton, George Michael ("Stahl"), 154, 154*n*
Whig, (Yazoo City, Mississippi), 21
Whig, 60*n*, 188*n*, 234*n*
Wills, Jim, actor, 309, 311

Yalobusha River, Mississippi, 307, 307*n*
Yankee, 8, 9, 10, 265*n*, 293
Yates, Norris, 3*n*, 5*n*, 60*n*, 70*n*, 88*n*, 95*n*, 133*n*, 194*n*, 220, 241*n*, 249, 255*n*, 292*n*
"Yazoo," 8, 14, 21, 21*n*, 49*n*, 50, 54, 57, 250
Yazoo City, Mississippi, 21*n*
Yazoo County, Mississippi, 21*n*, 62, 81
Yazoo River, Mississippi, 88, 307*n*
"Yazoo Sketches," (William C. Hall), 62*n*